AUSTRALIAN JOINT COPYING PROJECT

Handbook Part 8 Miscellaneous Series
Third Edition

Compiled by Ekarestini O'Brien

National Library of Australia
Canberra 1998

© National Library of Australia 1998
Third edition

Second edition published 1980

National Library of Australia Cataloguing-in-Publication entry

Australian Joint Copying Project handbook. Part 8.
    Miscellaneous (M series).

    3rd ed.
    ISBN 0 642 10696 7.

    1. Australian Joint Copying Project. 2. Documents on microfilm—Sources—Indexes. 3. Australia—History—Sources—Indexes. I. O'Brien, Ekarestini. II. National Library of Australia.

016.994

Publisher's Editor: Margaret Wells
Printed by Ligare Pty Ltd, Riverwood NSW

Front cover: *Towing Out* [an emigrant ship, the *St Vincent*, leaves Deptford for Sydney in April 1844]
             Engraving from *Illustrated London News*, 13 April 1844
             Rex Nan Kivell Collection NK 4182
             National Library of Australia

Contents

Introduction

Precursors of the Australian Joint Copying Project

Although original Australian sources in the Public Record Office had been used by F.P. Labillière, G.W. Rusden and James Bonwick in their historical writing, no systematic copying was done until Bonwick was appointed archivist by the New South Wales Government in 1887. The Government decided to publish his transcripts in the series *Historical Records of New South Wales, 1892–1901*. The original transcripts are now held in the Mitchell Library.

Following Federation, the editor of Historical Records of New South Wales, F.M. Bladen, urged the establishment of a Commonwealth archives office in association with a national library modelled on the Library of Congress in the United States of America. In reporting to the Commonwealth Parliament in 1903, he named the Public Record Office in London, one of the many he had just visited, as one of the finest archives offices in the world. He was especially impressed by the facilities it offered for taking certified copies of the records, and he recommended the extensive transcription of Australian material, for a 'very trifling cost'. He added that 'if when the transcriptions were made in London, one of the many contrivances for multiplying writing were used, and six additional copies made, one for each of the State Public Libraries, they would, I am sure, be treasured by those institutions as amongst their most valued possessions'. In his view, only the index, which he urged should be compiled at the time of transcription, needed to be printed.

The Commonwealth Parliamentary Library Committee accepted responsibility for preserving the records of national life and making them available, and in 1911 the Committee undertook the publication of the Historical Records of Australia, the successor to Bladen's work for New South Wales. Thirty–three volumes were published, until publication was suspended following editorial difficulties, the last volume having appeared in 1925.

The Australian Joint Copying Project

The development of microfilm in the interwar years opened new possibilities for an even more extensive and yet economic copying program. In 1939 the Commonwealth National Library and the Public Library of New South Wales jointly made proposals for copying at the Public Record Office. These proposals were upset by the outbreak of war, but in October 1945 an agreement was signed under which the two libraries would jointly microfilm material in the Public Record Office in London relating to Australia. Filming began in August 1948 and for ten years the work of the project was confined entirely to the Public Record Office. In 1960 Phyllis Mander-Jones was appointed the first full-time AJCP Officer and, while not neglecting the Public Record Office, she immediately set off in pursuit of private records of Australasian interest throughout the British Isles. Her work, which ultimately led to the publication of *Manuscripts in the British Isles relating to Australia, New Zealand and the Pacific* (1972), resulted in film being produced of records located in many of the smaller and lesser-known repositories in Britain and Ireland. In 1971 a second officer was appointed and the Project continued to have two full-time staff, based at the Australian High Commission in London, until it ended in June 1993.

Participation of Australian libraries in the Project fluctuated over the years. At a conference in 1949, agreement was reached that the State Libraries would participate to the extent of buying the microfilms of all material relating to their own State. Subsequently, however, some libraries withdrew from the AJCP, while others, notably the State Library of Victoria, participated more fully by acquiring copies of all or most of the film produced by the Project.

In the late 1940s the partners agreed that the geographical scope of the Project should be extended to include material relating to New Zealand and the Pacific. The Alexander Turnbull Library at Wellington joined the Project in 1953 and the filming of Colonial Office records relating to New Zealand and Fiji commenced shortly afterwards. In 1958 the scope was again extended to include much of Southeast Asia and Antarctica. This was found in practice to be too ambitious and in the 1970s the AJCP largely reverted to its original boundaries.

In 1988 the original partnership between the State Library of New South Wales and the National Library ended, with the withdrawal of the State Library of New South Wales from the Project. The AJCP continued under the sole direction of the National Library for a further five years, but with continued support from the State Library of Victoria, the National Library of New Zealand and the National Archives of New Zealand and, to a lesser degree, other State and university libraries. The AJCP Office was closed in June 1993, mainly on account of financial difficulties. The final reels were not received until 1997.

The Microfilm

The achievements of what is believed to be the longest-running microfilming project of its kind in the world were substantial. It located, listed and described thousands of classes and collections of Australian, New Zealand and Pacific records held in hundreds of institutions, organisations and homes in almost every part of Britain and Ireland. It produced and despatched to Australia over 10 000 reels of microfilmed records dating from 1560 to 1984.

For purposes of arrangement and description, the AJCP film is divided into two series: the Public Record Office Series and the Miscellaneous Series. Within the Public Record Office (PRO) Series, the records of the Colonial Office (CO) were predominant, joined more recently by the records of the Dominions Office. Almost half of the AJCP film is taken up by the despatches, correspondence, letterbooks and registers, dating from 1788 to 1951, of these two departments. In addition to the huge classes dealing specifically with the Australian, New Zealand and Pacific colonies, film has been acquired of many general classes referring to such subjects as colonial appointments, honours, emigration, overseas settlement schemes, the involvement of the Dominions in the World Wars, and imperial policies and relations generally.

Several other departments in the Public Record Office were also the subject of filming, including the Admiralty, Home Office, War Office, Air Ministry, Foreign Office, Privy Council, Treasury, Board of Customs and Board of Trade. Material copied varies from log books and station records (Admiralty) to muster books and pay lists for British regiments stationed in Australia (War Office), and material relating to the transportation and administration of convicts (Home Office).

The Miscellaneous Series

Archives and manuscripts filmed as part of the Miscellaneous Series range from those held in the British Library and the National Libraries of Wales, Scotland and Ireland to material in university libraries, county record offices, museums, religious archives, learned societies, business archives and private homes. Although private records predominate, the Miscellaneous Series encompasses some official records, including selections from the archives of the Hydrographic Office, the Post Office and the Ministry of Defence. There is also, anomalously, a small amount of film acquired from the Public Record Office. In addition, local government records, mostly relating to convict transportation, were filmed at several county and city record offices.

The great strength of the Miscellaneous Series is in material dating from the nineteenth century. This applies in particular to emigrant diaries and letters, convict records, the archives of missionary societies, scientific records and the papers of politicians and officials. Eighteenth-century material consists mainly of maritime records, including logs and journals of most of the early British explorers of the Pacific. Despite weakening links between Britain and its Pacific colonies, twentieth-century material is far from negligible and includes important sources on imperial relations, migration, trade, public finance, business, wars and defence, and scientific research.

The AJCP staff searched for Australian and Pacific records throughout England and Scotland. The wide coverage is apparent from the list of repositories on pages xii–xix. In Wales and Northern Ireland filming was largely confined to the National Library of Wales and the Public Record Office of Northern Ireland.

In Ireland the collections searched and filmed were mostly held in repositories in Dublin. No searching was undertaken outside Britain and Ireland. The Miscellaneous Series, however, incorporates a few European collections, especially German official records, which were acquired from various sources.

Most of the records filmed are held in repositories which, whether public or private, are in varying degrees open to the public. The remainder are personal papers which are in the possession of individuals or families. They range from the papers of well-known explorers and governors to letters and diaries sent back to Britain by ordinary emigrants and travellers. The AJCP never undertook any systematic search for records in private possession. Over many years, however, it benefited from information supplied by Australian and New Zealand researchers working in Britain, as well as from the knowledge of British archivists, and located and copied papers that had been largely unknown and inaccessible. Although the owners are recorded in this handbook, it must be borne in mind that in many instances their records were filmed 20–30 years ago and the originals may well be held elsewhere or may have been lost or destroyed.

Researchers should be aware of some of the gaps in the Miscellaneous Series. A small number of institutions would not allow their collections to be copied. In a few instances, notably the British Library, the Bodleian Library and Lambeth Palace Library, the AJCP was only allowed to copy records over 100 years old, because of copyright restrictions. Wherever possible, searching was thorough, making use of indexes and finding-aids and a close examination of collections likely to contain relevant material. Nevertheless, there were some categories of records that were extremely bulky and where references to Australia and New Zealand were thinly scattered and seldom of much significance. This applied in particular to parish records, records of Boards of Guardians, and financial papers and other records of businesses. In such cases filming was quite selective.

AJCP Handbooks

In 1972 the National Library published the first part of the Australian Joint Copying Project Handbook. To date, ten parts and some revised editions of the AJCP Handbooks have been issued. This present part of the AJCP Handbook is the third edition of Part 8, which was originally published in 1980.

The Handbook aims to provide a description of the microfilm at levels of progressively greater detail, linking descriptions with reel numbers. Description at both general and detailed levels enables a researcher to comprehend the context of particular records and to reach relevant material more quickly. The extent of the records microfilmed necessitates that the AJCP Handbook be issued in multiple parts. Attention is drawn to the synopsis of the Handbook on the back cover of each part, which lists the ten parts already published. The most concise summary of the microfilm is provided by Part 1, Shelf List of Copying in the Public Record Office, London; Shelf List of the Miscellaneous Series.

At the detailed level, Parts 2–7 and 9–10 are class and piece lists for Public Record Office records combined with a description of the contents of individual reels. Part 10 also provides descriptions down to file level. Part 8 provides a description of each Miscellaneous Series collection.

Users of the microfilm are also advised to consult the microfiche edition of the Public Record Office: Kew Lists (London: HMSO, 1988) and Phyllis Mander-Jones' Manuscripts in the British Isles relating to Australia, New Zealand and the Pacific (Canberra: Australian National University Press, 1972).

AJCP Handbook Part 8

The entries in Part 8 comprise collection or repository level descriptions based on the format used in the Guide to Collections of Manuscripts relating to Australia. Entries are arranged alphabetically by the name of the person or organisation that created or accumulated the records or, when more appropriate, by the name of the repository that houses the records.

Most entries contain brief biographical or historical information intended to help identify the person or organisation.

The first edition of Part 8, published in 1980, contained 168 entries, whereas the third edition has 512 entries. The large output of film in the final 15 years of the Project has necessitated briefer or more selective descriptions of many of the collections. In general, the descriptions in the first edition have not been altered. The new entries are less comprehensive and are intended to highlight the more important groups of records or items that were filmed. This is especially true of material filmed at county record offices or large libraries. The form of descriptions varies from entry to entry. In some cases the collections, or the selections filmed, are relatively homogenous and can be adequately described in a few sentences. In others, where a great diversity of records were copied, the entries comprise a number of brief paragraphs each dealing with a distinct record group or item. With some of the large collections, the entries indicate on which reels particular records appear.

The entries refer to the existence of more detailed descriptions or lists. These lists were not published, but are held in typescript or photocopied form in the libraries that hold copies of the film. They should be used in conjunction with the Handbook, especially in the case of large collections which extend to many reels.

An effort has been made to ensure that addresses are accurate. However, names and locations change quite frequently. The following name changes occurred after editorial work was completed. The British Museum (Natural History) is now the Natural History Museum, the Greater London Record Office is the London Metropolitan Archives and the Strathclyde Regional Archives is the Glasgow City Archives.

Access to Microfilm

A list of institutions holding M Series film can be found on pages viii–xi of this Handbook. AJCP film is available for purchase by libraries in Australia, New Zealand and the Pacific and also for interlibrary loan. Requests for interlibrary loans can be sent to the Document Supply Service, National Library of Australia.

Requests to purchase microfilm should be directed to the Manuscript Librarian, National Library of Australia, Canberra ACT 2600.

References to the Microfilm

Acknowledgement of use of the microfilm should refer to the location of the original material and to the Australian Joint Copying Project.

Citations should include reference to the original material and to the microfilm reel number. For example:

- PRO Series: Papers of Sir Otto Niemeyer, 1921–27, T. 176 (AJCP reels PRO 6777–6778).

- M Series: Journal of Capt. James Cook, 18 February–23 September 1770, British Library Add. MS 27885 (AJCP reel M1580).

Many of the records filmed are still in copyright. Readers wishing to publish or reproduce documents that were filmed should seek permission, in the first instance, from the owner of the original records.

Acknowledgement

I would like to thank the National Library's Manuscript Librarian Graeme Powell for his invaluable contribution to the compilation and editing of this part of the Handbook.

Ekarestini O'Brien
Manuscript Section
National Library of Australia

M Series Holding Institutions

Institution	M reels
Institution	*M reels*

AUSTRALIA

Australian Capital Territory

Australian Academy of Science: Basser Library	1907
Australian War Memorial	1198
High Court of Australia Library	1588–1614, 1678–1681
National Gallery of Australia	2611
National Library of Australia	COMPLETE

New South Wales

Archives Authority of New South Wales	2125–2229
Australian Genealogical Education Centre, Kiama	2125–2229
Australian National Maritime Museum	2225
Catholic Institute of Sydney	995–999
Charles Sturt University Regional Archives	2125–2229
Charles Sturt University: Wagga Campus Library	403, 987, 1172
Macquarie University Library	462, 465, 671, 788, 802–806, 824, 933–934, 971
Philatelic Association of New South Wales Library	1136–1153
Randwick CIty Council Library Service	2125–2229
Royal Botanic Gardens, Sydney	749–750
Society of Australian Genealogists	2125–2229
State Library of New South Wales: Mitchell Library	COMPLETE
University of New England Library	11, 72–74, 212–218, 224–225, 229, 232–236, 238–240, 337–366, 382, 385, 393, 398, 403, 411, 424, 460, 464, 468, 841
University of New South Wales Library	995–999, 1135, 1668, 2022
University of Newcastle: Auchmuty Library	118–405, 407–409, 411–433, 435–437, 440, 444–458, 460–600, 602–607, 671–675, 677–916, 933–971, 973–991, 993–1400, 1517–1547, 1549–1651, 1653–1675, 1682–1708, 1710–2246
Wollongong City Library	2125–2229

Institution	M reels

Northern Territory

Institution	M reels
Northern Territory Library Service	399, 403, 444, 463–464, 692, 857, 939, 972
Wadeye Community Library, Port Keats	984

Queensland

Institution	M reels
Department of Geographic Information	1199–1200
James Cook University of North Queensland Library	11–12, 91–101, 413–416, 468, 577–579, 596–597, 608–613, 660, 675–676, 680, 980, 1201–1335, 1401–1516, 1551–1556, 1559–1574, 1688, 2426–2435, 2468–2475
State Library of Queesland: John Oxley Library	1–116, 244–336, 367–372, 381, 387–388, 393–394, 408, 412, 418–420, 422, 437, 440, 442, 467–468, 580–581, 584, 591, 600, 608–671, 675, 680–688, 692, 708–714, 729–790, 794, 796–799, 801–806, 815–819, 821, 838–841, 845–847, 851, 866, 869–870, 872–874, 935, 939, 973, 978, 980–981, 983–984, 1000–1092, 1131, 1134, 1170–1172, 1176, 1363–1367, 1617, 1628–1639, 1642–1649, 1653–1658, 1667–1671, 1690–1703, 1822–1824, 1838–1839, 1854–1855, 1860, 1897, 1912–1913, 2050–2053, 2081, 2083–2084, 2119–2122, 2125–2229, 2184, 2468–2475, 2837, 2844–2846
University of Central Queensland Library	2728–2759
University of Queensland Library	118–215, 218–236, 238–243, 381, 398, 413–416, 468, 536–549, 582–583, 692, 789, 995–999, 1628–1637, 1914–1917, 1920
University of Queensland: Department of History	212
University of South Queensland Library	600, 675, 687–688, 729, 789–790

South Australia

Institution	M reels
Flinders University of South Australia Library	1–916, 933–2288, 2290–2337, 2339–3105
State Library of South Australia: Mortlock Library	373–381, 389–394, 397, 403, 407–408, 444, 464, 469, 687, 718, 723, 793, 837, 871–874, 972, 977, 1579, 2125–2229
State Records	418–420, 422, 601, 981, 983, 1122
University of Adelaide: Barr Smith Library	103–105, 159–166, 980, 993–994

Tasmania

Institution	M reels
Archives Office of Tasmania	377–380, 385, 396, 399, 417–419, 422, 438–440, 442–443, 445, 461–463, 581, 605–607, 671, 693–707, 719, 735–787, 938, 940, 945–946, 974, 976, 984

Institution	M reels

Port of Launceston Authority	465
State Library of Tasmania	2125–2229
University of Tasmania Library	995–999, 1093–1100, 1980–2003

Victoria

Australian Gallery of Sport and Olympic Museum	2401–2412
Deakin University Library	807–814, 828, 995–999, 1101–1113, 1226–1227, 1229, 1234, 1237–1240, 1628–1637, 1653–1660, 1697–1703, 1846–1853, 1864–1876, 1901–1903, 1907, 1909–1911, 1923, 2125–2229
Genealogical Society of Victoria	1574, 2125–2229
Monash University Library	379
National Museum of Victoria	853
Public Record Office	1171
State Library of Victoria: La Trobe Library	COMPLETE
University of Melbourne: Department of History	1–8, 118–172, 425–432, 536–549

Western Australia

Library and Information Services of Western Australia: Battye Library	381, 386, 397, 413–416, 465, 577–579, 584, 594, 691–692, 708–713, 720, 730–788, 791, 816–819, 822–823, 835, 837, 842–845, 945–947, 972, 976, 983, 995–999, 1539–1542, 2125–2229
Murdoch University Library	381, 464, 466, 823, 807–814, 828, 844, 1000–1076, 1454–1483, 1516
University of Western Australia Library	373–376, 582–583

FIJI

| Fiji Museum | 465 |
| Pacific Theological College | 157–158 |

NEW ZEALAND

Auckland Institute and Museum	590, 721, 728, 802–806, 824, 834, 1093–1100, 1906
Auckland Public Library	689–690, 815, 1170–1172, 1176, 1179, 1181–1182, 1192, 1194, 1363–1367, 2125–2229
College of St John the Evangelist	173–243, 411, 590, 715, 728, 802–806, 824, 993–994, 1093–1100, 1517–1534
National Archives of New Zealand	1120–1122, 2079–2090, 2123–2124

Institution	M reels
National Library of New Zealand: Alexander Turnbull Library	1–116, 118–243, 382–384, 402, 406–409, 411, 423, 465, 468, 536–549, 584, 590, 593, 595–597, 600, 605, 608–670, 679, 681–690, 693–713, 715, 718, 720, 722, 728, 730–788, 802–806, 824–827, 834, 869–874, 947, 973, 979, 982–986, 988–991, 993–1100, 1114–1129, 1132–1134, 1158–1169, 1173, 1176–1179, 1181–1182, 1190, 1192–1193, 11296–1200, 1337–1338, 1399–1583, 1585–1614, 1617, 1619, 1628–1685, 1688–1712, 1718–1845, 1854–1855, 1859, 1861, 1864–1907, 1912–1913, 1918–1922, 1924–1965, 1968–1972, 1976–2013, 2015–2063, 2066–2078, 2080–2089, 2091–2115, 2117–2124, 2230–2253, 2263–2342, 2346–2347, 2350–2394, 2396–2412, 2415–2421, 2426–2491, 2494–2500, 2502–2503, 2515–2519, 2523–2644, 2649–2684, 2686–2759, 2762–2836, 2838–2902, 2910–2911, 2924–2979, 2983–3086
University of Auckland Library	1–10, 14–68, 135–142, 159–165, 173–243, 387–388, 468, 596–597, 993–994, 1093–1100
University of Canterbury Library	1093–1110
University of Otago: Hocken Library	118–243, 382, 400, 465, 469, 537–545, 582–583, 590, 595, 679, 691, 721, 802–806, 824, 980, 1000–1100

PAPUA NEW GUINEA

University of Papua and New Guinea	11–12, 91–100, 109–116, 251–264, 608–613, 632–634, 657–660

UNITED STATES OF AMERICA

East–West Center, Hawaii	805–806
University of Hawaii Library	173–243, 367–372, 400, 465, 605, 608–670, 681–686, 689–691, 721, 802–806, 993–994, 2265–2270, 2318–2337, 2339–2342, 2350–2391, 2393, 2398, 2415–2421, 2426–2467

British and Irish Record Repositories

Institution	*Entry Numbers*
Berkshire	
Berkshire Record Office	35
Buckinghamshire	
Buckinghamshire Record Office	80, 177, 271, 390
Cambridgeshire	
Cambridge University Library	18, 85, 98, 125, 147, 203, 235, 362, 380, 386, 391, 395, 401, 474
Cambridgeshire Record Office	86
Fitzwilliam Museum	23
Haddon Library	40
Newton Library	193
Selwyn College Library	410
Cheshire	
Cheshire Record Office	96, 435
Chester City Record Office	97
Tameside Local Studies Library	304
Cleveland	
Cleveland County Office	103
Cornwall	
Cornwall County Record Office	113, 475
Cumbria	
Cumbria Record Office	119, 368
Derbyshire	
Derby Central Library	135
Derbyshire Record Office	136
Devon	
Devon Record Office	4, 137
North Devon Record Office	350

Institution	Entry Numbers
Humberside	
Brynmore Jones Library	79, 122, 338
Hull City Record Office	238
Hull Local Studies Library	239
Humberside Archive Service	240
Isle of Wight	
Isle of Wight County Record Office	251
Kent	
Kent Archives Office	264, 435
Lancashire	
Lancashire Record Office	268
Preston District Library	218
Rawtenstall Public Library	50
Leicestershire	
Leicestershire Record Office	274
Lincolnshire	
Lincolnshire Archives Office	279, 314
Greater Manchester	
Greater Manchester Record Office	211
Holyoake House	112, 231
John Rylands Library	99, 257–259, 323
Manchester Central Library	303
Merseyside	
Harold Cohen Library	383
Liverpool City Libraries	283, 284
Liverpool Record Office	133, 134
Merseyside Maritime Museum	319
Merseyside Record Office	320

Institution	Entry Numbers
SCOTLAND	
Aberdeen University Library	2, 505
Ayr Record Office	16
Edinburgh Central Library	500
Edinburgh University Library	156, 263, 525
Glasgow University Library	189
Hopetoun House	234
Mitchell Library, Glasgow	327
National Library of Scotland	101, 105, 176, 333, 340, 387, 459
Paisley Central Library	116
Scottish Record Office	301, 344, 408, 466
Strathclyde Regional Archives	5, 173, 441
Strathclyde University Archive	442
University of Glasgow, Business Record Centre	188, 194
WALES	
National Library of Wales	341, 458
NORTHERN IRELAND	
Armagh County Museum	10
Public Record Offiice of Northern Ireland	381
REPUBLIC OF IRELAND	
All Hallows College, Dublin	6
Genealogical Office, Dublin	182
National Archives of Ireland	336
National Library of Ireland	111, 146, 151, 269, 329, 339, 358
University of Dublin, Trinity College Library	465

Descriptive entries

Entry 1

Reels M1890–1892

Name **ABERDEEN, George Hamilton Gordon, 4th Earl (1784–1860)**

Title Papers

Inclusive dates 1828–55

Quantity 3 reels of microfilm

Location of original British Library, Great Russell Street, London WC1B 3DG, England

Note
Tory and Peelite politician. Foreign Secretary 1828–30; Secretary of State for War and Colonies 1834–35; Foreign Secretary 1841–46; Prime Minister 1852–55.

Description
Correspondence mostly dated 1841–46, dealing particularly with Anglo–French rivalry in the Pacific, the French annexation of Tahiti, actions of Sir James Brooke in Sarawak, and the Dutch East Indies.

Major correspondents are Queen Victoria and Prince Albert, Sir Robert Peel, Lord John Russell, Lord Palmerston, W.E. Gladstone, Lord Derby, Lord Ripon, Sir Charles Bagot, F.P.G. Guizot, Lord Clarendon, Sir James Graham, Lord Brougham, Duke of Newcastle, Sir George Grey, J.W. Croker, Sir Edward Disbrowe, Lord Cowley and Capt. T. Nicolas.

22-page list available for reference.

Entry 2

Reels M2398–2399

Name **ABERDEEN UNIVERSITY LIBRARY**

Title Collections

Inclusive dates 1800–1984

Quantity 2 reels of microfilm

Location of original Aberdeen University Library, King's College, Aberdeen, Grampian AB9 2UB, Scotland

Description
1) Diary 1843 of David Cargill on a voyage to Van Diemen's Land and Tonga.

2) Papers 1831–44 of Leslie Family of Warthill, including a letter of Patrick Leslie.

3) Papers 1800–13 of Alexander Seton, including letters of his brothers William Anderson and Robert Anderson at Sydney and Norfolk Island.

4) Papers 1891–1984 of John M. Bulloch on genealogy of Gordon Family, including cuttings, letters and a booklet about Adam Lindsay Gordon.

5) Papers 1889–93 of 10th Earl of Kintore, Governor of South Australia, including letters of Lord Salisbury, Lord Knutsford, Lord Carrington and Lord Hopetoun.

6) Typescript of Alice Hay describing her childhood in Western Australia.

7) Records 1964–72 of International Biological Programme collected by E.M. Nicholson relating to conservation of wildlife in the Pacific Islands.

8) Papers 1879–1974 of Dr William Wood, a Sydney physician.

Nine-page list available for reference.

Entry 3

Reels M2426–2435

Name **ABORIGINES PROTECTION SOCIETY**

Title Records

Inclusive dates 1837–1909

Quantity 10 reels of microfilm

Location of original Rhodes House Library, South Parks Road, Oxford OX1 3RG, England

Note
Founded in 1837, to carry out the recommendations of the 1835–37 House of Commons Select Committee on Aboriginal Tribes. The Society took a particularly strong interest in native affairs in Australia, New Zealand and the Pacific in the period 1866–88. It maintained close relations with the Anti-Slavery Society, and the two societies amalgamated in 1909.

Description
1) Letters received by Secretaries of the Aborigines Protection Society: Thomas Hodgkin (1837–66), F.W. Chesson (1866–88) and H.R. Fox-Bourne (1888–1909). They deal in particular with: the treatment of Aborigines in Queensland and Western Australia and of Maoris in New Zealand; charges made by Rev. J. Gribble in Western Australia; the visit of

Maori chiefs to England in 1882 and 1884; the Pacific labour trade and the treatment of Pacific Islanders in Queensland; the 1875 Pacific Islanders Protection Bill; cases involving *Jason*, *Carl* and other labour vessels; the annexation of New Guinea in 1884; and land rights and race relations in Fiji and Tonga.

2) Letters received by Secretaries of the Anti-Slavery Society: L.A. Chamerouzow (1852–70), Thomas Phillips (1870–74), Benjamin Millard (1871–75), Charles Allen (1879–98), Joseph Cooper (1871–79) and Edmund Sturge (1871–79).

Correspondents include W. Brookes, J. Sunderland, F. Chesson, Bishop C. Abraham, Sir Thomas Buxton, J. Cooper, Agnes Craig, Admiral J. Erskine, G.W. Rusden, J.B. Thurston, W.F. Parr, Sir George Grey, Rev. J.G. Paton, Te Wheoro, A. Davidson, R. Short and J. Douglas.

33-page list available for reference.

Entry 4   Reels M2055–2059

Name **ACLAND FAMILY**

Title Papers

Inclusive dates 1840–1902

Quantity 5 reels of microfilm

Location of original Devon Record Office, Castle Street, Exeter, Devonshire EX4 3PU, England

Note
The family members included Sir Thomas Dyke Acland (1809–1848), John Barton Arundel Acland (1823–1904), Sir Charles Dyke Acland (1842–1919), Sir Francis Dyke Acland (1874–1934) and Joanna Harper (nee Acland). Harper emigrated to New Zealand with her husband in 1864, returning to England in 1892–93. Sir Francis Acland visited Australia and New Zealand in 1897–98.

Description
Correspondence, diaries, newspaper cuttings and a photograph album.
The diaries 1863–93 of Joanna Harper contain brief entries referring to family activities, visitors, social events, shopping, church services, health, music and weather. Her letters contain family news, news from Australia and New Zealand, social events and church affairs.
The journal and letters 1897–98 of Francis Acland refer to social and sporting events, schools, universities, paintings, and governors and politicians in Australia and New Zealand.
Correspondents include Joanna Harper, J.B. Acland, Bishop G.A. Selwyn, Bishop Henry

J.C. Harper, Sir Fairfax Moresby, Sir Francis Acland and Sir Thomas Acland.

Nine-page list available for reference.

Entry 5   Reels M2679–2682

Name **AITKEN, LILBURN & CO LTD**

Title Shipping records

Inclusive dates 1867–1950

Quantity 4 reels of microfilm

Location of original Strathclyde Regional Archives, Mitchell Library, North Street, Glasgow G3 7DN, Scotland

Note
Glasgow-based shipping and ship-broking firm. Ships that visited Australia included the *Loch Torridon*, *Loch Carron* and *Loch Etive*.

Description
The records comprise a ledger, register book of ships, voyage books, sailing books and log books.

Five-page list available for reference.

Entry 6   Reels M871–874

Name **ALL HALLOWS COLLEGE, DUBLIN**

Title Correspondence and calendar

Inclusive dates 1842–77, 1956

Quantity 4 reels of microfilm

Location of original All Hallows College, Drumcondra, Dublin 2, Ireland

Note
Founded in 1842 by Father Hand as a seminary for the training of Roman Catholic priests. By 1863 the College had provided 50 secular priests for Australia; and one-quarter of that year's 218 students was destined for Australia. After the mid-1860s the College supplied the largest proportion of the mainly Irish clergy in the various dioceses of Australia and New Zealand.

Description
1) Thesis by Patrick F. Murray entitled 'Calendar of the Overseas Missionary Correspondence of All Hallows College, Dublin, 1842–77' (MA thesis, University College, Dublin, 1956). As well as the calendar itself, the thesis includes a history of the College and of each overseas diocese, arranged by geographic area, such as Australasia, then alphabetically by diocese.

2) Correspondence dealing with overseas missions, concluding with batches of letters arranged chronologically in groups of twelve with a summary note at the beginning of each group. These summary notes give the name of each correspondent, the date of the letter and its subject. The bulk of the correspondence consists of letters from bishops and priests addressed to the College presidents, and records of the ideas as well as the activities of Irish priests in Australia and New Zealand.

3) Correspondence from dioceses in Canada, Scotland and England.

4) A miscellaneous section of the correspondence contains letters 1858–60 to and from the Colonial Land and Emigration Commission relating to religious instruction on board emigrant ships, and letters 1845–69 of Rev. Thomas Heptonstall, who acted as agent for a number of Australian and New Zealand bishops on matters of emigration.

One-page list available for reference.

Entry 7 Reel M2492

Name **ANDREWS, Charles William (1866–1924)**
Title Papers
Inclusive dates 1887–1923
Quantity 1 reel of microfilm
Location of original Archives and Mineralogy and Palaeontology Libraries, British Museum (Natural History), Cromwell Road, South Kensington, London SW7 5BD, England

Note
Andrews joined the Geology Department of the British Museum (Natural History) in 1892 and later became Assistant Keeper. He visited Christmas Island on collecting expeditions in 1897–98 and 1908. He was the co-author of *A Monograph of Christmas Island*.

Description
Correspondence, photograph albums and notes relating to Andrews' visits to Java, Christmas Island and the Cocos Keeling Islands, and to the book *A Monograph of Christmas Island*. Includes a letter of Sir John Murray on the annexation of Christmas Island.

Three-page list available for reference.

Entry 8 Reel M2513

Name **ANGAS FAMILY**
Title Papers
Inclusive dates 1842–1988
Quantity 1 reel of microfilm
Location of original Mrs E. Bancroft, c/- Manuscript Section, National Library of Australia, Canberra ACT 2600

Note
John Howard Angas (1823–1904), the second son of George French Angas, was a South Australian pastoralist and politician. Lillian Angas (1862–1958) was his daughter.

Description
1) Correspondence 1906–54 of Lillian Angas, including letters of Sir Keith Angas, Fay Angas and H.F. Angas.
2) Watercolour by Charles Howard Angas.
3) Copy of a diary 1855 kept by John Howard Angas on a voyage from London to Adelaide on the barque *Fop Smit*.
4) Land grant 1842 to John B. White.
5) Manuscript biography of Lillian Angas by her grand-daughter Daphne Rance.

Four-page list available for reference.

Entry 9 Reel M2343

Name **ARCHER, Samuel (b.1835)**
Title Journal
Inclusive dates 1857
Quantity 1 reel of microfilm
Location of original Mrs G.H. Osmaston, Cumbria, England

Note
Surgeon on SS *Great Britain*, 1857.

Description
The journal describes a voyage on SS *Great Britain* from Liverpool to Melbourne February–April 1857, fellow passengers, life on board the ship, Archer's stay in Melbourne, places he visited in Victoria and the journey back to Liverpool via Cape Horn, May–August 1857.

One-page list available for reference.

Entry 10   Reel M389

Name **ARMAGH COUNTY MUSEUM**

Title Extracts

Inclusive dates (n.d.)

Quantity Portion of 1 reel of microfilm

Location Armagh County Museum, The Mall East, Armagh, County Armagh BT61 9BE, Northern Ireland

Description
1) Blacker manuscripts. Typescript abstract entitled 'Wentworth Family'. Contains recollections 'of D'Arcy Wentworth and his two sons, one of whom became a soldier and the other a surgeon who was convicted of highway robbery and transported to Botany Bay where his son also was a surgeon of some eminence'.

2) Raeburn manuscripts. Six-page typescript account of a voyage to Australia 1852–53. The journal, probably written by Samuel Pillow, concerns the voyage of the emigrant ship *Digby*. The writer mentions some of the Irish passengers by name and gives brief descriptions of events on board ship and on arrival in Melbourne. This typescript is also reproduced on reel M388.

Entry 11   Reel M411

Name **ARNOLD, Edward**

Title Letters

Inclusive dates 1841–43

Quantity 1 reel of microfilm

Location of original Mr G.A. Arnold, London

Note
Visitor to Australia and New Zealand. Arnold was employed in the service of Bishop G.A. Selwyn, first Anglican bishop of New Zealand. He accompanied the Bishop as a servant on the voyage to Australia, arriving in April 1842. After a brief visit to Sydney, where Selwyn stayed with Bishop Broughton, they sailed to Waimate in New Zealand, where Arnold remained for about a year.

Description
1) Four fragments of letters, two written by Arnold from Waimate, New Zealand. The only complete letter written to Arnold is addressed to Port Phillip and dated November 1843, from Isabella McCullum of Darlinghurst, New South Wales.

2) 11 letters 1841–43 from Arnold to his family in Windsor, England, some from Exeter and

Plymouth before his departure from England, the rest from Sydney, Geelong Harbour and Waimate, New Zealand. In addition to news of family interest the letters contain candid comments on places visited, people with whom Arnold and his employer stayed, and his attitude to the treatment of convicts and Maoris. They also provide brief descriptions of employment prospects, costs and living conditions in Sydney and Auckland.

Two-page list available for reference.

Entry 12   Reel M602

Name **ASHWORTH, Edward (1814–1896)**

Title Papers

Inclusive dates 1841–45

Quantity 1 reel of microfilm

Location of original Alexander Turnbull Library, Wellington, New Zealand

Note
Architect and surveyor. Ashworth left England in May 1842 in the *Tuscan* which sailed to Port Phillip and Auckland. He returned to Australia in February 1844 and stayed for three months in Sydney before leaving in the American ship *Navigator,* travelling to Hong Kong via Batavia and Macao.

Description
1) Journal and sketches 1842 of a voyage in the *Tuscan* from London to Auckland. It contains detailed descriptions of his short stay in Melbourne and of his long period of residence in New Zealand. There are many drawings of buildings.

2) Notebook in narrative form describing in detail his New Zealand and Australian visit, including many references to contacts with missionaries and Maori people, to political events and social and economic conditions.

3) Notebook 1844–45 of reminiscences of his journey to Batavia and Hong Kong and his residence in the colony.

4) Sketchbook and loose drawings of the landscape, buildings, people, flora and fauna of New Zealand, Australia, Batavia, China and Gibraltar; maps of Gibraltar and Macao.

5) Photograph of Ashworth's tombstone.

One-page list available for reference.

Entry 13   Reel M436

Name **ATKINSON, David**

Title Letters

Inclusive dates 1851–62

Quantity 1 reel of microfilm

Location of original National Library of Australia, Canberra ACT 2600

Note
Emigrant to New South Wales.

Description
Six letters from David Atkinson, mainly to his family in England. The first two letters, written in 1851, describe the weather and conditions on the emigrant vessel *Emperor*, carrying 300 passengers, most of them being Irish families. The remaining letters are from Sydney, Melbourne and Burrowa (Boorowa?), New South Wales. They discuss mainly family matters and give brief impressions of life in the colony.

One-page list available for reference.

Entry 14   Reels M1846–1853

Name **AUSTRALASIAN UNITED STEAM NAVIGATION COMPANY**

Title Records

Inclusive dates 1887–1961

Quantity 8 reels of microfilm

Location of original Guildhall Library, Aldermanbury, London EC2P 2EJ, England

Note
Formed in 1887 as a result of a merger between the Queensland Steamship Co and the Australasian Steam Navigation Co. The Company was one of the largest of the coastal shipping companies in Australia until 1961.

Description
1) Correspondence 1949–53.
2) Directors' meetings, minute-books and agenda books 1887–1939.
3) Voyage and foreign journals 1887–1932.
4) Ledgers 1937–48 and annual reports and accounts 1887–1959.
5) Papers 1960–61 of B.R.T. Greer, a director of the company, concerning the merger between AUSN Co and Macdonald Hamilton & Co.
6) Papers 1917–61 of Company Secretary.

7) Records 1903–16 of Eastern and Australian Steamship Co.

Correspondents include Lord Inchcape, Sir William Currie, Lord Huntingfield, B.R.T. Greer, Lord Simon, R. Loubser, I. Brodie, R. Macdonald and N. Campbell.

Two-page list available for reference.

Entry 15   Reel M461

Name **AUSTRALIAN JOINT COPYING PROJECT**

Title Search notes and filming instructions for Public Record Office material

Inclusive dates (n.d.)

Quantity 1 reel of microfilm

Note
The Australian Joint Copying Project began filming at the Public Record Office in 1948. Many Colonial Office classes were filmed comprehensively, but staff attached to the National Library Liaison Office in London searched other classes to identify relevant records. Mitchell Library staff also used the microfilm copies to compile lists.

Description
Search notes and instructions for filming of Public Record Office material. The typed lists have been marked up with AJCP reel numbers. The lists are arranged in numerical order within each record group, in the following sequence: Admiralty, Home Office, Privy Council, Board of Trade, Treasury, Audit Office, Paymaster General, War Office, Foreign Office, Board of Longitude, Colonial Office.

The search notes provide detailed contents lists for many of the AJCP reels, showing in some cases folio numbers of documents and an indication of their subject content. The Colonial Office listings complement the *Comprehensive List of Colonial Office Records* (the 'Blue Books'), reproduced on AJCP reels M418–421, in which documents are arranged by colony, and within each colony by subject.

Many of the notes reproduced on M461 are held in typescript form by the National Library of Australia and the Mitchell Library, and are available for consultation by users.

Entry 16   Reel M2683

Name **AYR RECORD OFFICE**
Title Collections
Inclusive dates 1862–95
Quantity 1 reel of microfilm
Location of original Ayr Record Office, Wellington Square, Ayr, Scotland

Description
1) Letters 1892–95 of Lord Glasgow, Governor of New Zealand, to his solicitor and Charles Shaw concerning social events, personal finances, constitutional problems, New Zealand politics, economic conditions and a visit to Melbourne.
2) Certificate 1862 appointing Alexander Morris as Harbour Master of Southland Province, New Zealand.

Two-page list available for reference.

Entry 17   Reel M397

Name **BAINES, Thomas (1822–1875)**
Title Sketches
Inclusive dates 1855–56
Quantity 1 reel of microfilm and 26 colour transparencies and photographs
Location of original Royal Geographical Society, 1 Kensington Gore, London SW7 2AR, England

Note
Artist and explorer. In 1855 he accompanied A.C. Gregory on his exploration of northern Australia. He produced numerous sketches of Albany Island, the Albert River and the Victoria River, as well as reports for the Colonial Office. In 1858 he was appointed artist to the Zambezi expedition under David Livingstone and later accompanied expeditions to Victoria Falls, the Tati goldfields and the Kaffir country of South Africa.

Description
Sketchbook 1855 kept by Thomas Baines on the A.C. Gregory expedition to Northern Australia comprising sketches of ships, flora and fauna, Aborigines, and landscapes of Sydney and Northern Australia.

One-page list available for reference.

Entry 18   Reel M2497

Name **BALDWIN, Stanley, 1st Earl (1867–1947)**
Title Papers
Inclusive dates 1923–38
Quantity 1 reel of microfilm
Location of original Cambridge University Library, West Road, Cambridge CB3 9DR, England

Note
Conservative politician. Chancellor of the Exchequer 1922–23; Prime Minister 1923–24, 1924–29, 1935–37; and Lord Privy Seal 1932–34.

Description
Correspondence and papers relating to defence, labour, trade and Empire affairs, Australian and New Zealand politics, and the 1928 Economic Mission to Australia.
Correspondents include Lord Derby, Sir Maurice Hankey, L.S. Amery, Malcolm MacDonald, Lord Stonehaven, S.M. Bruce, Lord Bledisloe, Lord Galway and Lord Huntingfield.

15-page list available for reference.

Entry 19   Reels M2527–2533

Name **BALFOUR DARWIN LTD**
Title Records
Inclusive dates 1902–40
Quantity 7 reels of microfilm
Location of original Sheffield Archives, 52 Shoreham Street, Sheffield S1 4SP, England

Note
Steel manufacturers founded in 1865. In 1915 the name changed to Arthur Balfour & Co Ltd. Ultimately it became Balfour Darwin Ltd in 1961.

Description
1) Daybooks 1908–40 Australia and New Zealand containing orders for steel drills, files, saw blades and miners' picks, and giving shipping details. Firms include Eagle & Globe Steel Co Ltd (Melbourne and Sydney), Toowoomba Foundry Co Ltd and Australian Agricultural Co.
2) Papers 1902–03 relating to formation of Eagle & Globe Steel Co.

Two-page list available for reference.

Name **BANK OF ENGLAND**

Title Records

Inclusive dates 1781–1960

Quantity 47 reels of microfilm

Location of original Archive Department, Bank of England, Threadneedle Street, London EC2R 8AH, England

Note
Founded in 1694 as the first public bank in the British Isles, and since that time it has been at the centre of the British banking system. The Bank was nationalised in 1946.

Description
Accounts, correspondence, memoranda and other papers relating to Australia, New Zealand and Southeast Asia. They originated in various departments, including Accounts, Administration, Cashier's, Exchange Control, Economic Intelligence, Governor's and Secretary's, Overseas. Among the topics covered are: issues of stocks; UK trade with the Empire; Empire Marketing Board; Empire cotton; finances of the Dutch East Indies; Empire trade; migration within the British Empire; banking legislation; banking statistics; exchange control; money supply; gold reserves; wool shipment; gold production; mineral reports; affairs of Commonwealth Bank of Australia and Reserve Bank of Australia; Bank of New Zealand; and the 1930 Niemeyer Mission to Australia. There are also some letters and petitions from convicted forgers and transportees to the Bank of England requesting assistance to purchase stores and clothing for the voyage to New South Wales.

Major correspondents include W.B. Gunn, Sir James Allen, Ernest Toms, Sir Claude Reading, H.C. Coombs, Sir Harry Sheehan, S.M. Bruce, Sir Ernest Riddle, Sir Granville Ryrie, J.R. Collins, Sir Otto Niemeyer, Leslie Lefeaux, Walter Nash, Sir Henry Batterbee, Sir James Parr, E.C. Fussell, Sir James Garrick, Sir Thomas Robinson, Sir Alfred Davidson, L.G. Melville, Sir John Forrest, A.H. Lewis, L.U. Rusden and R.W. Dalton.

127-page list available for reference.

Name **BANKS, Sir Joseph, 1st Baronet (1743–1820)**

Title Correspondence

Inclusive dates 1768–1819

Quantity 1 reel of microfilm

Location of original Botany Library, British Museum (Natural History), Cromwell Road, South Kensington, London SW7 5BD, England

Note
Naturalist and patron of science. Dawson Turner (1775–1858) was a banker, botanist and bibliophile. While working on Joseph Banks' biography, Dawson Turner transcribed his correspondence.

Description
Correspondence of Sir Joseph Banks, transcribed by Dawson Turner, relating to voyages of the *Resolution*, *Bounty*, *Discovery* and other ships to Australia, New Zealand and the Pacific.

Correspondents include Daniel Solander, Lord Sandwich, Capt. James Cook, Capt. William Bligh, Lieut. Matthew Flinders and George Caley.

25-page list available for reference.

Name **BANKS, Sir Joseph, 1st Baronet (1743–1820)**

Title Papers

Inclusive dates 1768–1820

Quantity 1 reel of microfilm

Location of original British Library, Great Russell Street, London WC1 B3DG, England

Note
Naturalist and patron of science. President of the Royal Society 1778–1820.

Description
1) Letters from European scientists, mainly concerning botanical, zoological and ethnological specimens collected from the South Seas and also referring to French and Spanish voyages. Correspondents include C.P. Thunberg, J.F. Blumenbach, P.M.A. Broussonet, A. Malaspina, Jacques-Julien H. de La Billardière and P.B. Milius.

2) Letters 1786–1802 from Sir Charles Blagden, Secretary of the Royal Society.

3) Miscellaneous correspondence concerning the publication of Cook's voyages, the charts and plates, voyages of W. Bligh and G. Vancouver, and specimens collected in Australia, the Pacific and the East Indies. Correspondents include J. Matra, J. Webber, G. Nicol, W. Roxburgh and Robert Brown.

14-page list available for reference.

Entry 23 Reel M469

Name **BANKS, Sir Joseph, 1st Baronet (1743–1820)**

Title Correspondence

Inclusive dates 1773–1815

Quantity 1 reel of microfilm

Location of original Fitzwilliam Museum, Trumpington Street, Cambridge CB2 1RB, England

Note
Naturalist and patron of science.

Description
Correspondence comprising about 300 letters addressed to Banks, mainly in his capacity as President of the Royal Society.

Principal correspondents are Sir Charles Blagden, Jonas Dryander, James Mario Matra, Daniel Solander, James Lind, William Richardson, Erasmus Darwin, the Geological Society of London, W.H. Yate and Lord Monboddo. The letters largely relate to botanical matters but also concern personal matters. There is also a folder of letters with enclosures, c.1783, sent to Banks relating to mermaids.

Other correspondents include William Bishop, J.F. Blumenbach, C.A. de Calonne, James Cross, George Cumberland, Mary Delany, J.A. De Luc, John Farey, Samuel Felton, Robert Graham, Matthew Gregson, C.F. Greville, J.W. Griffith, Charles Hatchett, T. Hennah, Charles Hutton, John Jeffries, Charles Lindgren, V. Lunardi, A. Mello, W.R. Notcutt, G. Rose, Dr Thomas Percy, G. Nicol, Henry Salt, William Sheffield, Charles Townley, Dawson Turner, H. Ussher, Luke Young, Thomas Velley and John Walsh.

As well as seven letters written by Banks concerning botanical collections and addressed to Major William Price, Sir William Herschel and Dawson Turner, there is an extract from *The Athenaeum,* 26 December 1796, commenting on the publication of Banks' *Endeavour* journal.

Four-page list available for reference.

Entry 24 Reels M1973–1975

Name **BARING BROTHERS & COMPANY LTD**

Title Records

Inclusive dates 1827–80

Quantity 3 reels of microfilm

Location of original Guildhall Library, Guildhall, Aldermanbury, London EC2P 2EJ, England

Note
The firm Johann and Francis Baring & Co was set up as an import and export commission house in 1763. A new partnership, Baring Brothers & Co, was formed in 1806 and for a time it became the leading banking company in Europe, with extensive business in America and the Far East.

Description
1) Letters of Paine, Stricker & Co concerning coffee and sugar production in Java.
2) Correspondence 1853–57 relating to the sugar estate of E. Horsman in Penang.
3) Memorandum 1838 on cotton and wool production in Australia.
4) Papers 1855–58 relating to a loan to the Victorian Government for railway construction, including letters of Sir Henry Barkly and H.C.E. Childers.
5) Correspondence 1844–48 with Sir Evan MacKenzie on trade between Brisbane and London.
6) Correspondence 1830–66 with Hope & Co on trade with Dutch East Indies.
7) Papers 1848–50 concerning Kapunda Copper Mine.
8) Ships' papers 1869–80.
9) Letter-books 1831–70 containing copies of Baring Brothers business letters. Recipients include E. Horsman, Paine, Sticker & Co, Russell and Sturgis, Revesby & Co, and H.C.E. Childers.
10) Statistics of general trade 1829–58.

20-page list available for reference.

Entry 25   Reel M594

Name **BARLEE, Sir Frederick Palgrave
         (1827–1884)**
Title Papers
Inclusive dates 1876–84
Quantity 1 reel of microfilm
Location of original Mrs M.C. Barlee, Hertfordshire,
England

Note
Colonial Secretary of Western Australia 1855–75
and ex-officio member of both the Executive and
Legislative Councils. Lieut. Governor of British
Honduras 1877–82 and Administrator of Trinidad
1884.

Description
1) Letters from Barlee to his brother, the Rev.
    William Barlee of Norwich. The six letters
    written in 1876, after Barlee's return to England,
    contain a few references to Australia, where he
    still had business interests, but they are mostly
    concerned with British politics and with the
    procrastinations of the Colonial Office in giving
    him further employment.
2) 61 letters written from British Honduras May
    1877–August 1882, and three from Trinidad
    June–August 1884, dealing chiefly with family
    matters in England and his work and travels in
    the colonies. A further 39 letters were written
    in England, September 1882–May 1884.
3) Notebook January–August 1884, containing
    financial accounts.

One-page list available for reference.

Entry 26   Reels M2581–2586

Name **BARTLETT, Ellis Ashmead (1881–1931)**
Title Papers
Inclusive dates 1915–29
Quantity 6 reels of microfilm
Location of original Mr F.E. Ashmead Bartlett,
Marbella, Spain

Note
Journalist. Bartlett was special war correspondent
in Japan (1904), Morocco (1907), Tripoli (1911) and
Gallipoli (1915).

Description
Diaries, correspondence, notes, articles and other
papers relating to Gallipoli and Bartlett's visit to
Australia, New Zealand and America in 1916.

Correspondents include William Burdett-Courts,
W. Graham Greene, V. Maxwell, Sir Roger Keyes,
C.R. Mackery, Keith Murdoch, Lord Curzon and
Lord Northcliffe.

11-page list available for reference.

Entry 27   Reel M1858

Name **BATEMAN, Gregory (1825–1895)**
Title Papers
Inclusive dates 1858–96
Quantity 1 reel of microfilm
Location of original Mr C.J. Bateman, Devon, England

Note
Emigrant. Bateman came to Australia in 1858.

Description
1) Letters of Gregory Bateman to his brother
    Rev. Stafford Bateman, written from Liverpool,
    Melbourne, Kerang, Bendigo and Moama. They
    describe Bateman's journey to Australia on
    board the *Marco Polo* in 1858, life in Australia
    and family news.
2) Papers relating to Bateman's death in 1895 and
    his estate.

Two-page list available for reference.

Entry 28   Reel M1169

Name **BATHURST, Henry, 3rd Earl (1762–1834)**
Title Papers
Inclusive dates 1798–1829
Quantity 1 reel of microfilm
Location of original British Library, Great Russell
Street, London WC1B 3DG, England

Note
Tory politician. Secretary of State for War and
Colonies 1812–27.

Description
Correspondence concerning administration of New
South Wales, Van Diemen's Land and Singapore,
referring especially to colonial appointments, land
grants, Samuel Marsden and other clergy, recall of
Governor Brisbane in 1824–25 and dismissal of
J. Gellibrand as Attorney-General in Van Diemen's
Land in 1826.

Correspondents include H. Goulburn, R.W. Hay,
Wilmot Horton, Lord Hastings and J. Macarthur.

Nine-page list available for reference.

Entry 29   Reel M394

Name **BEATH, David A.**

Title Letters

Inclusive dates 1842–53

Quantity Portion of 1 reel of microfilm

Location of original Mitchell Library, State Library of New South Wales, Sydney NSW 2000

Note
Scottish emigrant to Victoria. By 1862 he had become a partner in a warehousing and clothing firm in Melbourne, which was still operating in 1927 as Beath, Schiess & Co.

Description
Three letters from Beath to his father from Melbourne, Moonee Ponds and outside Geelong in Victoria, describing life in the colony. They contain family news as well as descriptions of his farm and stock, records of the prices of food and other commodities, land sales, effects of the gold rush and discussion of a recently built foundry and flour mills.

One-page list available for reference

Entry 30   Reels M1126–1129

Name **BEAVERBROOK, William Maxwell Aitkin, 1st Baron (1879–1964)**

Title Papers

Inclusive dates 1912–64

Quantity 4 reels of microfilm

Location of original House of Lords Record Office, Houses of Parliament, Westminster, London SW1A 0PW, England

Note
Canadian-born businessman, owner of *Daily Express*, *Sunday Express* and *Evening Standard*, Minister for Aircraft Production 1940–41, Minister for Supply 1941–42. Author of several political and historical books.

Description
1) General correspondence 1928–64 referring especially to Empire Free Trade Crusade of 1929–31, press and politics in Australia and New Zealand, and imperial trade. Correspondents include Sir James Parr, F.L. McDougall, Lord Bledisloe, J.H. Scullin, Theodore Fink, Sir Frederick Doidge, Sir Keith Murdoch, H.V. Evatt, G. Lansell, Lord Bruce, R.G. Casey and Ann Mozley.

2) Special correspondence, including correspondence with Sir Frederick Doidge, R.D. Elliott, Sir David Low and Sir Earle Page.

3) World War II papers concerning munitions production in Australia, Cable and Wireless Ltd, construction of American airfields in the western Pacific, and civil aviation in Australia and New Zealand.

4) Letters 1962–63 from Australians and New Zealanders supporting Beaverbrook's campaign against the European Common Market.

14-page list available for reference.

Entry 31   Reels M591, M821, M1659–1660

Name **BEDFORDSHIRE RECORD OFFICE**

Title Collections

Inclusive dates 1774–1945

Quantity 4 reels of microfilm

Location of original Bedfordshire Record Office, County Hall, Bedford MK42 9AP, Bedfordshire, England

Description
M591:
1) Papers of Lieut. Richard Bastard and logbooks: log 1816–18 of the convict ship *Sir William Bensley*; log March–September 1819 of the convict ship *Lord Wellington* en route to New South Wales; list 1819 of women and children, giving numbers but no names (probably those on board *Lord Wellington*); notes 1820 made by Bastard when passing the Great Barrier Reef and through Torres Strait.

2) Letters from settlers in Australia: Charles Cartwright, Illawarra, New South Wales, 1842 and 1844; Joel Croxford, Ironbarks goldfields, New South Wales, 1864; Richard Dillingham, Van Diemen's Land, 1831–39; Priscilla Dodson (later Huxley), Gympie, Queensland, 1886 and 1893; John Feazey, Melbourne, 1844; Dr George Witt, Sydney, 1851.

3) Newspaper cuttings: *Adelaide Observer* 1914 and *Bedfordshire Times* 1914; article 'Two Pioneers' relating to George Dodson and his wife.

4) Legal documents: probate of the will of Thomas Fyshe Palmer 1793; mortgage 1858 mentioning Gerard Phillips and William Northwood, timber merchant, for part of original town grant near Market Wharf, Sydney; mortgage 1841 on property of Thomas Potter Macqueen; probate 1877–80 of Henry Marshall, Bedford.

5) Journal July–October 1853 of a voyage to Sydney, possibly by Jemima Hitchcock.

M821:
1) Bedfordshire Quarter Sessions records: 'Transportation for life', 1825–52, and 'Transportations and sentences of penal servitude', 1801–78, giving names of convicts and ages, offences, sentences and disposals.

2) Board of Guardians records: selections from Bedford Union in-letters 1837–58, mainly from the Poor Law Commission, London, and the Land and Emigration Commission, London.

3) Bute Estate papers: letters and lists 1841–46 referring to the property of J.C.S. McDouall and his father, W. McDouall, in New South Wales and New Zealand.

4) Wilshere papers: correspondence 1818–23 of William Wilshere as Chairman of the Bedfordshire Quarter Sessions. Convicts mentioned include Richard Beardsley, Mr Arnold, Mr Barnes, William King, J. Gascoigne, George Smith and Norman Harkins.

5) De Grey papers: letters 1774 and 1780 from Jemima, Marchioness Grey and Baroness Lucas, regarding HMS *Adventure* and the death of Capt. James Cook.

6) Whitbread papers: letters and other papers 1793–1841 of Samuel Whitbread, MP, regarding the transportation of convicts, their employment in New South Wales, conditions on board the hulks, and the deposition of Governor Bligh. Correspondents include William Roscoe, Jorgen Jorgenson, Edward Abbott, R.H. Bennett and Thomas Fyshe Palmer.

7) Miscellaneous items: document 1827 containing terms upon which land was granted to settlers in New South Wales and Van Diemen's Land; letter 1892 from Albert H. Culpin, referring to the Broken Hill strike and maritime disturbances.

15-page list available for reference.

M1659–1660:
1) Documents 1896–1943 concerning properties of Howard Spensley in Melbourne.

2) Papers 1822–76 of Field Family, including letter of John Field in Melbourne and Octavius Field, Fred Martell and Henry Martell in Geelong, Ballarat and other towns in Victoria.

3) Documents and notebook 1926–38 of Rev. G.C.H. Phillips, a priest in the Diocese of Waikato, New Zealand.

4) Letters 1831–39 of Richard Dillingham, a convict in Van Diemen's Land.

5) Papers 1850–88 of Duncan Kennedy, including letters of Donald Kennedy, Jessie Kennedy and William Campbell in Melbourne referring to gold

discoveries, wool shipments, trade, prices, colonial politics and Scots in Victoria.

Nine-page list available for reference.

Entry 32   Reel M714

Name **BENNETT, Jonathon**

Title Logbook

Inclusive dates 1850–52

Quantity 1 reel of microfilm

Location of original Mr P.S. Laurie, Surrey, England

Note
Officer on the trading vessel *Margaret* which sailed in 1850 from Liverpool to San Francisco, visiting Tahiti, Sydney, Bombay and China.

Description
Logbook 24 May 1850–8 March 1852 recording the ship's voyage from Liverpool to China. The entries record daily routine aboard, weather observations, the navigational course of the ship, and behaviour of the crew, including desertions. Most of the crew were discharged at Port Jackson and new hands hired.

Two-page list available for reference.

Entry 33   Reels M2762–2765

Name **BENSON, Edward White, Archbishop (1829–1896)**

Title Correspondence

Inclusive dates 1883–96

Quantity 4 reels of microfilm

Location of original Library, Lambeth Palace, London SE1 7JU, England

Note
Bishop of Truro 1877–82, Archbishop of Canterbury 1882–96.

Description
Official correspondence relating to dioceses in Australia, New Zealand, Melanesia and Hawaii.

Main correspondents include W.T.T. Webber, G.W. Kennion, A. Willis, D.F. Sandford, E.W. Benson, S. Thornton, H.H. Montgomery, W. Saumrez Smith, Alfred Barry, S.T. Nevill, Henry J.C. Harper, H.L. Jenner, J.R. Selwyn, M. Thomas, W.G. Cowie, A. Willis, S.E. Marsden, James Moorhouse, A.B. Suter, R.H. Codrington, H.W. Tucker and R.T. Davidson.

124-page list available for reference.

Entry 34 Reel M1684

Name **BENTHAM, Jeremy (1748–1832)**

Title Papers

Inclusive dates 1790–1820

Quantity 1 reel of microfilm

Location of original British Library, Great Russell Street, London WC1B 3DG, England

Note
Social philosopher and author of books, pamphlets and articles on jurisprudence, criminal law, political theory, ethics and economics.

Description
Selections from papers mainly relating to Bentham's interest in penal reform, his opposition to the transportation of convicts to Botany Bay, and his unsuccessful attempts over many years to persuade the Government to adopt his scheme of penitentiary houses (panopticons).

Correspondents include Sir John Parnell, Sir Charles Bunbury, Capt. J. Hunter, Spencer Perceval, Sir Frederick Eden and David Collins.

Six-page list available for reference.

Entry 35 Reels M713, M866

Name **BERKSHIRE RECORD OFFICE**

Title Collections

Inclusive dates 1744–1887

Quantity 2 reels of microfilm

Location of original Berkshire Record Office, Shire Hall, Shinfield Park, Reading, Berks RG2 9XD, England

Description
M713:
1) Bouverie-Pusey Family: letter 1854 enclosing letter from Sir William Denison to the Duke of Newcastle requesting authority for the purchase of agricultural implements.
2) Benyon Family: two letters 1836 regarding a convict, Thomas Mills of Sydney.
3) Cooke, Cooper and Barry, solicitors: papers 1846–83 relating to marriage settlements including references to John W. Boyce of Bundaberg, Queensland, and William C. Hulme of Bendigo, Victoria.
4) Buscot Estate papers: letters 1864 from R.C. Crawford, Hill End, New South Wales, concerning affairs in New South Wales and containing a brief mention of the Maori Wars.

5) Crawford Family: correspondence 1839–87 mainly of Capt. James C. Crawford, including letters from his wife Jane relating to his emigration to New Zealand, geological work and their property, Miramar, in New Zealand; naval orders 1811–12 to Capt. Crawford, mainly on the *Hussar* in the East Indies.
6) Lenthall Family: 14 photographs of the family in Australia.
7) Pleydell-Bouverie Family: correspondence 1853–56 of William, 3rd Earl of Radnor, concerning his sponsorship of Mary Ann Sherwood as an emigrant to Melbourne.
8) Broome Pinniger, solicitor: two printed maps 1840–41, one of New Zealand by James Wylde, the other of Wellington by Francis Molesworth.
9) Stevens Family of Bradfield: documents 1744–65 relating to the private trade of John Stevens in the East Indies and China.
10) Walter Family: title deeds 1861–81 concerning the Barklamb Family of Benalla, Victoria.
11) Reynolds Family of Faringdon: documents 1838–56 mainly relating to Robert Huntley of Balmain, New South Wales, and his family.
12) Williams Family of Warfield: correspondence 1843–50 relating to Thomas Williams of Adelaide.
13) Tilehurst parish records: three printed statements 1829, 1835, on emigration to Western and South Australia.

M866:
1) Correspondence 1840–66 of the Barrett Family, including letters from James W. Barrett describing the gold diggers riot in 1854 at Ballarat, Victoria, and visits to New Zealand.
2) Letters 1852–56 of Frank H. Weedon and Edward M. Weedon describing conditions on the goldfields in Victoria, and farm work in New Zealand.
3) Account 1838 of Josh Mason of his experiences on being transported to New South Wales after the agricultural riots of 1830.

Eight-page list available for reference.

Entry 36   Reels M2616–2618

Name **BEVERIDGE, Sir William Henry, 1st Baron (1879–1963)**

Title Papers

Inclusive dates 1921–62

Quantity 3 reels of microfilm

Location of original British Library of Political and Economic Science, London School of Economics and Political Science, 10 Portugal Street, London WC2A 2HD, England

Note
1st Baron Beveridge (created 1945). Director, London School of Economics 1919–37, Master of University College, Oxford 1937–44. Liberal MP 1944–45. Author of many works including *Full Employment in a Free Society* (1944).

Description
General and personal correspondence, a diary and other papers relating to Beveridge's visit to Australia and New Zealand in 1948, and papers relating to his lectures and broadcasts, and the 'Crusade for world government'.

Correspondents include Lucy Mair, Sir Douglas Copland, G. Fitzpatrick, Sir Walter Nash, Sir Richard Boyer, D. Raphael, A.G. Downs, Sir Patrick Duff and G. Billing.

13-page list available for reference.

Entry 37   Reels M825–827, M2118

Name **BIRMINGHAM CITY ARCHIVES**

Title Collections

Inclusive dates 1824–1953

Quantity 4 reels of microfilm

Location of original Birmingham Central Library, Chamberlain Square, Birmingham B3 3HQ, England

Description
M825–827:
1) Alston collection: correspondence and documents 1780–1851 concerning a disputed title to property of the Egginton Family, including letters from Walter Egginton, transported to New South Wales.
2) Lee collection: 18 agreements 1881–91 for the sale of patents for improving cable tramways; two plans 1842–43 of Nelson, New Zealand, showing settlement blocks.
3) Papers of Sir Charles Adderley, 1st Baron Norton: minutes 1850–51 of the Council of the Society for the Reform of Colonial

Governments; receipts for New Zealand stock c.1892–1908 from banks and institutions.
4) Travel diaries 1893–1914 of Helen Caddick, containing descriptions of India, Australasia, Pacific Islands and China.
5) Printed material: *Colonization Circular, Part VI, New South Wales* (1880), *Information for Emigrants and Others* (1881), *Mount Victoria Goldfield: Report* (1903) and *Railway Guide of New South Wales* (1881).
6) Photographs 1893–1914 from Helen Caddick's diaries of Hawaii, Australia and New Zealand; photographs 1870–1901 taken by Sir Benjamin Stone, including inauguration of the Australian Commonwealth in Sydney 1901, scenes in New Zealand, Fiji, Hawaii, Samoa and an album 1873 on Eastern Asia containing photographs of Borneo, Java, Singapore, Sumatra and Batavia.

Two-page list available for reference.

M2118:
1) Papers 1888–1937 of Sir Richard Threlfall, including letters, photographs and papers written while Professor of Physics at Sydney University.
2) Records 1922–30 of John Holt concerning organs supplied to churches in New Zealand.
3) Cadbury Collection, including photographs of cocoa estates in Samoa, letters of George Cadbury to Thomas Cooper, the representative of Cadbury Brothers in Australia (1888–1922), and letters written by Barrow Cadbury on a visit to Australia in 1930.
4) Drawings of railway locomotives and other rolling stock supplied by Metropolitan Cammell Carriage and Railway Co to railways in Australia and New Zealand.

Five-page list available for reference.

Entry 38   Reel M97

Name **BLACKBURN, David (d.1795)**

Title Correspondence

Inclusive dates 1785–96

Quantity 1 reel of microfilm

Location of original Mr T. Grix, Norfolk, England

Note
Master HM Armed Tender *Supply*. He sailed with the First Fleet when it left England in May 1787. In early 1791 the *Supply* was placed under his command to carry a detachment of the New South

Wales Corps, settlers and stores to Norfolk Island whence it returned with Capt. Hunter and the crew of HMS *Sirius*.

Description
Correspondence of David Blackburn with his sister Margaret and his mother. His letters provide an interesting account of early life at Port Jackson describing Aborigines such as Bennelong, his acquaintance with Governor Phillip and the problems of inadequate food supplies. Early letters concern the preparations for the departure of the *Supply* from Portsmouth and mention a delay while a code of laws was being drawn up for the colony. There are descriptions of Norfolk Island and the discovery of Lord Howe Island.

The collection contains certificates belonging to Blackburn, and includes instructions, signed by Governor Phillip, to sail to Norfolk Island in 1791.

Other letters are from Blackburn's acquaintances and family, concerning his death at the Royal Naval Hospital at Haslar.

One-page list available for reference.

Entry 39   Reels M2806–2819

Name **BLACKWOOD, Beatrice (1889–1975)**
Title Papers
Inclusive dates 1929–74
Quantity 14 reels of microfilm
Location of original Pitt Rivers Museum, Oxford University, South Parks Road, Oxford OX1 3PP, England

Note
Anthropologist and ethnologist. Blackwood worked in America, Melanesia and New Guinea. She worked for over 30 years at the Pitt Rivers Museum.

Description
1) Working papers: diaries, notebooks and notes relating to Blackwood's research in North Solomons, New Guinea, New Britain, Java, Sumatra, Borneo and Sarawak (1929–37).
2) Correspondence 1931–74 concerning Blackwood's work. Main correspondents are A.P. Elkin, A.C. Haddon, M.J. Herskovitz, C.G. Seligman, H.D. Skinner, F. Speiser and J. Wingate Todd.
3) Material relating to the publication of *Both Sides of the Buka Passage* (1935).

18-page list available for reference.

Entry 40   Reel M853

Name **BLANDOWSKI, William (b.1822)**
Title Photographs
Inclusive dates 1862
Quantity 1 reel of microfilm
Location of original Haddon Library, Museum of Archaeology and Ethnology, Cambridge CB2 3DZ, England

Note
Naturalist, Victorian government zoologist 1854–57. Led an expedition to explore the natural history of the region at the junction of the Murray and Darling Rivers in 1856–57.

Description
Album of 142 photographs of engravings, mostly of Australian Aborigines, entitled *Australien in 142 Photographischen*.

Four-page list of the photograph titles available.

Entry 41   Reel M824

Name **BLENCOWE, John Walcot, Rev. (1886–1964)**
Title Papers
Inclusive dates 1908–32
Quantity 1 reel of microfilm
Location of original Mrs M. Blencowe, Sussex, England

Note
Missionary and schoolteacher, attached to the Melanesian Mission 1909–12. Ordained in 1913 and was an army chaplain during World War I. Guy F. Bury went to Norfolk Island in 1911 to work as a missionary, but died shortly after his arrival.

Description
1) Correspondence comprising 24 letters 1909–11 from Blencowe to his parents describing his voyage to Australia and his work on Norfolk Island and Santa Cruz; five letters 1908–13 to Blencowe and his father about his appointment to Melanesia and news of the mission, and 16 letters 1910–15 in the Melanesian language.
2) Two notebooks containing brief entries May–October 1910 arranged by village and a Mota–English vocabulary arranged alphabetically.
3) Miscellaneous documents including a list of the voyages made by Blencowe 1909–18, a printed list of Melanesian Mission personnel 1911,

a report headed 'Conversations with J.W. Blencowe 26 June 1932', six drafts for speeches and letters, printed map of the Santa Cruz group of islands and newspaper cuttings about HMS *Torch* and HMS *Mongolia*.

4) Printed material comprising:*Thoughts We All Share* by the Rev. John Walcot Blencowe (99 p.); *Home Letters* by Guy F. Bury, addendum by J.W. Blencowe; *My Last Voyage* by Bishop Cecil Wilson, describing a journey in 1911 around the islands of Melanesia.

5) Photographs, mainly by J.W. Beattie of Hobart, of Melanesian Mission personnel, islanders and their dwellings, boats, churches, in the New Hebrides, Solomon, Torres and Banks Islands, San Cristobal, Santa Cruz and Norfolk Island.

Five-page list available for reference.

Entry 42   Reels M1924–1926

Name **BODLEIAN LIBRARY**
Title Collections
Inclusive dates 1676–1894
Quantity 3 reels of microfilm
Location of original Bodleian Library, University of Oxford, Broad Street, Oxford OX1 3BG, England

Description
1) Acland Papers 1841–92 including letters of W. Acland written from the Australian Naval Station 1883–85 and correspondence with the entomologist Rev. William Cotton 1841–46.

2) Papers 1839–52 of the poet Arthur H. Clough, including letters of J.P. Gell and Thomas Arnold in Hobart.

3) Letter-books 1813–31 of Calcutta merchant John Palmer. Correspondents include Lachlan Macquarie, E. Riley, T. Harrington and R. Jones.

4) Letters 1851–56 of Sir Edmund Du Cane to his family concerning his life in Western Australia, treatment of convicts, road-building, travels and racial conflict.

5) Letters 1798–1802 of Rev. Richard Johnson to William Gilpin referring to his work in Sydney.

6) Papers 1840–52 of Jacob Hagen concerning properties in South Australia.

7) Letters 1869–85 of W. Henley Rawlings to Caroline Napier describing life in Queensland and New South Wales.

8) Letters 1872–94 of historian and Victorian politician Charles H. Pearson concerning political and social conditions in Australia, visit of A. Deakin to England in 1887, and writings

on democracy. Correspondents include James Bryce, Sir Charles Dilke, Sir George Goschen and John Morley.

9) Letters 1862–64 of E.C. Dunn of Geelong to book collector Sir Thomas Phillipps.

10) Letters 1862–84 of Sir George Grey and J. Henniker Heaton to bookseller Bernard Quaritch.

11) Papers 1846–69 of Sir Henry Taylor, Colonial Office official.

12) Papers 1791–1870 of William Wilberforce and Bishop Samuel Wilberforce relating to missions in the Pacific Islands, the Church in New Zealand, convict transportation, the endowment of colonial bishoprics, the 1852–53 Colonial Church Bill, and the establishment of the Melanesian Mission. Correspondents include Rev. S. Marsden, Bishop G.A. Selwyn, Angela Burdett-Coutts, W.E. Gladstone, Sir James Stephen, Bishop E. Hobhouse, Bishop F.R. Nixon, Bishop T. Staley and Bishop F. McDougall.

13) Correspondence 1854–82 of sculptor Thomas Woolner and copy of a diary he kept on the Victorian goldfields 1852–53.

28-page list available for reference.

Entry 43   Reel M724

Name **BOND, John James (1831–1922)**
Title Diary
Inclusive dates 1915
Quantity 1 reel of microfilm
Location of original Misses A. and E. Bond, Somerset, England

Note
Visitor to Australia in 1853–54, where he stayed with his uncle at Benalla, Victoria. On his return to England he farmed in Somerset until his retirement in 1889.

Description
Diary (89 p.) written in 1915 by Bond recalling his voyage to and stay in Australia 1853–1854. He quotes from letters he wrote to his mother at this time and adds some details gathered from letters written to him from Australia in 1868 and 1874. The first part of the diary describes the voyage to Australia in the *Lady Flora*. He continued his voyage to Sydney and returned to Melbourne in the steamer *Waratah*. He stayed with his uncle at Benalla, Victoria, for some months and gives a detailed account of the town and its residents.

He also gives his impressions of Sydney and Melbourne and notes in some detail the features of buildings and the prices of certain commodities. Before sailing from Melbourne in the *Marco Polo* Bond visited the Victorian goldfields of Ballarat and Bendigo and describes problems experienced on the diggings, such as lack of water and poor communications.

Two-page list available for reference.

Entry 44   Reel M2578

Name **BOOTH FAMILY**
Title Papers
Inclusive dates 1864 and 1957–64
Quantity 1 reel of microfilm
Location of original Mr Chris Booth, Cheshire, England

Note
Lieut. Col. Henry Jackson Booth (b.1864) and his son Lieut. Col. Henry Booth served in the 43rd Light Infantry in New Zealand. Henry Jackson Booth was killed at the Battle of Gate Pa, Tauranga in 1864.

Description
Correspondence, cuttings and souvenir programs kept by Booth and his son.
Correspondents include Major F. Synge, Lieut. Col. G. Garland, Fienne M. Colville, Thomas Horan, Phillip Booth and Sir Bernard Fergusson.

One-page list available for reference.

Entry 45   Reel M1863

Name **BOURKE FAMILY**
Title Papers
Inclusive dates 1809–55
Quantity 1 reel of microfilm
Location of original Mrs Bridget Agate, Pewsey, England

Note
Sir Richard Bourke (1777–1855), Governor of New South Wales 1831–38. His son Richard Bourke (1812–1904) served as his private secretary in Sydney and his daughter Anne married Edward Deas Thomson, the Colonial Secretary.

Description
1) Diary 1831 of Anne Bourke on the voyage from England to New South Wales on the *Margaret.*

2) Family correspondence 1822–55, including letters of Sir Richard Bourke, Elizabeth Bourke, Richard Bourke, Anne Bourke and T. Spring-Rice.

Three-page list available for reference.

Entry 46   Reel M2349

Name **BOURNER FAMILY**
Title Papers
Inclusive dates 1960–88
Quantity 1 reel of microfilm
Location of original Mrs Sheila Bourner, Somerset, England

Note
Sheila Bourner (nee Carpenter) submitted three entries into the Historical Association's Australian Bicentenary Competition, based on her research into her family history. Charles Carpenter (1801–1887) was her great-great-grandfather who was transported to Australia in 1832.

Description
The papers include manuscripts by Sheila Bourner concerning Charles Carpenter, his early life, transportation to Van Diemen's Land in 1832, his marriage to Charlotte Yaxley, and letters and photographs from Australian relations Alan Wass, Lilian Robinson and Winifred Birchall.

One-page list available for reference.

Entry 47   Reel M1920

Name **BOWEN, Sir George Ferguson (1821–1899)**
Title Cutting book
Inclusive dates 1868–78
Quantity 1 reel of microfilm
Location of original Mr Peter Newman, Devon, England

Note
Governor of Queensland 1859–68, Governor of New Zealand 1868–73, Governor of Victoria 1873–79, Governor of Mauritius 1879–82 and Governor of Hong Kong 1882–86.

Description
The cutting book was kept by Sir George Bowen in New Zealand (pp. 1–357) and Victoria (pp. 358–550). It includes an index and annotations by Bowen, but the cuttings are mainly undated.

Two-page list available for reference.

Entry 48   Reels M1174–1175

Name **BOXER, C.R., Professor (b.1904)**

Title Manuscripts

Inclusive dates 1569–1811

Quantity 2 reels of microfilm (film quality is uneven as these manuscripts did not reproduce well)

Location of original Professor C.R. Boxer, Hertfordshire, England

Note
The manuscripts were collected by C.R. Boxer, Camoens Professor of Portugese at the University of London, 1947–51 and 1953–67, and author of many books on the Portuguese and Dutch maritime empires.

Description
1) Letter-book 1615–20 of Capt. William Keeling describing the third voyage undertaken by the East India Co and referring to trade with the East Indies and Anglo–Dutch rivalry.
2) Manuscript copy 1569 of description by Gabriel Rebello of the Spice Islands and disputes of the Portuguese and Spanish for their possession.
3) Journal 1731–32 of voyage of the *Flora* from Batavia to the Netherlands.
4) Manuscript 1733–41 on the trade and commerce of Java.
5) Spanish journal 1590 describing the Far East and South East Asia.
6) Logs 1634–36, 1668, of galleons on voyages from Manila to Acapulco.
7) Letter of appointment 1632 of Anthony Van Diemen as Commander of the Dutch East India Co fleet.

Two-page list available for reference.

Entry 49   Reels M2634–2635

Name **BOYLE FAMILY**

Title Papers

Inclusive dates 1892–1901

Quantity 2 reels of microfilm

Location of original Rt Hon. the Earl of Glasgow, Ayrshire, Scotland

Note
David Boyle, 7th Earl of Glasgow (1833–1915), was Governor of New Zealand 1892–97.

Description
1) Papers 1892–1901 covering the 7th Earl of Glasgow's term as Governor of New Zealand, including correspondence, addresses, cuttings, photographs and scrapbooks. Correspondents include Lord Glasgow, Richard Seddon and Lord Ranfurly.
2) Papers of Robert Elphinstone Boyle, including letters from his brother Lord Glasgow and nephew Lord Kelburn in New Zealand and Samoa.

Five-page list available for reference.

Entry 50   Reel M977

Name **BRENNAND, Stephen**

Title Papers

Inclusive dates 1842–61

Quantity 1 reel of microfilm

Location of original Rawtenstall Public Library, Haslingden Road, Rossendale, Lancashire BB4 6QU, England

Description
1) Journal kept by Stephen Brennand aboard the clipper ship *Harbinger* during a voyage from England to Adelaide, August–November 1883. The journal gives an account of conditions on board, weather experienced, and the diarist's impressions of the crew and his fellow passengers. The journal concludes with a list of passengers on board, together with a list of deaths among the passengers. A typescript copy of the journal follows the manuscript version.
2) Two letters from members of the Preston Family 1860–61 written from Heathcote, Victoria.
3) 15 letters from America 1842–57 written by members of the Hopkinson and Livesey families.

Entry 51   Reels M3061–3067

Name **BRIDGE, Sir Cyprian (1839–1924)**

Title Papers

Inclusive dates 1881–1904

Quantity 7 reels of microfilm

Location of original National Maritime Museum, Romney Road, Greenwich, London SE10 9NF, England

Note
Joined the Royal Navy in 1851. Bridge was in Australia in command of HMS *Espiegle* (1881–85) and was Commander-in-Chief of the Australian Station (1894–98).

Description

1) Journals 1895–98. Subjects include visits to Australian and New Zealand ports, movement of French and German ships and steam trials.

2) Letter-books 1881–98. Subjects include Pacific labour trade, *Isabelle* massacre, Presbyterian missionaries, trial of seamen on *Flora*, registration of titles to land by British subjects in Melanesian islands, and steam trials.

3) Other papers 1894–1904. Subjects include Australian Federation, possible French annexation of New Hebrides, defences of Australia and New Zealand, Australian Naval Agreement Bill, Samoan affairs, surveying, and socialism in Australia.

Seven-page list available for reference.

Entry 52   Reel M1919

Name **BRISTOL RECORD OFFICE**
Title Collections
Inclusive dates 1833–1905
Quantity 1 reel of microfilm
Location of original Bristol Record Office, 'B' Bond Warehouse, Smeaton Road, Bristol BS1 6XN, England

Description

1) British Corporation of the Poor: contracts 1833 for the passages of paupers to Australia.

2) Correspondence 1858–61 between G. Chick of Bristol and James B. Gibbs of Avoca, Victoria, and Adelaide.

3) Letters 1840–49 of Daniel R. Lang and Susannah M. Lang of Melbourne.

4) Journal 1852 kept by a steerage passenger on a voyage of SS *Great Britain* to Melbourne.

5) Letters 1848–79 of John Clement of Glen Innes and Armidale, New South Wales.

Three-page list available for reference.

Entry 53   Reels M2669–2677

Name **BRITISH LIBRARY**
Title Collections
Inclusive dates 1642–1888
Quantity 9 reels of microfilm
Location of original British Library, Great Russell Street, London WC1B 3DG, England

Note

Selections from several major collections at the British Library were filmed separately and are entered under the names of the individuals or organisations that created them.

Description

1) Journal 1683–86 of W.A. Cawley on a voyage to East Indies and China.

2) Journal 1681–91 of voyages of William Dampier and others.

3) Petition and letters 1712–16 of J. Welbe for expedition to discover Terra Australis.

4) Journal 1813 of G. Blaxland on expedition across Blue Mountains.

5) Order book 1740–43 of Commander G. Anson referring to voyage around the world.

6) Account 1790–92 by J. McCluer of voyage to New South Wales and East Indies.

7) Account 1772–74 of second Pacific voyage of Capt. James Cook.

8) Papers 1801–06 of Philip Yorke, 3rd Earl of Hardwicke, referring to transportation of Irish convicts.

9) Papers 1826–67 of mathematician Charles Babbage including letters of Sir John Franklin, R.H. Horne and Sir Richard MacDonnell.

10) Order book 1813–16 of Lieut. Governor T. Davey of Van Diemen's Land.

11) Correspondence 1840–79 of zoologist Sir Richard Owen. Correspondents include Sir William Martin and Lady Martin in New Zealand.

12) Papers 1859–86 of writer Samuel Butler, mainly relating to his life in New Zealand 1859–65, and correspondence with Julius von Haast.

13) Papers 1854–86 of Mary Gladstone, including letters of Sir Arthur Gordon and H. Cust.

14) Papers 1862–88 of naturalist Alfred Wallace, including letters of Charles Darwin, F. von Mueller, F.W. Hutton and E. Atkinson.

15) Records 1830–87 of publisher Richard Bentley and Son, including agreements and correspondence with Ada Cross, Rosa Praed, Marcus Clarke and E.A. Petherick.

16) Manuscript poem by Richard Horne entitled 'Ancient Idols'.

17) Papers of Charles Fox, including memorandum 1783 of J. Matra on colonisation of NSW.

18) Papers 1836–50 of Lord Palmerston referring to French activities in the Pacific.

19) Papers 1834–37 of Sir Charles Napier referring to colonisation of South Australia.

71-page list available for reference.

Name **BRITISH LIBRARY OF POLITICAL AND ECONOMIC SCIENCE**

Title Collections

Inclusive dates 1816–1948

Quantity 4 reels of microfilm

Location of original British Library of Political and Economic Science, London School of Economics and Political Science, 10 Portugal Street, London WC2A 2HD, England

Description
1) Correspondence 1920–34 of economist Edwin Cannan, including letters of D.B. Copland, F.C. Benham and A.G.B. Fisher.
2) Diaries 1930 and a notebook 1932 of Sir Walter Citrine, General Secretary of Trade Union Congress, kept during a world tour.
3) Papers 1937–48 of Hugh Dalton, including a diary of a visit to Australia and New Zealand.
4) Papers 1845–63 of Sir Joshua Jebb relating to transportation of convicts to Australia.
5) Papers 1939–40 of anthropologist Phyllis M. Kaberry relating to her work in the Sepik district of New Guinea. Includes correspondence from Margaret Mead.
6) Papers 1884–1940 of politician George Lansbury including references to land development in Australia 1929–30.
7) Papers 1853–93 of the philosopher John Stuart Mill and Harriet Taylor, including letters of Arthur Hardy of Adelaide.
8) Papers 1898–1904 of Sidney and Beatrice Webb, including diary and letters relating to their visit to New Zealand and Australia in 1898.
9) Papers 1904–30 of economist and political scientist Graham Wallas, including letters of R.C. Mills.
10) Correspondence 1866–76 of Florence and Rosamund Davenport-Hill.
11) Papers 1895–1911 of W. Pember Reeves, New Zealand Agent General in London, including letters of E. Treagear, M. Cohen, Sir Joseph Ward, Sir Henry Atkinson and R. Seddon.

34-page list available for reference.

Name **BRITISH MEDICAL ASSOCIATION**

Title Records

Inclusive dates 1914–58

Quantity 2 reels of microfilm

Location of original Contemporary Medical Archives Centre, Wellcome Institute for the History of Medicine, 183 Euston Road, London NW1 2BE, England

Note
Founded in 1832 by Sir Charles Hastings. The first Australian branch was set up in South Australia in 1879. In 1962 the six BMA branches in Australia were formally dissolved and the Australian Medical Association was founded.

Description
The records include correspondence, minutes and extracts relating to the Australian branches of the BMA. Correspondents include Dr R.H. Todd, Sir Henry Brackenbury, Dr J.C. Matthews, Dr J. Newman Morris, George S. Thompson, Dr Robert V. Storer and Dr John G. Hunter.

Seven-page list available for reference.

Name **BRITISH MUSEUM, Department of Ethnography**

Title Paintings

Inclusive dates c.1830–80

Quantity 1 reel of microfilm and black and white prints

Location of original Department of Ethnography, British Museum, Great Russell Street, London WC1B 3DG, England

Note
Thomas Bock (1790–1857) was transported to Van Diemen's Land in 1823 and was granted a full pardon in 1833. He operated a gallery in Hobart and was the first portrait painter to practise professionally in Tasmania. As well as painting portraits of many of the well-known residents of Hobart, he also did a series of studies of Aborigines for Lady Franklin.

Robert Dowling (1827–86) came to Tasmania with his father, Rev. Henry Dowling, in 1839. He received lessons from Thomas Bock and exhibited at the Royal Academy, London, 1859–1882.

Description
23 watercolours comprising selections from a folder labelled 'Portfolio 4118 Tasmanian Aborigines'. They comprise drawings and paintings of Tasmanian Aborigines by Thomas Bock and Robert Dowling and a painting by Benjamin Duterreau, also of a Tasmanian Aborigine.

16-page list available for reference.

Entry 57   Reels M2523–2526

Name **BRITISH MUSEUM (NATURAL HISTORY)**
Title Case and policy files
Inclusive dates 1919–72
Quantity 4 reels of microfilm
Location of original Archives Department, Natural History Museum, Cromwell Road, South Kensington, London SW7 5BD, England

Description
Directors' correspondence, cuttings, photographs, reports, memoranda, circulars and minutes of meetings on:
1) Australian bird expedition 1961–66.
2) Harold Hall Australian expeditions 1961–68.
3) Expeditions to search for tertiary mammals in Western Australia 1966–67.
4) L.E. Cheeseman's Pacific expeditions 1928–58.
5) Expeditions to Galapagos Islands 1935–60.
6) Expeditions to Gunong Benom, Malaysia, 1966–67.
7) Expeditions to New Guinea 1963–65 and 1969–70.
8) Expeditions to North Borneo 1947–63 and 1960–64.
9) Expeditions of W.J. Potter to New Guinea 1919–22.
10) Expeditions to Rennell Island 1950–62.
11) Expeditions of John Rowett and Ernest Shackleton to Antarctica 1921–23.
12) Expeditions to Solomon Islands 1946–66.
13) Expeditions of Capt. G.H. Wilkins to Australia and the Arctic 1923–59.
14) Plumage Bills 1920–25, 1921, 1921–27 and 1959–68.
15) Australian Museum, Sydney, 1931–66.
16) A. Liversidge collection of minerals 1927.
17) G. Rigg collection of minerals and ethnological items 1944–47.
18) A.F. Wollaston collection of New Guinea ethnological specimens 1921–39.

19) Botanic Gardens, Bogor, Java, 1970–71.
20) Colonial Office 1922–55.

21-page list available for reference.

Entry 58   Reels M2768–2769

Name **BRITISH MUSEUM (NATURAL HISTORY), Anthropology Library and Archive Section**
Title Records
Inclusive dates 1884–1962
Quantity 2 reels of microfilm
Location of original Natural History Museum, Cromwell Road, South Kensington, London SW7 5BD, England

Description
1) Papers c.1884–90 of Sir William Flower on physical anthropology.
2) Papers of George Williamson relating to his collection of human skulls.
3) Correspondence 1910–57 of Anthropology Department, mostly relating to skeletal remains.
4) Subject files 1946–62 of Anthropology Department.

12-page list available for reference.

Entry 59   Reel M2708

Name **BRITISH MUSEUM (NATURAL HISTORY), Arachnida Section**
Title Correspondence
Inclusive dates 1892–1940
Quantity 1 reel of microfilm
Location of original Archive Section, Natural History Museum, Cromwell Road, South Kensington, London SW7 5BD, England

Description
1) Correspondence 1892–1903 of R. Pocock, relating to spiders, scorpions and other specimens from Australia, New Zealand, Malaya, New Guinea and Fiji.
2) Correspondence 1906–34 concerning spiders, scorpions, mites and other specimens. Correspondents include A. Dixie, J.B. Cleland and Gilbert Archey.

Ten-page list available for reference.

Entry 60   Reels M2903–2909

Name **BRITISH MUSEUM (NATURAL HISTORY), Bryozoa Section**

Title Collections

Inclusive dates 1858–1987

Quantity 7 reels of microfilm

Location of original Bryozoa Section, Natural History Museum, Cromwell Road, South Kensington, London SW7 5BD, England

Description
1) Papers 1858–1905 relating to scientific papers. Correspondents include P.H. MacGillivray.

2) Papers 1900–14 concerning Antarctic expeditions.

3) Correspondence 1875–1987 of Bryozoa Section, including letters of Eliza Jelly, Sir Douglas Mawson, David Brown, Dennis Gordon, Douglas Hall, Garry Russ, Robin Wass and Michael Cooper.

4) Papers of F.W. Hutton on New Zealand polyzoa.

16-page list available for reference.

Entry 61   Reels M2643–2644

Name **BRITISH MUSEUM (NATURAL HISTORY), Coelenterata Section**

Title Correspondence

Inclusive dates 1903–68

Quantity 2 reels of microfilm

Location of original Archives Department, Natural History Museum, Cromwell Road, South Kensington, London SW7 5BD, England

Description
Correspondence of successive heads of the Coelenterata Section, concerning the acquisition, loan and exchange of specimens, enquiries from both professional and amateur zoologists, and coelenterate research relating to Australia, New Zealand and the Pacific.

Correspondents include Baldwin Spencer, Arthur K. Totton, W.M. Bale, E.A. Briggs, W.T. Wells, Sir Douglas Mawson, E.J. Batham, H. Boschma, Cyril Crossland, Beatrice Grey, Loisette Marsh, R. Denison Purchon, C.M. Yonge and John Wells.

14-page list available for reference.

Entry 62   Reels M2709–2713

Name **BRITISH MUSEUM (NATURAL HISTORY), General Library**

Title Autograph letters and collections

Inclusive dates 1804–1959

Quantity 5 reels of microfilm

Location of original General Library, Natural History Museum, Cromwell Road, South Kensington, London SW7 5BD, England

Description
M2709: Autograph letters
Autograph letters or fragments of handwriting of biologists and geologists, including W.B. Clarke, Sir Edgeworth David, John B. Brazier, Robert Etheridge, Richard Daintree, Henry B. Guppy, Charles Hedley, Sir William MacGregor and Bernard Woodward.

Seven-page list available for reference.

M2710–2713: Collections
1) Letters to and from malacologists 1882–1959, including Joyce Allan, Edwin Ashby, C.E. Beddome, Bernard Cotton and A.W. Powell.

2) Papers 1824–98 of naturalist on HMS *Blonde*, Andrew Bloxam, including diary, notes and other papers relating to the voyage.

3) Papers of Charles Darwin, specimens collected during voyage of HMS *Beagle*.

4) Letter-book 1880–81 of F.D. Godman concerning butterflies and other specimens from New Guinea. The recipients are A. Goldie and W.M. Macleay.

5) Diaries 1835–39 and 1836–40 of naturalist Richard B. Hinds on the voyages of HMS *Sulphur* with Capt. E. Belcher. Subjects include sugar cane, local languages and population, flora, birds and shells.

6) Australian landscapes 1860–61 by Conrad Martens.

7) Sowerby Family Papers 1865–1907, including letters of James E. Bryant and his wife Ellen F. Bryant to his parents, James and Charlotte Bryant, and other family members concerning voyage to Australia on the *Countess of Elgin*, economic conditions and specimens sent.

8) Letters 1856–58 of Alfred R. Wallace to Samuel Stevens, discussing a new bird of paradise, butterflies, monkeys, and cultivation of Bali and Lombok islands.

12-page list available for reference.

Entry 63   Reels M2599–2610

Name **BRITISH MUSEUM (NATURAL HISTORY), Keeper of Zoology Archives**

Title Letters

Inclusive dates 1840–1969

Quantity 11 reels of microfilm

Location of original Archives Department, Natural History Museum, Cromwell Road, South Kensington, London SW7 5BD, England

Description

1) Correspondence 1858–1945. Subjects include: New Zealand lizards; mud fish from Hokitika, New Zealand; lizards and butterflies from New Hebrides; sponges from the Philippines; butterflies and insects from New Guinea; appointment of taxidermist for Public Library, Museum and National Gallery of Victoria; and sale of Gilbert Raynor's collection of Australian lepidoptera.

2) Foreign letters 1841–69. Subjects include birds from Australia, New Zealand, New Guinea and Sumatra, and the collecting of shells and crustacea.

3) Reports and minutes to Trustees 1840–50. Subjects include fishes of Port Jackson, birds and shells from New South Wales and John Gould's collection.

4) Miscellaneous subject files. Subjects include: *Animal Protection and Game Act 1921–22*; British, Australian and New Zealand Antarctic research expedition 1929–31; Harold Hall expeditions 1960–69; North Borneo expedition 1956; and New Guinea expedition 1964–65.

5) Great Barrier Reef expedition files 1922–63.

6) Curator of Birds correspondence 1896–1918.

7) Official documents and correspondence of the Vertebrate Section 1893–1915.

129-page list available for reference.

Entry 64   Reels M2597–2598

Name **BRITISH MUSEUM (NATURAL HISTORY), Mammals Section**

Title Collections

Inclusive dates 1868–1984

Quantity 2 reels of microfilm

Location of original Natural History Museum, Cromwell Road, South Kensington, London SW7 5BD, England

Description

1) Michael R. Oldfield Thomas correspondence 1868–1928. Subjects include collecting expeditions to Australia, Malaya, Indonesia and the Pacific and dispatch of skulls and other specimens. Correspondents include Wilfrid B. Alexander, Tom Carter, Charles W. De Vis, Joseph Fletcher, Charles Hedley, Frederic Wood Jones and Sir Hubert Wilkins.

2) Collectors' notes. Subjects include: Hubert Wilkins' Australia and Islands expedition 1923–24; expeditions to Malaysia 1967, 1974; Cambridge Sumatra expedition 1984; and mammals of Oceania and Eastern New Guinea.

27-page list available for reference.

Entry 65   Reels M2702–2707

Name **BRITISH MUSEUM (NATURAL HISTORY), Mineralogy Department and Mineralogy Library Archives**

Title Records

Inclusive dates 1828–1957

Quantity 6 reels of microfilm

Location of original Natural History Museum, Cromwell Road, South Kensington, London SW7 5BD, England

Description

1) Correspondence 1889–1934. Subjects include: samples of Australian and New Zealand minerals; Australian meteorites; sales of collections of Australian minerals; and collecting expeditions.

2) Individual collections 1861–1957 concerning meteorites found in Australia.

3) Collection notes, reports and correspondence 1886–1957, including papers of Archibald Liversidge. Correspondents include William Poole, G.F. Herbert Smith and T. George Sweet.

4) Notebooks and diaries of Lazarus Fletcher, Philip Game, George Prior and Walter Smith relating to their visits to Australia, New Zealand and Antarctica 1886–1953.

5) Mineralogy Library Archives including papers of Henry Guppy and Frank Debenham.

41-page list available for reference.

Entry 66   Reel M2500

Name **BRITISH MUSEUM (NATURAL HISTORY),**
        Mollusca Section

Title Collections

Inclusive dates 1869–1977

Quantity 1 reel of microfilm

Location of original Natural History Museum,
Cromwell Road, South Kensington, London
SW7 5BD, England

Description
Papers 1869–1977, including correspondence,
notebooks, drafts, notes and memoranda,
concerning mollusca specimens and collecting
expeditions in Australia and New Zealand.

Two-page list available for reference.

Entry 67   Reels M2770–2771

Name **BRITISH MUSEUM (NATURAL HISTORY),**
        Murray Library

Title Papers

Inclusive dates 1839–1922

Quantity 2 reels of microfilm

Location of original Murray Library, Natural History
Museum, Cromwell Road, South Kensington,
London SW7 5BD, England

Description
1) Surveys 1873–1912 of oceanographic
   expeditions. The ships include HMS *Penguin*,
   HMS *Waterwitch*, USS *Albatross* and HMS
   Egeria.
2) Papers 1839–43 of Joseph D. Hooker, including
   drawings, manuscripts, notes and diary of
   invertebrate animals made during the Sir James
   Ross Antarctic expedition.
3) Notes, correspondence, photographs and other
   records 1891–1910 collected on USS *Albatross*.
4) Data 1840–1921 collected by SS *Britannia*,
   HMS *Egeria*, HMS *Iris*, HMS *Myrmidon*,
   USS *Nero*, HMS *Penguin*, HMS *Rambler*,
   USS *Tuscarora*.
5) Data 1890 collected by F.G. Pearcey.

Nine-page list available for reference.

Entry 68   Reels M2878–2887

Name **BRITISH MUSEUM (NATURAL HISTORY),**
        Department of Palaeontology. Archives

Title Papers

Inclusive dates 1839–1968

Quantity 10 reels of microfilm

Location of original Archive Section, Natural History
Museum, Cromwell Road, South Kensington,
London SW7 5BD, England

Description
1) Departmental correspondence 1846–1916
   concerning dispatch of specimens and fossils,
   exchange of specimens, identification of
   specimens, and other research. Correspondents
   include F.W. Whitehouse, Duncan Merrilees,
   David Ride, B.D. Webby, A.B. Walkom,
   Rev. Robert T. Wade, Martha Small, Michael
   Waldman, Arthur Wade and R.J. Tillyard.
2) Correspondence 1839–1930 relating to
   acquisition, loan and exchange.
3) Fossil Mollusca Section: correspondence
   1893–1924 of Richard Newton.
4) Fossil Echinodermata Section: correspondence
   and papers 1898–1929 of Francis Bather.
5) Fossil Brachiopoda Section: correspondence
   1948–55 of W.N. Benson.

72-page list available for reference.

Entry 69   Reel M2767

Name **BRITISH MUSEUM (NATURAL HISTORY),**
        Palaeontology Library

Title Collections

Inclusive dates 1831–1964

Quantity 1 reel of microfilm

Location of original Palaeontology Library,
Natural History Museum, Cromwell Road,
South Kensington, London SW7 5BD, England

Description
Correspondence, typescripts and drafts concerning
fossils and other geological specimens and remains
of animals.

11-page list available for reference.

Entry 70   Reels M2339–2342

Name **BRITISH MUSEUM (NATURAL HISTORY), Sub-Department of Ornithology Library**

Title Collections

Inclusive dates 1910–34

Quantity 4 reels of microfilm

Location of original Natural History Museum, Akeman Street, Tring, Hertfordshire HP23 6AP, England

Note
The museum at Tring was built by Lionel Walter Rothschild. He bequeathed the museum to the nation in 1938 and it now forms an annex to the Natural History Museum.

Description
Correspondence, official documents, notes, press cuttings, minutes and memoranda concerning birds in Australia, New Zealand and New Guinea, Plumage (Prohibition) Bill 1914 and importation of plumage.

Six-page list available for reference.

Entry 71   Reels M2825–2830

Name **BRITISH MUSEUM (NATURAL HISTORY), Zoology Library**

Title Collections

Inclusive dates 1772–1966

Quantity 6 reels of microfilm

Location of original Zoology Library, Natural History Museum, Cromwell Road, South Kensington, London SW7 5BD, England

Description
1) Notebooks c.1776–79 of William Anderson relating to zoological discoveries on Cook's second and third voyages.
2) Notebooks 1910–13 of Edward L. Atkinson containing data on parasite protozoa collected on British Antarctic expedition.
3) Notes 1886 of T.H. Bower of birds collected in north and northwestern Australia.
4) Field notebooks 1887–1922 of Tom Carter recording Australian birds.
5) Lists and notes 1832–45 of Charles Darwin relating to reptilia and amphibia obtained during voyage of HMS *Beagle*, and mounted manuscript sheet list of cirripeds.
6) Catalogue of drawings and animals collected by Johann Forster on Cook's second voyage.
7) Correspondence 1870–89 of John Gurney and James Reeves concerning Australian birds of prey.

8) Notes 1898–1904 of Ambrosius Hubrecht relating to specimens of Nemertina collected in the Antarctic regions during the expeditions of *Southern Cross* and *Discovery.*
9) Papers 1962–66 of Desmond S. Johnson on crustacea of the Far East.
10) Catalogue 1846–50 of radiata and mollusca compiled by John MacGillivray on voyage of HMS *Rattlesnake.*
11) Drawings and descriptions 1863–83 of Richard Laishley on natural history of New Zealand.
12) Correspondence 1950 of Frederic Sawyer and K.A. Hindwood of Sydney and drawings of Australian birds in Lambert, Latham and Watling collections.
13) Notes c.1915 of J. Kidson Taylor on shells.
14) Notebooks 1855–61 of Alfred Wallace giving localities of birds and insects in Malay Archipelago.
15) Diary, notes and drawings 1901–11 by Edward Wilson of seals, whales and birds of the Antarctic.

13-page list available for reference.

Entry 72   Reel M468

Name **BRITISH WOMEN'S EMIGRATION ASSOCIATION**

Title Records

Inclusive dates 1861–1901, 1949

Quantity 1 reel of microfilm

Location of original Fawcett Library, Calcutta House, Old Castle Street, London E1 7NT, England

Note
The Female Middle Class Emigration Society was founded in 1862 by Maria Rye and Jane Lewin. Its aim was to assist unemployed educated women to emigrate and find suitable employment, usually as governesses and occasionally as clerks, in Australia, New Zealand, South Africa and Canada. In 1892 the Society was absorbed by the British Women's Emigration Association.

See entry 164 for further records of the British Women's Emigration Society.

Description
1) Letter-books 1862–82 containing copies of letters, with index, from women emigrants in Australia, New Zealand and South Africa, mainly to Maria Rye and Jane Lewin, giving first impressions of the colonies and details of employment. There are also letters from the Society's New Zealand representative, Harriet Herbert.

2) Press cuttings 1880–95 from English and Canadian journals and newspapers relating to women's emigration.

3) Minutes of the Finance Committee of the United Englishwomen's Emigration Association, March 1885–March 1886, with statements of its aims and organisation.

4) Letter 1949 from G.F. Plant and typewritten reply concerning the history of the Female Middle Class Emigration Society and the Colonial Intelligence League.

5) Minutes of the Council and some sub-committees of the United British Women's Emigration Association, May 1896–December 1901.

6) Published addresses: *Emigration of Educated Women* (1861) by Maria S. Rye and *Female Middle Class Emigration* (1863) by Jane E. Lewin.

7) Printed annual reports of the Female Middle Class Emigration Society 1861–72, 1874–79 and 1883–85.

Three-page list available for reference.

Entry 73   Reels M582–583

Name **BROOKS, ROBERT AND COMPANY**
Title Records
Inclusive dates 1822–90
Quantity 2 reels of microfilm
Location of original National Library of Australia, Canberra ACT 2600 (apart from 1862–90 correspondence)

Note
London firm of merchants and one of the largest importers of Australian wool. In 1842 Robert Towns was appointed the Sydney agent to replace Ranulph Dacre. He quickly established himself as a mercantile agent and later involved the firm in his cotton growing project in Queensland in the 1860s.

Description
1) Correspondence 1862–90, mainly with Robert Towns and Co of Sydney, regarding the cotton plantation on the Logan River, Queensland. Includes letters from R. Towns, A. Stuart, C. Lett and W.T. Walker; inventories, statements and a plan of the plantation.

2) Journal January 1822–September 1828 giving details of supplies sent to ships from London (2 vols).

3) Ledgers 1826–32 (2 vols).

4) Acceptance book containing bills accepted from Australian companies and merchants 1846–53.

5) Cash book 1855–56.

6) Letter-book February 1841–May 1843. Includes copies of letters to W.C. Wentworth, Campbell & Co, W. Campbell & Co, R. Dacre, James Cain, R. Towns and other Australian pastoralists and businessmen, regarding shipment and sale of wool and other products.

One-page list available for reference.

Entry 74   Reel M1877

Name **BROWN, Charles (1786–1842)**
Title Papers
Inclusive dates 1841–1983
Quantity 1 reel of microfilm
Location of original Keats Memorial Library, Keats House, Wentworth Place, Keats Grove, Hampstead, London NW3 2RR, England

Note
Charles Armitage Brown, a friend of the poet John Keats, emigrated to Taranaki, New Zealand, in 1841 with his son Charles (Carlino) Brown (1820–1901).

Description
The papers include a notebook, correspondence and official documents. The notebook was kept by Charles Armitage Brown on the voyage to New Zealand on board the *Oriental*. Correspondents include W.S. Landor.

Three-page list available for reference.

Entry 75   Reels M849–850

Name **BROWN, John**
Title Papers
Inclusive dates 1838–51
Quantity 2 reels of microfilm
Location of original Mrs Margaret Brown, County Londonderry, Northern Ireland.

Note
Surgeon John Harris (1754–1838), who arrived in New South Wales in 1790, was proprietor of large estates including Harris Park at Parramatta, Ultimo, Shane's Park and the Killangan station near Yass. On his death, his estate was bequeathed to three brothers in Ireland who sent sons and a son-in-law John Brown to Australia to look after their interests.

Description

The papers deal with the management of the properties of John Harris, emphasising the financial and legal aspects. Included is Brown's diary 1840–45 commencing with his departure from England for Australia and concluding with the return journey via Port Phillip and Valparaiso.

Seven-page list available for reference.

Entry 76   Reels M1193, M2494–2496

Name **BROWN, Robert (1773–1858)**

Title Papers

Inclusive dates 1800–55

Quantity 4 reels of microfilm

Location of original

Reel M1193: British Library, Great Russell Street, London WC1B 3DG, England

Reels M2494–2496: British Museum (Natural History), Cromwell Road, South Kensington, London SW7 5BD, England

Note

Naturalist on HMS *Investigator* in 1801–03 and, after his return to England in 1805, librarian to the Linnean Society and Sir Joseph Banks. Author of *Prodromus Florae Novae Hollandiae* (1810).

Description

M1193:

The early correspondence describes: the exploration of the southern and northern coasts of Australia; botanical discoveries made on the voyage and at New South Wales; Brown's return to England; the captivity of M. Flinders at Mauritius; work in describing and classifying botanical discoveries; and the publication of *Prodromus*. Later letters deal with: the botanical and ornithological work of G. Caley; specimens sent from Australia and the East Indies; the exchange of plants and publications with European scientists; and efforts to secure a pension for the widow of M. Flinders.

Correspondents include Sir Joseph Banks, Ferdinand Bauer, George Caley, Allan Cunningham, Matthew Flinders, Sir William Hooker, P.G. King, P.P. King, Sir Thomas Mitchell and Olaf Swartz.

Four-page list available for reference.

M2494–2496:

Correspondence and manuscripts relating to Brown's career as a naturalist and librarian. The manuscripts include: accounts of his travels in Australia; drafts of *Prodromus Florae Novae Hollandiae et Insulae Van Diemen;* corrections to the appendix of M. Flinders, *A Voyage to Terra Australis*; and catalogues of plants and fossils.

Main correspondents include A. Cunningham, Rev. W. Buckland, Sir William Hooker, Sir Thomas Mitchell and C. Stokes.

11-page list available for reference.

Entry 77   Reels M858–863

Name **BROWN FAMILY**

Title Letters, papers and family photographs

Inclusive dates 1829–99

Quantity 6 reels of microfilm

Location of original Lady Redcliff-Maude, Oxford, England, and Mrs A. Weir, London, England

Note

The Brown Family lived in Glasgow in the early 1850s, when the head of the family was Mrs Margaret A. Brown. Her children included Jane Hay Brown, schoolteacher, Jessie, Maggie and James W. Brown, a Presbyterian minister. The Hoey Family were old friends of the Browns.

Description

Correspondence, initially between James Hoey, who migrated to Victoria in 1852 with his brother Thomas, and the Brown Family, describing life in Melbourne. Maggie Brown travelled to Australia in 1854 to marry James Hoey and their letters to the family in Scotland relate domestic news and tell of conditions on the goldfields at Bendigo and Eaglehawk, where Thomas and James Hoey began prospecting in 1856 with their brother-in-law John Buckie. Jane Hay Brown arrived in Australia in 1859 on the *Royal Charter* to care for her sister Maggie, who died later that year. All correspondents refer to activities of fellow Scots in Australia.

M862 contains a journal kept by Andrew Hamilton in 1852, describing in detail his departure for Australia in July 1852 on the *Birmingham,* his arrival in Melbourne and journey to the diggings at Ballarat with Thomas Hoey. Jane married Andrew Hamilton in 1860, but continued to care for her sister Maggie's two children. James Hoey was principal of St Mungo Mining Co, Eaglehawk, and the Hamilton letters tell of their move to Eaglehawk to try their luck at prospecting following Andrew's lack of success in business. Church and family affairs, as well as business affairs and economic conditions, are discussed. The discovery of gold in New Zealand prompted James Hoey to travel to Dunedin in 1863 with his new wife. The letters tell of James and Maggie's children being left orphans in 1865, and of the son Robert being sent to Paisley, Scotland, to live with his uncle James W. Brown.

The final letters were written by Jane's nephew Robert Hoey, who went to Fiji in 1883, but by 1895 was living in Sydney. Family and domestic news predominate, but employment prospects and financial conditions are referred to, as well as Jane Hamilton's death c.1898. Family photographs are included on reel M863.

59-page list available for reference.

Entry 78   Reels M2476–2491

Name **BRYANT AND MAY ARCHIVES**

Title Records

Inclusive dates 1879–1973

Quantity 16 reels of microfilm

Location of original Hackney Archives Department, Rose Lipman Library, 43 De Beauvoir Road, London N1 5SQ, England

Note
William Bryant (b.1804) and Francis May (b.1803), the match manufacturers, became business associates in 1839. In 1884 their business became a public company. By 1927 it had established branches in Australia, New Zealand, Brazil, Canada and South Africa.

Description
1) Bryant and May Ltd records, including directors minute-books 1884–1937 and income tax files.
2) Papers 1885–1910 of Gilbert Bartholomew, managing director of Bryant and May 1885–1901, concerning sale figures, shipment of goods, Arthur Bryant's visit to Australia and general business matters. Recipients of the letters include H. Nathan, J. Hoffnung, H. Hayman and James Service.
3) Correspondence 1890–97 of Arthur B. Bryant.
4) Correspondence 1960–73 concerning Bryant and May Pty Ltd, Richmond, Victoria, including correspondence concerning integration of Australian companies. The chief correspondent is Brian Bath.
5) Correspondence 1927–67 with Federal Match Co Pty Ltd concerning financial and general business matters.
6) Correspondence 1931–50 with Western Australia Match Co Ltd.
7) Newspaper cuttings 1923–54 concerning Bryant and May in Australia and matches in general.
8) Records 1909–59 of Bryant and May Ltd, Bell and Co, and Australasia Ltd.

33-page list available for reference.

Entry 79   Reels M2649–2656

Name **BRYNMOR JONES LIBRARY**

Title Collections

Inclusive dates 1817–1975

Quantity 8 reels of microfilm

Access conditions Partly closed

Location of original Brynmor Jones Library, Hull University, Cottingham Road, Kingston upon Hull, Humberside HU6 7RX, England

Description
1) Letters 1963–75 of Peter Porter and other writers sent to publisher Harry Chambers concerning the poetry magazine *Phoenix* (closed until 2005).
2) Records 1942–49 of Union of Democratic Control concerning Australia, Malaya, Sumatra and Philippines. Subjects include: migration to Australia; independence movements; and Japanese treatment of Malays.
3) Correspondence 1939–51 between J. Henry Lloyd and Dr J. Bell Ferguson of South Yarra. Subjects include: Tasmanian sweepstake; BMA opposition to a national health service in Australia; Ferguson's job as physician at Royal Melbourne Hospital; and political views.
4) Records 1945–54 of Revolutionary Communist Party, including: campaign against military intervention in Java and Indo-China; resolution of the Labour Socialist Group of Australia on forthcoming conference of RCP; strikes by painters and dockers in Australia; and position of communism in Australia.
5) Southeast Asian manuscripts 1823–1948, including letter of Charles S. Brett referring to: conditions on a rubber estate due to economic climate in 1929; typescript 'Education in the Netherlands Indies' by B.H.M. Vlekke; 'Anthology of Malaya' by H.R. Cheeseman; diary of an officer in the Public Works Department in Penang 1890–92 and photograph albums.
6) Papers 1850–1909 of William M. Baines who lived in Auckland in 1851–68. Includes: a diary describing voyage to New Zealand on the *Sir Edward Paget* in 1850; accounts of life and conditions of early settlers in New Zealand; timber mill; accounts of Baines voyage to England on the *Kate Waters* in 1868; Mount Eden Gold Mining Co; sinking of the *Tauranga*; and family news. Correspondents include W.P. Fooks, M.V. Baines, P.V. Dixon, J.W. Dixon, E.V. Dixon, A. Hunter and R.C. Dyer.
7) Emigrant letters 1862–69 sent to Marmaduke C. Maxwell. Correspondents include nephews Robert, Wilfred and Edward Maxwell, who worked on sheep stations in New Zealand.

8) Papers 1871–1910 of Beilby Lawley, 3rd Baron Wenlock, who accompanied the Duke and Duchess of Cornwall and York to Australia and New Zealand in 1901.

9) Papers 1854–78 of Sir Charles Hotham, Governor of Victoria 1854–55. Subjects include: land question; colonial governorships; colonial finances; *Convict Prevention Act 1854*; Commission of Enquiry into the Gold Fields in Victoria; customs legislation; Victorian goldfields; mining legislation; travels in the colony; military defence; Eureka uprising; Constitution of Victoria; and steam postal communication between England and Australia. Correspondents include Duke of Newcastle, Sir George Grey, Lord John Russell, C.J. La Trobe, Beaumont Hotham and Sir William Molesworth.

64-page list available for reference.

Entry 80   Reels M1667–1671

Name **BUCKINGHAMSHIRE RECORD OFFICE**

Title Collections

Inclusive dates 1789–1923

Quantity 4 reels of microfilm

Location of original Buckinghamshire Record Office, County Hall, Aylesbury, Buckinghamshire HP20 1UA, England

Description
1) Calendars of prisoners 1789–1855 in Aylesbury Gaol, including many sentenced to transportation.

2) Papers 1794–1803 of Robert Hobart, Lord Hobart, Secretary of State for War and Colonies 1801–04, referring to: trade with East Indies and Philippines; British annexations in Moluccas; proposed settlement at Port Phillip Bay; appointments in New South Wales; and an account of the colony written by David Collins. Correspondents include R.T. Farquar and D. Collins.

3) Papers 1883–1923 of 5th Earl of Rosebery concerning his property interests in Sydney and Darwin. They include letters from his Australian agents, legal papers, plans, maps and cuttings.

4) Portion of autobiography c.1889 by Rev. John A. Greaves describing his voyage to Australia and his work as an Anglican Minister in the Hunter Valley and Sydney 1857–66.

5) Letter 1836 of Anne Russell in Launceston referring to difficulties of employment for emigrant women in Van Diemen's Land.

6) Letters 1854–55 of John Dukes in South Australia and William Dukes in Sydney.

Nine-page list available for reference.

Entry 81   Reels M1909–1911

Name **BUNBURY FAMILY**

Title Papers

Inclusive dates 1824–72

Quantity 3 reels of microfilm

Location of original Argyll Etkin Ltd, 55 New Bond Street, London W1Y 9DG, England
Photocopies of the papers are held at the National Library of Australia (MS 8098).

Note
Capt. Richard Hanmer Bunbury (1813–1857), youngest son of Lieut. General Sir Henry Bunbury, migrated to Port Phillip in 1841 with his wife Sarah and her father Robert K. Sconce. They returned to England in 1857.

Description
Letters of Richard Hammer Bunbury to Sarah Bunbury 1840–57, Sir Henry Bunbury 1840–50, Lady Bunbury 1840–44, Robert K. Sconce 1839–40 and George Repton 1842–43. Subjects include: descriptions of the voyage to Australia; first impressions of Melbourne; explorations in Victoria; conflict with Aborigines; and personal news. Other correspondents include Sarah Bunbury, Sir Henry Bunbury and Robert K. Sconce.

Three-page list available for reference.

Entry 82   Reels M2555–2562

Name **BURGON AND BALL LTD**

Title Records

Inclusive dates 1867–1952

Quantity 8 reels of microfilm

Location of original Sheffield City Archives, 52 Shoreham Street, Sheffield S1 4SP, England

Note
Makers of shears, hammers and agricultural tools. Charles Burgon and James Ball formed a partnership in 1866. They established branches in America and Australia in 1870.

Description

1) Financial and legal papers 1867–1952.

2) Papers relating to patents 1869–1911.

3) Papers 1881–99 of Charles and Frederic Burgon, including letters written by Burgon during an Australian tour 1887–88.

4) Cutting books 1886–1947 comprising cuttings mostly from Australian newspapers.

5) Letters 1900–06 of J.H. Baines, company secretary, mainly to W.H. Eyres and J.H. Young in Sydney.

6) Letters 1868–78 from shipping agents.

7) Agreements and correspondence 1877–1929 with Australian agents.

8) Correspondence 1898–1906 between Benjamin Hind in Sheffield and James Hind in Sydney.

9) Letters 1903–07 from Alfred de Lissa, solicitor in Sydney.

10) Correspondence 1908–44 with Australian branches and agents.

20-page list available for reference.

Entry 83   Reel M605

Name **BYRON, John, Vice-Admiral (1723–1786)**
Title Journal
Inclusive dates 1764–66
Quantity 1 reel of microfilm
Location of original National Maritime Museum, Romney Road, Greenwich, London SE10 9NF, England

Note
Navigator. Commanded HMS *Dolphin* in a voyage round the world 2 July 1764–9 May 1766.

Description
Journal of HMS *Dolphin* 21 June 1764–9 May 1766 with marginal notes probably by John Hawkesworth. As well as giving meteorological and navigational information, the journal gives brief descriptions of places visited, especially their geographical features, and mentions the activities of the crew on board.

Entry 84   Reel M46

Name **CADELL, Francis, Capt. (1822–1879)**
Title Papers
Inclusive dates 1837–80
Quantity 1 reel of microfilm
Location of original Mrs F.A.M. Chitty, Hertfordshire, England

Note
Murray River steamboat owner. Formed the River Murray Navigation Co which traded on the Murray 1853–58. Continued trading on the river until 1861 when he went to New Zealand. In 1867–68 he explored part of the Gulf of Carpentaria and he was later engaged in pearling in the Arafura Sea.

Description

1) Three books of newspaper cuttings 1852–60 and 1867–68 referring to Cadell's trade on the River Murray and his Northern Territory expedition.

2) Documents relating to navigation of the River Murray including copies of dispatches from the Governor of South Australia and correspondence between Cadell and the Governor 1853 on the navigability of the Murray. There is also a rough sketch of the canvas boat in which Cadell first sailed down the Murray River from Swan Hill in 1852, and an address by the Murray settlers of New South Wales and Victoria to Cadell.

3) Memorials and addresses outlining the life of Cadell and his explorations in Australia, including a manuscript entitled 'Australia' and a copy of a letter from the First Government Secretary of Batavia, 25 February 1880, giving an account of the death of Cadell.

Two-page list available for reference.

Entry 85   Reels M2591–2595

Name **CAMBRIDGE UNIVERSITY LIBRARY**
Title Collections
Inclusive dates 1719–1959
Quantity 5 reels of microfilm
Location of original Cambridge University Library, West Road, Cambridge CB3 9DR, England

Description

1) Papers 1791–94 of astronomer William Gooch who sailed on the *Daedalus*. They include: an account relating to part of the journey; notes on the inhabitants of the Falkland Islands,

Marquesas Islands and Sandwich Islands; and a statement written by Thomas Dobson giving details of Gooch's murder in 1792 in Woahoo (Oahu).

2) Log 1823 of Capt. Thomas Alexander kept on HMS *Alligator*.

3) Papers 1884–1903 of mathematician and scientist William Thomson, 1st Baron Kelvin, relating to papers for the Royal Society of New South Wales on Mt Morgan, Queensland, his professorship in Glasgow and the metric system.

4) Correspondence 1855 of Sir James Stephen. The letter was written by his brother Sir George Stephen on board the *Oliver Lang* describing the voyage and his impressions of Melbourne.

5) Correspondence and transcripts 1835–63 of geologist Rev. Adam Sedgwick. Subjects include: dispatch of specimens and fossils; geological explorations in Australia; Sydney sandstone; and discussion of Leichhardt and his expedition.

6) Correspondence 1860–98 of mathematician and scientist Sir Gabriel Stokes. Subjects include: the founding of a school and laboratory for physical sciences in Victoria; thoughts on evolution; construction of a school of physical science at Melbourne University; and correspondence relating to the Royal Society. Main correspondents are Graham Berry and A. Le Sueur.

7) Papers 1835–53 of Sir James Stephen referring to the 1846 New Zealand Bill, constitutions for Australian colonies and the 1853 Colonial Church Regulation Bill.

8) Sketchbooks of Conrad Martens while draughtsman on HMS *Beagle* and en route to Australia.

9) Records 1933–59 of the Church Army, a Church of England organisation.

10) Papers 1907–10 of Sir Robert Crewe-Milnes. Subjects include governorships of Western Australia, Tasmania, New South Wales and South Australia and governor-generalship of Australia. Includes correspondence from Alfred Deakin.

11) Papers 1835–82 of naturalist Charles Darwin, including notes on the geology of places visited during voyage of the *Beagle* 1831–36, coral formations on Great Barrier Reef, Philosophical Institute at Canterbury and astronomy.

12) Papers 1914–18 of Charles Hardinge, 1st Baron Penhurst. Subjects include: Australian and New Zealand military forces; operations in the Dardanelles; and indentured labour. Main

correspondents are Sir Ronald Munro-Ferguson and Lord Birdwood.

72-page list available for reference.

Entry 86   Reel M1896

Name **CAMBRIDGESHIRE RECORD OFFICE, Cambridge**

Title Collections

Inclusive dates 1826–1919

Quantity 1 reel of microfilm

Location of original Cambridgeshire Record Office, Shire Hall, Castle Hill, Cambridge CB3 0AP, England

Description

1) Parish records 1827–54. Records of Cherry Hinton, Melbourne and Orwell relating to emigration to Australia.

2) Papers 1855–56 of Baumgartner Family concerning postal services, Victorian goldfields and platypus hunting.

3) Papers of Holsworthy Family of Bromley and Elsworthy, including diary of Joseph M. Holsworthy on a voyage to Melbourne on the *Lusitania* 1877–78.

4) Records 1902 of Cambridge Women's Suffrage Association.

5) Papers 1917–19 of Collins Family, referring to property of Lewis P. Collins of Launceston, Tasmania.

Four-page list available for reference.

Entry 87   Reels M1854–1855

Name **CAMBRIDGESHIRE RECORD OFFICE, Huntingdon**

Title Collections

Inclusive dates 1842–1911

Quantity 2 reels of microfilm

Location of original Cambridgeshire Record Office, Grammar School Walk, Huntingdon PE18 6LF, England

Description

1) Records of H. Wilson, Clerk of the City of Peterborough Education Committee, relating to the exchange of flags between St Peter's Church School, Sydney, and St John's School, Peterborough, 1911.

2) Papers 1856–93 of George Montagu, 6th Duke of Manchester, and William Montagu, 7th Duke of Manchester, concerning properties in Australia, Australian Transcontinental Railway and Queensland Emigration Scheme.

3) Papers 1885–1900 of Linton Family of Stirtloe, Buckden, concerning the estate of Sydney Linton, Bishop of Riverina, and the marriage of Frederick Chamberlin and Helen Kaye.

Seven-page list available for reference.

Entry 88   Reel M385

Name **CAMPBELL, John**

Title Diary

Inclusive dates 1850–51

Quantity 1 reel of microfilm

Location of original Mrs E.H. Campbell, Northumberland, England

Note
Surgeon on the ship *William Jardine* carrying convicts to Van Diemen's Land.

Description
1) Diary 15 July–21 November 1850 kept on *William Jardine*, noting daily routine of the surgeon, some incidents with the convicts on board, land sightings and the weather.

2) List of the 261 male convicts on board, compiled by John Byron, a convict sentenced to ten years transportation for forgery. The list gives name, age, marital status, birthplace, sentence, crime, original trade or occupation, conduct in prison, whether they could read or write, years of separate confinement and public works, conduct on board, height and sometimes weight on embarkation.

3) 'General regulations to be observed by prisoners on board the *William Jardine*', 'The Daily Routine', and a list of overseers, constables, cooks, barbers and clothesmen.

4) Notes by Campbell on the health of the convicts, guards and their families summarising the symptoms and treatment of the most common diseases.

5) Drafts of letters by Campbell to officials in Hobart and London, November 1850 and May 1851, describing the health and conduct of the convicts and guards who had arrived on the *William Jardine*.

One-page list available for reference.

Entry 89   Reel M393

Name **CAMPBELL & COMPANY**

Title Letter

Inclusive dates 1840

Quantity 1 reel of microfilm

Location of original Mr D.F.O. Dangar, Devon, England

Note
Mercantile firm operating in Sydney owned and operated by Robert Campbell (1769–1846) and his descendants. It was a general merchant business engaged in fulfilling contracts for supplies including livestock and spirits.

Description
Letter 1840 from Campbell & Co to Henry Dangar, Neotsfield, Hunter River, New South Wales, concerning his account and usual charges on transactions in the colony, also mentioning that his arrangement with Campbell & Co about his wool was satisfactory.

One-page list available for reference.

Entry 90   Reels M917–932

Name **CARRINGTON, Charles Robert Wynn-Carrington, 1st Earl (1843–1928)**

Title Papers

Inclusive dates 1864–1913

Quantity 16 reels of microfilm

Location of original Brigadier A.W.A. Llewellen Palmer, Channel Islands, England

Special conditions Permission to copy is required from the copyright owner.

Note
Charles Wynn-Carrington, 3rd Baron Carrington, 1st Earl Carrington (created 1895), 1st Marquess of Lincolnshire (created 1912). Liberal politician, Governor of New South Wales 1885–90.

Description
1) Four volumes of speeches and notes by Lord Carrington 1879–1905.

2) Notes and copies of correspondence with King Edward VII and Lord Rosebery.

3) Correspondence of Lord and Lady Carrington with their family, especially their son Rupert;

with other State Governors, namely Sir Robert Hamilton, Lord Hopetoun, Lord Kintore, Sir Henry Loch, Sir Anthony Musgrave, Sir William Robinson, Sir Hercules Robinson and Sir Henry Norman; and Governors of New Zealand Sir William Jervois and Lord Onslow, and with various individuals including Sir George Dibbs, Lord Knutsford, Edward Stanhope, Lord Normanby, Sir Henry Parkes, Sir Alfred Stephen, Lord Carnarvon, Sir Edmund Barton, James Bryce, Sir Arthur Ellis, General Arthur Fremantle, Lord Aberdeen, Lord Hamilton, Lord Lansdowne, Cardinal Manning, Lord Selborne and Lord Jersey.

4) Memoirs of Lord Carrington.

5) Cuttings and printed articles about the Mount Rennie Rape Case 1886.

6) Speeches by Sir Henry Parkes.

7) Diaries of Lord Carrington 1888–93 and Lady Carrington 1881–1913.

Eight-page list available for reference.

Entry 91   Reel M1618

Name **CARTER, John**

Title Diary

Inclusive dates 1844–50

Quantity 1 reel of microfilm

Location of original Lieut. Col. R.P. Carter, Surrey, England

Note
Carter emigrated to New South Wales in 1845 and worked as a superintendent on stations in the Molong district.

Description
A diary kept on a voyage to Australia on the *General Hewett* 1844–45 and on a journey from Sydney to the Monaro region of New South Wales. It resumes in 1847 and describes work on sheep stations of A. Hood and T. Hood, financial transactions, litigation and sporting activities.

One-page list available for reference.

Entry 92   Reels M2088–2089

Name **J & J CASH LTD**

Title Records

Inclusive dates 1890–1955

Quantity 2 reels of microfilm

Location of original Coventry City Record Office, Mandela House, Bayley Lane, Coventry CV1 5RG, England

Note
John and Joseph Cash founded their ribbon weaving company in 1846. In 1906 the company set up subsidiaries in the United States, Canada and Australia. The Australian company was based in Richmond, Melbourne. In 1928 it amalgamated with the Australian Weaving Co Ltd.

Description
Ledgers, minutes of meetings of directors of the Melbourne company, financial papers and correspondence. Correspondents include W.J. Roberts and A.E. Webb of Melbourne and R.J. Cash of Coventry. Includes plans of the factory in Melbourne.

Four-page list available for reference.

Entry 93   Reel M944

Name **CATCHPOLE, Margaret (1762–1819)**

Title Papers

Inclusive dates 1845–1965

Quantity 1 reel of microfilm

Location of original Central Library, Northgate Street, Ipswich, East Suffolk, England

Note
Convict and New South Wales pioneer. In 1800 she was sentenced to transportation and arrived in Sydney in December 1801 on the *Nile*. She worked for John Palmer and then the Rouse Family and in 1814 was pardoned. She spent the rest of her life keeping a small store at Richmond and acting as nurse and midwife in the area.

Description
1) Clyde collection: newspaper cuttings 1845 on Rev. Richard Cobbold's book *The History of Margaret Catchpole* (London, 1845).

2) Woolnough collection: Vol.1: Letters 1908–11 relating to Margaret Catchpole, documents and photographs, including a letter from Gregory M. Mathews and a handbill and cuttings regarding a production of the play *Margaret Catchpole*

starring Laurence Irving at Ipswich; Vol. 2: Transcript of article in the *Ipswich Journal* 1800 recording her escape from prison; an article on the Cobbold house at Ipswich; certificate of burial of Margaret Catchpole; correspondence and notes 1914–18 on material in the Mitchell Library; typed transcripts of letters by Margaret Catchpole 1803–11; pamphlet by F.J. Foakes Jackson 1916 on Rev. Richard Cobbold; and cuttings from English newspapers 1915, 1932–65 on Margaret Catchpole.

One-page list available for reference.

Entry 94   Reels M2640–2642

Name **HMS *CHALLENGER***

Title Papers

Inclusive dates 1873–90

Quantity 3 reels of microfilm

Location of original Mineralogy and Zoology Libraries, and Bryozoa Section, British Museum (Natural History), Cromwell Road, South Kensington, London SW7 5BD, England

Note
HMS *Challenger* carried out a physical and biological survey of the oceans of the world 1872–76. The director of the scientific staff was Professor Sir Charles W. Thomson.

Description
1) Diaries of Sir John Murray 1874–75, John J. Wild 1874–75, Sir Charles W. Thomson 1874–75 and Rudolph von Willemoes-Suhm 1874–75 describing the voyage to Australia and the Pacific.
2) Logs of HMS *Challenger* 1874–75.
3) Letter-book 1883–90 of the zoologist Sir John Murray.
4) Letters 1874–78 of Joseph Matkin containing descriptions of Melbourne, Sydney and places in the Pacific, and work on board the ship.
5) Journal 1874–75 of Henry N. Moseley describing the voyage from Melbourne across the Pacific.

16-page list available for reference.

Entry 95   Reel M2395

Name **CHATTERTON, John Henry (1835–1928)**

Title 'My life: a record of events and the experience of'

Inclusive dates 1835–1855

Quantity 1 reel of microfilm

Location of original Mr David Vines White, London, England

Note
Chatterton came to Australia, visiting Adelaide, Melbourne and Tasmania, in 1852.

Description
Autobiography based on diaries kept on Chatterton's visit to Australia and letters he wrote to his family in England 1835–55.

Two-page list available for reference.

Entry 96   Reels M845–847

Name **CHESHIRE RECORD OFFICE**

Title Collections

Inclusive dates 1749–1914

Quantity 3 reels of microfilm

Location of original Cheshire Record Office, Duke Street, Chester CH1 1RL, England

Description
1) Quarter Sessions Records: Orders by Quarter Sessions and Chester Sessions for transportation of convicts 1749, 1803–29; Orders by Secretary of State for transportation of convicts to hulks 1802–40; reports and returns of convicts transported and under sentence of transportation 1802–56; circulars and correspondence on the transportation of convicts 1802–51; convict lists sent to the Commissioners of County Rates, 11 March 1835.
2) Genealogical notes and letters of the Whittell Family and the Woolfield Family of Papatoetoe, New Zealand.
3) Stanley of Alderley: Family correspondence: journal by Owen Stanley's mother, Catherine; correspondence, including 24 letters 1846–49 to Capt. Owen Stanley concerning family matters; correspondence 1847–53 of Charles Edward Stanley and his wife Elizabeth; letters from T.H. Huxley relating to J. MacGillivray's *Narrative of the Voyage of HMS Rattlesnake;* letters 1834–c.1843 from Catherine Stanley to Louisa Dorothea Stanley; correspondence 1844–49 of Catherine Stanley Vaughan.

4) Wilson of Sandbach collection: petition 1849 by passengers on the emigrant ship *Cheapside;* journals 1849–51 of John Ayre, surgeon on the *Cheapside* and *Duchess of Northumberland;* hotel bills and accounts for photographic equipment purchased by T.N. Wilson during a journey to Australia and New Zealand in 1889. Ayre's journals contain descriptions of conditions aboard emigrant ships, details of treatment of the sick, and relations between passengers.

Three-page list available for reference.

Entry 97   Reel M848

Name **CHESTER CITY RECORD OFFICE**
Title Collections
Inclusive dates 1833–1938
Quantity 1 reel of microfilm
Location of original Chester City Record Office, Town Hall, Chester, Cheshire CH1 2HJ, England

Description
1) Letters 1849–84 from John Brown to his family in Chester describing the gold diggings around Ballarat and Gippsland in Victoria, in the Snowy River district, and in various parts of New Zealand. Also a solicitor's letter and newspaper cutting 1907 relating to John Brown's estate.
2) Copy of extract of will 1905 of Edward Davies of Melbourne bequeathing five pounds per annum to the Blue Coat School, Chester, for an annual prize; and in every fourth year for an essay on Imperial Federation. Copies of prize-winning essays, letters and accounts 1905–38.
3) Letters, financial statements and reports 1900–05 of the South Australia Development Syndicate Ltd and the Murninnie Mine, Spencer Gulf, in the papers of Joliffe, Wickham and Wood, solicitors.
4) Deeds 1833–46 relating to Port Pool Meadow, one party being Philip Oakden of Launceston, Van Diemen's Land.

Seven-page list available for reference.

Entry 98   Reel M1687

Name **CHILDERS, Hugh Culling Eardley (1827–1896)**
Title Papers
Inclusive dates 1850–95
Quantity 1 reel of microfilm
Location of original University of Cambridge, West Road, Cambridge CB3 9DR, England

Note
Liberal politician. Emigrated to Victoria 1850, Member of Legislative Council 1852–55, Collector of Customs 1853–55, Member of Legislative Assembly 1856–57. Returned to England in 1858, held office in governments of W.E. Gladstone 1868–73, 1880–85 and 1886.
Papers formerly held by the Royal Commonwealth Society, London.

Description
1) Diary 1850 kept by Childers on voyage from Plymouth to Melbourne.
2) Diaries 1852–53 and 1855–56 of Emily Childers describing life in Melbourne, social events, household duties and political activities of her husband.
3) Papers 1878–86 concerning Rowland Childers, including letters to his father relating to his life in Melbourne and on stations in New South Wales and Queensland and bills, receipts and correspondence concerning his debts. Correspondents include Sir George Bowen, C. Heneage, J.C. Tyler and Emily Hammond.

Two-page list available for reference.

Entry 99   Reels M2576–2577

Name **CHRISTIAN BRETHREN ARCHIVE**
Title Records
Inclusive dates 1875–1976
Quantity 2 reels of microfilm
Location of original John Rylands University Library of Manchester, University of Manchester, Oxford Road, Deansgate, Manchester M3 3EH, England

Note
The Brethren was a puritanical Christian sect which rejected all church orders and outward forms. Its first centre was established in Plymouth in 1830 by John N. Darby (1800–1882) and the name Plymouth Brethren came to be used.

Description

1) Papers 1875–80 of John N. Darby, including descriptions of visit to New Zealand and floods in Motueka Valley.

2) Papers 1934–37 of bible scholar, teacher and missionary Harold St John concerning lectures given in Australia and New Zealand.

3) Papers 1974–75 of Ransome W. Cooper, including drafts of his poems and articles and lists of names and addresses of British World War II refugees and other emigrants to New Zealand.

33-page list available for reference.

Entry 100   Reels M173–243; M1825–1827

Name **CHURCH MISSIONARY SOCIETY**

Title Records

Inclusive dates 1799–1914

Quantity 74 reels of microfilm

Location of original Birmingham University Library, PO Box 363, Birmingham B15 2TT, England

Note

The Church Missionary Society for Africa and the East was founded in London in 1799 by a group of Anglican evangelicals. The New Zealand mission began in 1814 and the Australian mission in 1825, due to the efforts of the Rev. Samuel Marsden. The New Zealand mission was known as the Australasian Mission until 1841, when the parent English Society's work in Australia ceased. In 1884 work amongst the Maoris became the responsibility of the church in New Zealand, although grants to New Zealand continued until 1903.

Description

M173–198:

Committee and sub-committee meeting minutes 1799–1884. With the exception of the material on reel M199, the minutes of committees and sub-committees are entered in the same volumes in chronological order, and contain extracts from and summaries of reports, letters and other items dealt with by the committees, as well as decisions reached. Many of the Society's affairs were handled by sub-committees, such as the Clerical sub-committee, which received correspondence from aspiring missionaries, including testimonials, and recorded appointments and retirements; the Accounts sub-committee minutes include lists of expenses, supplies to be forwarded to the mission stations, bequests and donations; the Correspondence sub-committee received correspondence covering the whole range of missionary activity, such as medical reports from missionaries wishing to return home, complaints from Colonial Governors about political activity of Society personnel, and requests for guidance on policy towards employing indigenes as lay teachers in schools.

M199:

Sub-committee minutes 1799–1818, of the following: Accounts, 1808–17; Correspondence, 1799–1818; Funds, 1812–15; and Special Committees, 1799–1815. The minutes are followed by four letters from William Hall and John King 1809–11, the three written from Parramatta referring to Rev. Samuel Marsden and the delay in establishing a New Zealand mission, together with an extract of a letter dated 22 November 1821 written from the Bay of Islands, New Zealand, by Rev. J. Williams. The second half of reel M199 contains letter-books of correspondence from Society officials to missionaries in New Zealand 1852–83.

M200–211:

Mission books 1820–80, containing copies made in London from incoming correspondence, for which separate name indexes exist. Included are annual reports of the various missionaries, journals documenting local political, economic and social conditions or describing journeys undertaken, and details of dealings with colonial officials.

M212:

Sydney Corresponding Committee minutes 1821–41. Copies of minutes prepared for the English Society, arranged in order by the date of their receipt in London. After 1830 New Zealand and Australian business was usually dealt with at separate meetings, but there were exceptions to this practice.

M212–214:

Bishops' correspondence 1830–80. Mainly letters to the Church Missionary Society secretaries, but letters to officials such as the Colonial Secretary are also to be found in this group; minutes of missionaries' meetings, with reports and accounts, 1823–77. Correspondents include Bishops W.G. Broughton, G.A. Selwyn, W.G. Cowie, E.C. Stuart and O. Hadfield.

M215:

Sydney Corresponding Committee correspondence 1820–52, being letters to and from the New Holland Mission 1821–37, and between the Committee and missionaries and others, mainly in New Zealand, 1827–52. Correspondents include Rev. S. Marsden, Rev. R. Hill and Rev. W. Cowper.

M215–216:
Missionaries' joint reports 1836–58. Reports of the New Zealand mission stations, as well as personal reports; correspondence between missionaries and the New Zealand Mission secretary 1831–66. Correspondents include Rev. H. Williams, Rev. W. Colenso, Rev. R. Maunsell, Rev. R. Vidal and Rev. G. Clarke.

M217:
Letters from New Zealand Mission secretaries to Home Secretaries 1826–69.

M218:
Station estimates and accounts 1823–80, statistics 1872–80, medical certificates 1847–74, correspondence 1821–35 about the Australian Mission and the Committee of Native Institution; documents concerning land matters 1845–76; miscellaneous papers 1820–55 and pamphlets 1856–76; letters to Home Secretaries 1821–68.

M218–236:
Papers of missionaries, agents and lay workers at the various stations, arranged alphabetically by the writer's surname.

M237:
New Zealand letters 1822–60, approximately 700 pages of typescript, from Rev. H. Williams and others, many of the letters touching on land dealings.

M238:
Home papers relating to the New Zealand Mission including papers relating to S. Kempthorne 1843–48, and miscellaneous General Secretary's papers relating to New Zealand 1835–75, concerned mainly with relations between Bishop G.A. Selwyn and missionaries of the Church Missionary Society, Rev. H. Williams and land problems, and re-organisation of the New Zealand Mission 1852.

M238–241:
Home letter-books, Out 1824–75 and In 1808–67; miscellaneous correspondence 1845–74; documents concerning Norfolk Island.

M242–243:
Indexes to Society minutes 1799–1900, including indexes of names, subjects dealt with, and precis indexes arranged by country.

75-page list available for reference.

M1825–1827:
Correspondence and precis books 1879–1914 concerning grants to missionaries in New Zealand. Correspondents include Bishop W.L. Williams, A.F. Williams, Bishop E.C. Stuart, W. Goodyear, Bishop W.G. Cowie, Bishop O. Hadfield, J. McWilliam, G. Maunsell and E. Clarke.

Four-page list available for reference.

Entry 101   Reels M1551–1556, M1864–1876

Name **CHURCH OF SCOTLAND**

Title Records

Inclusive dates 1836–1936

Quantity 19 reels of microfilm

Location of original National Library of Scotland, George IV Bridge, Edinburgh EH1 1EW, Scotland

Note
In 1842 about a third of the ministers of the Church of Scotland seceded to form the Free Church of Scotland. In 1847 the United Secession Church and the Relief Church combined to form the United Presbyterian Church and its missionaries were active in Victoria and South Australia in 1847–57. The Free Church took over the Presbyterian missions in the New Hebrides in 1876. The Free Church and the United Presbyterian Church amalgamated in 1900 to form the United Free Church of Scotland, which united with the Church of Scotland in 1929.

Description
M1551–1556:
1) Letter-books and minutes 1836–1929 of the Foreign Mission Committee and other committees of the Church of Scotland referring mainly to missions of the Presbyterian Church of Australia in India.

2) Letter-books 1847–1936 of the Foreign Mission Committee of the United Presbyterian Church referring to missionaries sent to Australia, New Zealand and the New Hebrides, disputes in Presbyterian Church in Victoria in 1856–59, work of missions at Aneityum and Futuna, and translations by Rev. W. Gunn.

3) Letter-books and correspondence 1856–1934 of the Foreign Mission Committee and other committees of the Free Church of Scotland relating mainly to the New Hebrides Mission and also missions in India. They include letters of Rev. R. Steel, Rev. A. Watt, Rev. J.G. Paton and Rev. T. Macmillan, a file of letters 1891–1900 on the New Hebrides Mission, and a file of correspondence 1923–31 with Rev. F. Bowie and others on the Mission and the future of the New Hebrides Condominium.

4) Two albums of photographs of the New Hebrides Mission, c.1890.

79-page list available for reference.

Description
M1864–1876:
1) Minutes 1845–1900 of United Presbyterian Church Mission Board.
2) Minutes 1872–1900 of Free Church of Scotland Foreign Mission Committee.
3) Minutes 1900–29 of United Free Church of Scotland Foreign Mission Committee.
4) Minutes 1836–1936 of Church of Scotland Colonial Committee.
5) Minutes 1843–1900 of Free Church of Scotland Colonial Committee.
6) Minutes 1900–10 of Free Church of Scotland Colonial Committee.
7) Minutes 1910–29 of United Free Church of Scotland Colonial and Continental Committee.

23-page list available for reference.

Entry 102   Reels M2004–2006

Name **CLARENDON, George Villiers, 4th Earl (1800–1870)**
Title Papers
Inclusive dates 1843–70
Quantity 3 reels of microfilm
Location of original Bodleian Library, University of Oxford, Broad Street, Oxford OX1 3BG, England

Note
Whig politician. Lord Lieutenant of Ireland 1847–52; Foreign Secretary 1853–58, 1865–66 and 1868–70.

Description
Papers 1843–70 of Lord Clarendon, relating to his career as Lord Lieut. of Ireland, and Foreign Secretary. Subjects include female Irish emigration, convicts, the 1848 rebellion in Ireland and transportation of W.S. O'Brien and other political prisoners, creation of Bishopric of Labuan, and the threatened United States annexation of Sandwich Islands. Major correspondents include Sir George Grey, Lord Grey, T.F. Elliot, Lord John Russell and T. Redington.

18-page list available for reference.

Entry 103   Reels M2854–2856

Name **CLEVELAND COUNTY ARCHIVES**
Title Collections
Inclusive dates 1803–1950
Quantity 3 reels of microfilm
Location of original Cleveland County Archives, Exchange House, 6 Marton Road, Middlesbrough, Cleveland TS1 1DB, England

Description
1) Records 1880–1950 of Middlesbrough Borough Clerk's Department, including arrangements for Australian cricket match 1880, photographs of sites or monuments associated with Capt. James Cook and celebrations of bicentenary of Cook's birth in 1928.
2) Papers 1834–40 of Daniel Wheeler, including correspondence with missionaries in the Pacific and accounts of Wheeler's voyages to Australia and the Pacific.
3) Records 1865–1917 of Meek, Stubbs and Barnley, solicitors.
4) Papers 1930–35 of Pennymen Family of Ormesby Hall, including account of voyages to Australia and Indonesia.

Nine-page list available for reference.

Entry 104   Reel M1191

Name **CLUNIES-ROSS, John (1786–1854)**
Title Papers
Inclusive dates 1824–54
Quantity 1 reel of microfilm
Location of original British Library, Great Russell Street, London WC1B 3DG, England

Note
John Clunies-Ross formed a settlement on the Cocos–Keeling Islands in 1825, and his descendants lived there for the next 150 years.

Description
The papers consist primarily of autobiographical writings of Clunies-Ross referring especially to his relations with Alexander Hare and the visit of HMS *Beagle* to Cocos in 1836.

Three-page list available for reference.

Name **COCHRANE, Sir Thomas John (1789–1872)**

Title Papers

Inclusive dates 1840–49

Quantity 23 reels of microfilm

Location of original National Library of Scotland, George IV Bridge, Edinburgh EH1 1EW Scotland

Note
Admiral, Second in Command 1842–45 and Commander-in-Chief, East Indies Station 1845–47.

Description
1) Personal and family correspondence 1842–48, including letters of introduction and recommendation. Other correspondence concerns surveys in HMS *Samarang* and HMS *Vernon* near Mauritius, and reports from Sir William Parker in Manila, Singapore, Hong Kong and from the China Station. Includes letters from Capt. Alexander Maconochie seeking a loan from Cochrane and letters mentioning piracy, and the treatment of scurvy on convict ships.

2) East Indies Station papers: letters 1842–46, chiefly semi-official, to Cochrane or to his Secretary, Edward Waller. Correspondents include Sir James Brooke, Rajah of Sarawak, and Sir John Davis, Governor of Hong Kong. Includes: minutes of courts martial 1843–47; miscellaneous papers 1842–47, including instructions for the hospital and lists of personnel; journals 1842–47; books of semi-official letters to Cochrane 1842–46 and a book of semi-official letters by Cochrane 1843–47; Admiralty letters 1842–47, with index; Admiralty enclosures 1844–47, including correspondence regarding Hong Kong and the Malay Archipelago; Admiralty letters sent 1842–47, with index, and Admiralty Department letters 1842–47, with index; letters by Cochrane to the Indian Government 1842–47; account books 1844–47; dinner lists 1845–47; freight list for the East India Station 1844–47; list of persons recommended to Cochrane, with remarks; various logbooks, registers, returns and orders for the East India Station 1842–47.

3) Account-book 1842.

4) Plan of the cabin of Cochrane's flagship, HMS *Agincourt* 1847.

5) Private journals 1840–49, including descriptions of life in Hong Kong and cruises to the Malay mainland, Borneo, Sarawak and the Ryukyu (Lu-Chu) Islands.

6) Private letter-book 1840–45.

27-page list available for reference.

Name **CODRINGTON, Robert H., Rev. (1830–1922)**

Title Journals and Letters

Inclusive dates 1867–82

Quantity 2 reels of microfilm

Location of original Melanesian Mission, 15 Denewood Close, Watford, Hertfordshire WD1 3SE, England

Note
Anglican missionary and teacher in Melanesia, headmaster of St Barnabas' College, Norfolk Island 1867–87, pioneer Pacific anthropologist and lexicographer.

Description
Three journals 1872–75, describing Codrington's travels in Melanesia, life among the Mota people, slave trading, and island legends, customs and crafts. The killing of Lieut. James H.C. Bower of HMS *Sandfly* in 1880 is described in the third journal.

The letters 1867–82 were written to Codrington's brother Tom and give detailed descriptions of: life on Norfolk Island; travels in Melanesia; the impact of European culture on island life; and the death of Bishop J.C. Patteson. They reveal his interest in anthropology and language.

Four-page list available for reference.

Name **COGHLAN, Sir Timothy Augustine (1856–1926)**

Title Papers

Inclusive dates 1878–1929

Quantity 9 reels of microfilm

Location of original National Library of Australia, Canberra ACT 2600

Note
Statistician and Agent-General. First New South Wales Government Statistician 1886–1905, Agent-General for New South Wales in London 1905–26. Author of several major works on Australian statistics and economic history.

Description
M807–814:
1) Correspondence 1878–1929, including 18 letters 1905–08 from Alfred Deakin discussing Federal politics and legislation, letters 1887–1920 from Andrew Fisher, B.R. Wise, Sir Henry Parkes, Sir George Dibbs,

R.E. O'Connor, and J. Le Gay Brereton; letters, telegrams and cards of congratulations on his knighthood in 1914, and miscellaneous correspondence in chronological order on private and official matters.

2) Letter-books 1906–15 containing copies of letters to 325 friends, business contacts, politicians and officials. They relate to official matters and to his activities as Agent-General for New South Wales, as well as to routine and domestic affairs. Principal correspondents include Sir Joseph Carruthers, Alfred Deakin, Sir Charles Dilke, Sir George Reid, J.W. Holliman, W.M. Hughes, N.C. Lockyer, William Macleod and D.C. McLachlan.

3) Invitations, programs and club membership documents 1888–1925.

4) Legal documents and printed material including notification of honours and letters of condolence on his death.

5) Family correspondence 1885–1926, containing mainly correspondence with his wife and children.

6) Newspaper cuttings 1885–1926 including references to his career in Sydney and London and his contributions to the *Bulletin.*

7) Photographs of family and of railway construction in Sydney 1922.

17-page list available for reference.

M828:
Album with index of criminals, containing entries for 53 criminals generally giving name, place and date of birth and particulars of convictions, with accompanying portraits. The album was probably compiled at the end of the last century.

Entry 108   Reels M413–416, M577–579

Name **COMMONWEALTH AND CONTINENTAL CHURCH SOCIETY**

Title Records

Inclusive dates 1834–1957

Quantity 7 reels of microfilm

Location of original School of Oriental and African Studies, University of London, Thornhaugh Street, Russell Square, London WC1H 0XG, England

Note
In 1835 the Colonial Missionary Society was founded to meet the needs of the new settlement in Western Australia. This Society soon united with the Colonial Church and School Society, already at work in Newfoundland and Canada. In 1861 the

Society changed its name to the Colonial and Continental Church Society and in 1953 adopted its present title. In 1920 in Australia a sub-group was formed, known as the Bush Church Aid Society, to enable the Anglican Church in Australia to support outback people.

Description
M413–416:
Annual reports of the Society 1834–1957. These are printed reports and in some cases only the sections relating to Australia have been microfilmed. There is an index to the earlier volumes. Each report lists missionaries and agents, and shows financial returns, as well as detailing colonial operations in Australia, New Zealand, India, Africa, Canada and North America.

M577–579:
Minutes of meetings of the Society in London 1839–1901, excluding 1843–50. They are contained in six volumes, each of which has an index. As well as detailing financial matters and affairs in England, the minutes give summaries of letters from missionaries in Perth; Goulburn and Armidale, New South Wales; Queensland; and Christchurch, New Zealand.

Four-page list available for reference.

Entry 109   Reels M2570–2574

Name **CONTEMPORARY MEDICAL ARCHIVES CENTRE**

Title Collections

Inclusive dates 1885–1977

Quantity 5 reels of microfilm

Location of original Contemporary Medical Archives Centre, Wellcome Institute for the History of Medicine, 183 Euston Road, London NW1 2BP, England

Special conditions Microfilm must be purchased from the Wellcome Institute

Note
Sir Henry Wellcome (1853–1936) built up a medical museum and library which was opened to the public in 1949. The Institute (so called since 1968) houses the library and the academic research centre. The Contemporary Medical Archives Centre was set up in 1979.

Description
1) An account 1942–45 by Richard Philps of his experiences as a Royal Air Force Medical Officer in POW camps in Indonesia. It refers to:

accounts of the fall of Singapore; Japanese invasion of Java; conditions in POW camps in Surabaya and Semarang; internment in Changi, and news of atomic bombs.

2) Papers 1957–64 of physiologist Professor Ernest B. Verney, including manuscripts written at University of Melbourne.

3) Typescript diary 1915 of surgeon Alfred H. Tubby kept while serving with the British Mediterranean Expeditionary Force, referring to ANZAC forces, treatment of wounded from Gallipoli hospitals, and visits to Australian and New Zealand hospitals in Alexandria.

4) Papers 1969–76 of Sir Ernest Chain. Subjects include establishment of Florey Memorial Fund, Beecham Research Symposia held in Auckland, Sydney and Melbourne (1970) and 46th ANZAAS Congress in Canberra (1975).

5) Papers 1891–1934 of physiologist Sir Edward Schafer, including letters of his brother Ernest Sharpey on the Western Australian goldfields, Sir Charles Martin in Sydney and John Malcolm in Dunedin.

6) Papers 1947–59 of Grantley Dick-Read referring to childbirth practices, including natural childbirth in Australia and New Zealand.

7) Papers 1965 of Professor Sir George and Lady Pickering relating to a visit to Australia.

8) Paper 1919–55 of Marie C.C. Stopes referring to sex education and family planning in Australia and New Zealand and sales of her book *Married Love* in Australia.

9) Papers 1950–54 of Sir Edward Mellanby referring to: establishment of graduate medical school at Australian National University; medical research in Australia and academic appointments; and his visit to Australia in 1951. Correspondents include Sir Douglas Copland, H.W. Florey, Douglas Wright, Derek Denton and Sir George Paton.

10) Papers 1925–77 of Professor Percy C.C. Garnham relating to malaria research in Malaysia and Australia. Correspondents include I.M. Mackerras, John Field, A.S. Dissanaike and J.F.B. Edeson.

11) Papers 1900–31 of Sir Leonard Rogers relating to cholera, leprosy and tuberculosis.

12) Records 1930–74 of Abortion Law Reform Association.

13) Records 1901–33 of Lister Institute.

14) Research 1957–74 of Multiple Sclerosis Society of Great Britain and Ireland.

50-page list available for reference.

Entry 110   Reels M1580–1582

Name **COOK, James, Capt. (1728–1779)**

Title Journals

Inclusive dates 1770–84

Quantity 3 reels of microfilm

Location of original British Library, Great Russell Street, London WC1B 3DG, England

Note
Navigator and explorer.

Description
Journals and logs kept by Cook on his three voyages to the Pacific on HMS *Endeavour* and HMS *Resolution,* together with notes by Joseph Gilbert, William Wales and Henry Roberts.

Two-page list available for reference.

Entry 111   Reel M722

Name **COOK, James, Capt. (1728–1779)**

Title Journal

Inclusive dates 1772–75

Quantity 1 reel of microfilm

Location of original National Library of Ireland, Kildare Street, Dublin, Ireland

Note
Navigator and explorer. On his second major voyage 1772–75 Cook circumnavigated the world in HMS *Resolution,* accompanied by HMS *Adventure.* On this voyage he probably became the first navigator to sail south of the Antarctic Circle.

Description
Copy of Cook's journal of the second voyage, 9 April 1772–29 July 1775, in two folio vols (416 p. and 558 p.).

The inscription on the title page reads *A Journal of the Proceeding of His Majesty's Sloop the Resolution in a Voyage of Discoveries Towards the South Pole and Round the World* by Capt. James Cook 1772, 3, 4 and 5.

Detailed description at beginning of reel.

Entry 112   Reel M865

Name **COOPERATIVE UNION LTD**

Title Letters

Inclusive dates 1830–1905

Quantity 1 reel of microfilm

Location of original Holyoake House, Hanover Street, Manchester M60 0AS, England

Note

The Cooperative Central Board, later the Cooperative Union, was set up in 1869, with its headquarters in Manchester, as an advisory body for cooperative societies in Britain. The businessman and socialist Robert Owen (1771–1858) was one of the founders of the cooperative movement. George Holyoake (1817–1906) became an Owenite in 1838, supported the Rochdale Cooperative Society in the 1840s, and was one of the leading propagandists of the cooperative movement.

Description

1) Papers 1830–55 of Robert Owen, referring to National Colonisation Society, transportation of Dorsetshire labourers in 1834, and other matters. Correspondents include Robert Gouger.

2) Papers of George Holyoake 1852–1905 referring to emigration, activities of relatives and friends in Australia, the case of Gerald Supple in Melbourne, politics in the colonies and the cooperative movement. Correspondents include Horatio Holyoake, Gerald Supple, Sir Henry Parkes and Emma Hornblower.

Six-page list available for reference.

Entry 113   Reel M1897

Name **CORNWALL COUNTY RECORD OFFICE**

Title Collections

Inclusive dates 1844–1924

Quantity 1 reel of microfilm

Location of original Cornwall County Record Office, County Hall, Truro TR1 3AY, England

Description

1) Papers 1872–1924 of the Victor Family concerning estate of Richard Victor in South Australia.

2) Papers of Bundrett & Co 1862–1906, including estate of Richard Hancock of Adelaide.

3) Reports and papers 1917–20 of F.C. Cann concerning gold mining in New Zealand and Australia.

4) Letters 1859–62 of Thomas Medlyn of Adelaide.

5) Letters 1855–62 of Peter Matthews describing Ballarat goldfields.

6) Memoirs 1922 of Hannah Glasson referring to Cornish settlements in New Zealand.

7) Letters and papers 1899–1913 of J. Langdon Bonython of Adelaide.

Four-page list available for reference.

Entry 114   Reels M580, M1363–1367

Name **CORPORATION OF LONDON RECORDS OFFICE**

Title Records

Inclusive dates 1756–1840

Quantity 6 reels of microfilm

Location of original Corporation of London Records Office, PO Box 270, Guildhall, London EC2P 2EJ, England

Description

Records of criminal cases tried at London Criminal Court (Old Bailey) and of prisoners held in Newgate Gaol.

1) Index to persons indicted 1756–1834. The lists give name and date and an abbreviated indication of the offence, and sometimes of the sentence.

2) Sessions Minute-books (Fair Entry Books) 1783–1834. Each session is divided into:

(a) Gaol Delivery, giving names of justices, jurors and those tried with a note of their offences and sentences;

(b) Oyer and Terminer trials, where appropriate, giving names of jurors and recognisances brought forward;

(c) Gaol Calendar giving names of prisoners arranged by sentence.

3) Transportation Account 1829–40. It contains clerks' charges for drawing up documents and other contracts connected with the transportation of convicts, arranged chronologically by ship.

4) Bills 1791 of Keeper of Newgate in respect of persons sentenced to transportation.

Two-page list available for reference.

Entry 115   Reel M857

Name **COTTON, W.J.**

Title Diaries

Inclusive dates May 1874–January 1876

Quantity 1 reel of microfilm

Location of original M.W. Gregory, Hampshire, England

Note
Master of the yacht *Goshawk*. Cotton was a keen photographer, developing his own film on board the *Goshawk*.

Description
1) Diary kept by Cotton between December 1874, when the *Goshawk* set sail from England, and January 1876, when it returned. During the round trip, the *Goshawk* called at Cadiz, Algiers and Malta, then was towed 1450 miles through the Suez Canal and Red Sea to Aden. After spending some time in Ceylon it sailed to Batavia, Singapore, Bangkok and then to Darwin. The return voyage to England was made via Batavia, Mauritius and Cape Town. The journal includes lively descriptions of the gentlemen passengers and of customs and people observed at the various ports of call. Details are recorded of the fauna and flora observed during the trip, together with weather and navigational information.

2) Diary May–August 1874 written during a voyage from Cowes, England, to Hammerfest and Spitzbergen in Norway. During the voyage the *Goshawk* sailed far north, over the 80 degrees line of latitude, to allow its passengers to hunt seals. Cotton evidently had a keen interest in the dress and customs of the inhabitants of the region, as well as the wildlife.

One-page list available for reference.

Entry 116   Reel M978

Name **CRAIG, James Whitelaw (1849–1880)**

Title Diary

Inclusive dates September 1873–March 1877

Quantity 1 reel of microfilm

Location of original Local History Library, Central Library, High Street, Paisley, Scotland

Note
Engineer from Paisley, Scotland. Craig was a keen naturalist and gave a large collection of specimens to the Paisley Museum.

Description
Diary, September 1873–March 1877. The first portion of the diary records an expedition to the south of France, during which he collected specimens of birds, insects, butterflies and plants, which he later presented to the Paisley Museum. Craig added to his collection while in Australia in 1874–77. The record of his activities during this period make up the second portion of his diary. The daily entries are very detailed, recording several temperature readings most days, together with general meteorological notes and observations on the natural history of the area being visited. Although Craig spent time in Melbourne and Sydney and travelled around the surrounding countryside, he spent the largest part of his stay in or near Brisbane. He befriended many Aborigines and his diary contains extensive notes on their attitudes, behaviour and customs, the notes often being accompanied by drawings. Accounts of his collecting activities frequently include local lore related to events such as bushfires, and to the disappearance of species from a locality.

One-page list available for reference.

Entry 117   Reels M600, M687–688

Name **CRAWFORD, James Coutts (1817–1889)**

Title Papers

Inclusive dates 1837–80

Quantity 3 reels of microfilm and 20 black-and-white photographs

Location of original Brigadier H.N. Crawford, Fife, Scotland

Note
Explorer and settler. Crawford first visited Australia and New Zealand in 1838–39. In 1845 he rented 'Forest Lodge', Sydney, and purchased 'Eton Vale', Darling Downs, Queensland, in partnership with Sir Arthur Hodgson. In 1847–48 he observed geological structures throughout New South Wales and in 1862 made a geological survey of the Province of Wellington, New Zealand. He settled at Miramar in New Zealand and constructed a tunnel there in 1858 to drain the waters into the sea. He was a member of the Legislative Council for seven years and resigned to become magistrate and sheriff at Wellington for more than 12 years. He published *Recollections of Travel in New Zealand and Australia* (1880).

Description
1) 11 volumes of diaries covering 1837–64 (excluding 1849–56). They contain detailed entries describing Crawford's journeys and places visited, as well as his work in Australia and New Zealand.

2) Letters to Crawford 1840–75, relating to family and business matters and mentioning building activity in New Zealand, the Fitzroy mines and the Richmond Hill silver mine, Victoria. Correspondents include Capt. William Loring, J.C. Bidwill and B.W. Mountfort.

3) Two manuscripts entitled 'Drafts for Book Australia Section 1838–39' and 'Reminiscences', perhaps drafts for New Zealand section of book. These drafts give fuller descriptions than corresponding chapters in his book, *Recollections of Travel in New Zealand and Australia* (1880).

4) Sketchbook covering a journey up the Wanganui River, depicting Maori people, settlements and landscapes and a collection of watercolours and drawings of Australia and New Zealand. Subjects include Glebe 1844–49, and other parts of Sydney; Eton Vale, Queensland; Mount Egmont and Taranaki, New Zealand.

Nine-page list available for reference.

Entry 118   Reels M1829–1830

Name **CRUTCHLEY, Ernest Tristram (1878–1940)**

Title Papers

Inclusive dates 1928–40

Quantity 2 reels of microfilm

Location of original Mr Brooke Crutchley, Cambridge, England

Access conditions Microfilm is to be used for reference and research purposes only.

Note
British civil servant, whose posts included British Government Representative for Migration in Australia (1928–31) and Representative in Australia of Her Majesty's Government in the United Kingdom (1932–35).

Description
1) Typescript of unfinished autobiography includes account of Crutchley's early life and his appointment in 1928 as the British Government Representative for Migration in Australia.

2) Diaries 1928–40 containing: a detailed record of Crutchley's travels in Australia; meetings with public figures; social life in Canberra, Sydney and Melbourne; negotiations with British settlers; impressions of Australian politics; reflections on migration; British–Australian relations; and the 'bodyline' controversy.

3) Correspondence 1931–35.

Five-page list available for reference.

Entry 119   Reels M983, M2078

Name **CUMBRIA RECORD OFFICE**

Title Collections

Inclusive dates 1863–1939

Quantity 2 reels of microfilm

Location of original Cumbria County Office, The Castle, Carlisle, Cumbria CA3 8UR, England

Special conditions Permission to reproduce is required from the County Archivist.

Description
M983:
1) Scott family papers: 20 letters 1819–52 written to Miss Scott of Sandgate Hall, Penrith, by M.J. (Mrs John) Wood of Sydney and her daughter Mary, who married a Mr Lowe of Bathurst. The letters contain comments on conditions in the colony, and on family, church and political affairs.

2) Crerar papers: correspondence 1938–39 between Dr J.W. Crerar of Maryport, Cumberland, and Alexander Morrison, Town Clerk, Adelaide, concerning the introduction in Australia of municipal elections by means of secret ballot. Thomas English, Mayor of Adelaide 1862–63 and a native of Maryport, claimed to have introduced the practice to Australia.

3) Papers of Ken Graham, Dalton & Kennedy of High Crosby: Chart of Swan River 1827; map of the Vasse district, Western Australia; letters 1829–37 from Georgiana Molloy and her husband John, written on board ship and after their arrival in Western Australia to Georgiana's mother and brothers in Rugby and Cheltenham. The letters include descriptions of the Swan River settlement, Augusta and Cockburn Sound, local and domestic news, and notes on the excursion to the Vasse district in January 1833.

4) Four letters 1854–58 from John Gibson, stonemason of Parramatta, to his mother in England. One letter dated 1874 refers to the probable death of Gibson.

5) McMorrans scrapbook. Two volumes of photographs accompanied by an index. Archie and John McMorran migrated to Australia in 1884, their nephew James arrived in Australia in 1911.

6) Madgen Family letters 1854–86. Correspondence of Stephen Madgen to his family in England; letters of Samuel and Margaret White of Ipswich, Queensland, to the Madgens. The letters include news of conditions on the gold diggings in Victoria, New Zealand and Queensland, noting local prices and referring to coal mining and cotton growing in Queensland. The final letter is from Robson and Mary Urwin, describing conditions in Adelaide.

7) F.W. Woolworth & Son, Whitehaven. Conveyance dated 23 June 1905, referring to premises in Whitehaven. Document includes reference to James Wilfred Marsden of Nelson, New Zealand.

8) Printed material: *A General Chart Exhibiting the Discoveries Made by Capt. James Cook in This and his Two Preceding Voyages*, by Lieut. Henry Roberts of His Majesty's Royal Navy (n.d.); *A New and Complete Chart of the World, displaying the tracks of Capt. Cook,* by T. Bowen (n.d.), bound as part of *A Treatise on Naval Affairs* (1790); Obituary from the *Carlisle Journal, 28* March 1871, of Francis Jollie, agent in Nelson of the New Zealand Company, and former Colonial Treasurer.

Ten-page list available for reference.

M2078:
1) Diary April–July 1863 of Joshua Hughes on a voyage from Liverpool to Brisbane on the *Montmorency*, recording the weather, life on board the ship, and sightings of porpoises, flying fish and other ships. The diary ends with his first few days in Brisbane.

2) Diary 1898 of John Swainson Littlewood on a voyage from Liverpool to Adelaide and Port Augusta on the *Oakhurst.*

One-page list available for reference.

Entry 120   Reel M692

Name **CUNNINGHAM, Allan (1791–1839)**
Title Papers
Inclusive dates 1814–39
Quantity 1 reel of microfilm
Location of original Botany Library, British Museum (Natural History), Cromwell Road, South Kensington, London SW7 5BD, England

Note
Botanist and explorer. Arrived in Australia in 1816 and joined John Oxley on his expedition to the Lachlan River. In 1817, 1820 and 1821 sailed with Capt. P.P. King on voyages to Western and Northern Australia. In 1827 he discovered the Darling Downs in Queensland.

Description
Transcripts of some papers in the Mitchell Library, Sydney.
1) 'Journal of the Proceedings of Mr James Bowie and Mr Allan Cunningham' 1814–15 with continuations by Cunningham to 1819.

2) Letters 1817–19 to Sir Joseph Banks and W.T. Aiton.

3) Lists of seeds and specimens 1816–22.

4) Draft 1822 entitled 'Original MS of Appendix to P.P. King's "Survey"'.

5) Correspondence between Cunningham and Robert Brown 1822–39, and further lists of specimens collected and plants observed by Cunningham 1819–27.

Three-page list available for reference.

Entry 121   Reel M1941

Name **DALE, Sir Henry (1875–1968)**
Title Papers
Inclusive dates 1935–64
Quantity 1 reel of microfilm
Location of original Royal Society, 6 Carlton House Terrace, London SW1Y 5AG, England

Note
First Director of National Institute for Medical Research 1928–42, Director of Royal Institution 1942–46, Secretary of Royal Society 1925–35, President of Royal Society 1940–45, Chairman of Scientific Advisory Committee to War Cabinet 1942–47, President of British Association 1947, President of Royal Society of Medicine 1948–50 and President of British Council 1950–55.

Description
1) Papers 1941–43 of the British Commonwealth Science Committee of the Royal Society regarding H.C. Webster and inter-dominion scientific collaboration.

2) Correspondence 1944 between Dale and Sir Howard Florey on the manufacture of penicillin in Australia.

3) Papers 1944–46 concerning the Empire Scientific Conference in 1946. Correspondents include Sir Henry Tizard and Sir David Rivett.

4) Papers concerning Dale's tour of New Zealand and Canada in 1950, including letter by F.R. Callaghan.

5) Papers 1951–56 relating to a biography of Lord Rutherford, including letters of E. Marsden and J. Rutherford.

6) Correspondence 1942–49 with E. Singer of Melbourne concerning paper on the influence of metals on diphtheria intoxication and Singer's application for the Chair of Bacteriology at Queensland University.

Eight-page list available for reference.

Name **DALLEY, Frederick W. (1885–c.1960)**

Title Papers

Inclusive dates 1920–56

Quantity 4 reels of microfilm

Location of original Brynmor Jones, Hull University, Cottingham Road, Kingston Upon Hull, Humberside HU6 7RY, England

Note

Trade unionist. Co-author of *Trade Unions in Malaya and Singapore* (1948).

Description

Correspondence, memoranda, notes, cuttings and other papers relating to trade union movements in Malaya and Singapore. Correspondents include M. Buttrose, W.L. Blythe, R. Caddick, John Brazier, Alex Simpson and P.P. Narayanan.

Eight-page list available for reference.

Entry 123 Reel M1862

Name **DANNOCK, James (1831–1907)**

Title Autobiography

Inclusive dates 1898

Quantity 1 reel of microfilm

Location of original Mr George Dannock, Norwich, England

Note

Born in Norfolk in 1831 and emigrated with his family to Australia on the *Castle Eden* in 1848. James Dannock died in Melbourne in 1907.

Description

Life history of James Dannock, written in 1898 and copied by his son Jesse Dannock of Box Hill, Victoria, in 1909. The manuscript contains: an account of the voyage from England to Australia in 1848 on board the *Castle Eden*; Dannock's work on farms near Sydney; bullock driving near Kilmore; the Black Thursday bushfires; the Victorian, New South Wales and Western Australia goldfields; experience with Aborigines near Swan Hill; his illness and old age.

Two-page list available for reference.

Name **DANVERS, Frederick Charles**

Title Transcripts

Inclusive dates 1893–95

Quantity 27 reels of microfilm

Location of original India Office Library, 197 Blackfriars Road, London SE1 8NG, England

Note

Registrar and Superintendent of Records of the India Office 1834–98. Between 1893 and 1895 he made a number of visits to the State Archives in The Hague to inspect and arrange for the copying of official Dutch records of the seventeenth century relating to the East Indies.

Description

Transcripts of selected Dutch documents relating to India and the East held in the State Archives in The Hague. They deal with all activities of the Dutch in the East from the regulation of trade to the treatment of indigenous people, and particularly relations with Chinese, French, Spanish, English and Portuguese traders and officials.

The following three groups of records have been microfilmed:

1) Letters from India 1600–99 with English translations 1600–70.

2) Letters from the Dutch East India Company to India 1614–1700, with English translations.

3) Letters from the Governor-General at Batavia (Dutch East Indies) to various factories 1617–99, with English translations 1617–43.

One-page list available for reference.

Entry 125 Reels M2520–2521

Name **DEACON, Arthur B. (1903–1927)**

Title Papers

Inclusive dates 1907–34

Quantity 2 reels of microfilm

Location of original Cambridge University Library, West Road, Cambridge CB3 9DR, England

Note

Anthropologist. Deacon arrived in Malekula, New Hebrides in 1926 and travelled extensively, visiting Bushman's Bay, Atchin, Big Nambas Territory and Ambrym. His work *Malekula : A Vanishing People in New Hebrides,* edited by Camilla Wedgwood, was published in 1934. The Deacon Papers form part of the A.C. Haddon Papers at Cambridge University Library.

Description
Correspondence, biographical notes, cuttings, notes on Malekula and linguistics, and other papers relating to Deacon's fieldwork in the New Hebrides and posthumous publication of *Malekula*. Correspondents include Camilla Wedgwood, A.C. Haddon and A.R. Radcliffe-Brown.

Seven-page list available for reference.

Entry 126   Reel M440

Name **DEANE, Mathilde E. (b.1870)**

Title Index

Inclusive dates 1925

Quantity 1 reel of microfilm

Location of original Typescript copies held in the Mitchell Library, State Library of New South Wales, Macquarie Street, Sydney NSW 2000; National Library of Australia, Canberra ACT 2600; and State Library of Victoria, 328 Swanston Street, Melbourne VIC 3000

Note
In 1920 Deane was commissioned by the three libraries to make typescript copies of the dispatches of Governors of Victoria 1851–60, held in the Governor's Office in Melbourne. She worked on this project for several years and in 1926–30 she also copied Victorian dispatches held in the Public Record Office, London, which were not held in Australia.

Description
Index to Dispatches relating to the Colony of Victoria 1851–1860 ... serving as an index to Colonial Office, Victoria. Original correspondence and entry books (dispatches) 1851–1860 and War Office. Out-letters Secretary of State (Victorian dispatches) 1851–1854, compiled by M.E. Deane.

This subject index covers persons, places and subjects mentioned in the dispatches of the Governor of Victoria and the Secretary of State for the Colonies. Each index entry summarises briefly a subject referred to in a dispatch, indicating whether the dispatch originated in Britain or Victoria, the dispatch number and date, and the page number of the dispatch in the typed transcripts made by M.E. Deane (held in the Mitchell Library, National Library of Australia and State Library of Victoria).

One-page list available for reference.

Entry 127   Reel M716

Name **DE CHAIR, Sir Dudley (1864–1958)**

Title Memoirs

Inclusive dates 1931–47

Quantity 1 reel of microfilm

Location of original Imperial War Museum, Lambeth Road, London SE1 6HZ, England

Note
Admiral. Governor of New South Wales 1924–30. Entered the Royal Navy in 1878 and was Naval Secretary to the First Lord of the Admiralty 1912–14.

Description
Two typescript volumes 1924–30, containing reminiscences of his time as Governor of New South Wales. They describe vice-regal life and include a section on the constitutional struggle initiated by J.T. Lang to abolish the Legislative Council in 1926. Descriptions of social life and entertainment at Government House and his visits to various parts of New South Wales are contained in the journals. The last section records his voyage back to England via Singapore, Japan and China, and his reception in London.

Entry 128   Reel M717

Name **DE CHAIR, Henry Graham Dudley, Commander (b.1905)**

Title Journals

Inclusive dates 1927–31

Quantity 1 reel of microfilm

Location of original Commander H.G.D. de Chair, Hertfordshire, England

Note
Commander in the Royal Navy, ADC to his father, Sir Dudley de Chair, 1929–30 while he was Governor of New South Wales.

Description
1) Journal, October 1927–April 1929, kept while Lieutenant on HMS *Laburnum*. The *Laburnum* served at the New Zealand Station and visited Fiji, Samoa and the Society Islands, June–October 1928. The journal records life on the ship, excursions and entertainments on shore and impressions of places visited. There are a number of watercolour, crayon, and pen and ink sketches by the author.

2) Journal, April–December 1929, kept while ADC to his father, Sir Dudley de Chair. It describes life at Government House, Sydney, and in country districts and includes a description of a skiing trip to Mount Kosciusko.

3) Journal, April–July 1930, recording portion of the journey of Sir Dudley de Chair and his party from Sydney to England and giving a detailed description of travel in the East Indies and Asia. About 13 pages at the beginning deal with de Chair's experiences as ADC to his father and there are also comments on the Chinese and Japanese as emigrants to Australia.

4) Journal, November 1930–November 1931, kept while lieutenant on HMS *Nelson* on a voyage from England to the West Indies, Balboa, Gibraltar and return to England.

One-page list available for reference.

Entry 129   Reel M1136–1153

Name **DE LA RUE COMPANY LTD**

Title Records

Inclusive dates 1865–1946

Quantity 18 reels of microfilm

Location of original National Postal Museum, King Edward Building, King Edward Street, London EC1 A1LP, England

Note
London printing firm founded in 1816. In 1855 it secured the printing of British postage stamps, and from 1860 onwards it produced postage stamps, revenue stamps, currency and other items for many of the colonies. It also supplied plates, dandy rolls, stamp paper and other stationery to the colonies.

Description
Selections from correspondence books comprising correspondence with Agents-General in London and the Office of the Crown Agents for the Colonies concerning the design, printing and supply of postage stamps, revenue stamps, postal stationery, printing plates and other items. The records relate to all the Australian colonies (later States), New Zealand, Straits Settlements, Malay States, Borneo, Sarawak, Labuan, Tonga, Fiji, Gilbert and Ellice Islands, and Solomon Islands.

100-page list available for reference.

Entry 130   M465

Name **DENHAM, Sir Henry Mangles (1800–1887)**

Title Sketches and paintings

Inclusive dates 1852–69, 1958

Quantity 1 reel of microfilm

Location of original Capt. H.M. Denham, London, England

Note
Commander of HMS *Herald* engaged in exploring and surveying in the South Pacific. The first cruise began in February 1853 from Sydney and proceeded to Bass Strait to examine Port Dalrymple, then Lord Howe Island and the New Hebrides. In 1854 the survey was extended to the Isle of Pines, Fiji Islands and Sunday Island. Later expeditions surveyed Norfolk Island, Port Jackson, Dirk Hartog Island and the Great Barrier Reef.

Description
1) Approximately 80 drawings and paintings, many of which are by J. Glen Wilson. They were commissioned by Capt. Denham to record the voyages of HMS *Herald*. Subjects include: Isle of Pines; Lord Howe Island; St Paul Island; the New Hebrides; Balls Pyramid; Shark Bay; and Fiji. There are also sketches of Fijians, and fish, flora and birds.

2) Photographs of J. Glen Wilson and the captain and crew of the *Herald* 1860.

3) Letter 1958 with photographs and report on the site of the grave of Fleetwood Denham, son of the commander of the *Herald*.

Entry 131   Reels M606–607, M671

Name **DENISON, Sir William Thomas (1804–1871)**

Title Papers

Inclusive dates 1846–65

Quantity 3 reels of microfilm

Location of original Col. W.M.E. Denison, Nottinghamshire, England (M606-607); National Library of Australia, Canberra ACT 2600 (M671)

Note
Lieut.-Governor of Van Diemen's Land 1846-54, Governor of New South Wales 1854–61, Governor of Madras 1861–66.

Description

M606–607:

1) Letter-books (six vols) 1846–64 containing copies of letters written by Sir William Denison. Many of the letters are on official subjects although they are marked private. The first volume 1846–49 is indexed and contains memoranda and diary entries. Inserted in several of the volumes are letters received from Lord Grey, Sir Charles Wood and Lord Canning.

2) Journal September–October 1857 of a trip to Norfolk Island containing Denison's impressions of the island and its inhabitants, as well as recording day-to-day events.

3) Letters 1855–59 from Lady Denison to their sons, mainly discussing domestic events.

M671:

Letters 1856–57 from Sir William Denison discussing: the settlements on Norfolk Island and at Moreton Bay; A.C. Gregory's expedition to North Australia; legal tender in the colony and the political situation. In addition, there are letters 1856 from Rev. George Hobbs and G.M. Frederick Young and a letter 1857 from an unknown correspondent describing Norfolk Island. Also included are newspaper clippings 1856 relating to the separation of Moreton Bay, and an address by Sir William Denison.

Eight-page list available for reference.

Entry 132   Reels M1615–1616

Name **DENISON FAMILY**

Title Papers

Inclusive dates 1819–1915

Quantity 2 reels of microfilm

Location of original Mrs P. Goedhuis, Nottinghamshire, England

Note
Sir William Denison (1804–71), Lieut.-Governor of Van Diemen's Land 1847–54, Governor of New South Wales 1854–61. His brother Sir John Denison (1800–73) was Speaker of the House of Commons 1857–72 and his nephew Edward Denison was a politician who died during a visit to Australia in 1870.

Description
A large collection of letters written mainly to William and Frank Denison by their parents Sir William and Lady Denison and their brothers and sisters in Sydney 1855–60. Apart from family news, they refer to: travels in New South Wales; a visit to Norfolk Island and New Zealand; church affairs; sport; theatre and other social activities; and Australian natural history. Includes letters from the Duke of Newcastle and Sir George Grey, estate papers, official papers and correspondence about armorial bearings.

Two-page list available for reference.

Entry 133   Reels M1969–1972

Name **DERBY, Edward Henry Stanley, 15th Earl (1826–1893)**

Title Papers

Inclusive dates 1852–85

Quantity 4 reels of microfilm

Location of original Liverpool Record Office, Liverpool City Libraries, William Brown Street, Liverpool L3 8EW, England

Note
Conservative MP 1848–69, Secretary of State for Colonies February–May 1858, Foreign Secretary 1866–68, 1874–78 and Secretary of State for the Colonies 1882–85.

Description

1) Papers 1858–59 relating to Derby's position as Secretary of State for the Colonies and India. Subjects include Australian Federation and separation of the Straits Settlements from the Government of India.

2) Papers 1866–68, 1874–78 relating to Derby's position as Foreign Secretary. Subjects include: the *Sandwich Islands Treaty* (1875); American interest in a Hawaiian protectorate; treaty with Samoa (1878); war in Aceh, Sumatra; Pacific labour trade; and French interest in New Guinea.

3) Papers 1882–85 relating to Derby's position as Secretary of State for the Colonies. Subjects include: British and German annexation of New Guinea; Australian Federation; representation of natives in New Zealand Parliament; Australian representation on Suez Canal Technical Committee; and Fijian land claims.

4) Diaries 1882–85. Subjects include: annexation of New Guinea; Monroe Doctrine in Pacific; Australian Federation; offer of Australian troops for Sudan; and Australasian Federal Council Bill.

Major correspondents include Lord Carnarvon, Sir Edward Thornton, H.C.E. Childers, Sir Arthur Gordon, Sir John Pope Hennessy, Sir Henry Wrenfordsley, Lord Selborne, T. Sanderson,

Sir George Bowen, Sir Robert Herbert, Sir Henry Loch, Lord Normanby, Lord Augustus Loftus and Sir Frederick Weld.

36-page list available for reference.

Entry 134   Reel M2077

Name **DERBY, Edward Smith Stanley, 13th Earl (1775–1851)**

Title Papers

Inclusive dates 1813–51

Quantity 1 reel of microfilm

Location of original Liverpool Record Office, Liverpool City Libraries, William Brown Street, Liverpool L3 8EW, England

Note
President of Linnean Society 1828–33, President of Zoological Society of London 1831–51.

Description
Correspondence and manuscripts. Subjects include: natural history collections; dispatch of birds and other specimens from Australia, New Zealand, New Guinea and East Indies for Derby's collections; appointment of J. MacGilivray as naturalist on HMS *Rattlesnake*; Maori disturbances 1843 and fighting against Maoris at Kawati Pah; and John Gould's *Birds of Australia*. Correspondents include J. Gray, Sir William Hooker, G.W. Earl, J.W. Willis, Edward Stanley, John Gould and T.M. McDonnell.

Five-page list available for reference.

Entry 135   Reels M791–793

Name **DERBY CENTRAL LIBRARY**

Title Records

Inclusive dates 1704–1878

Quantity 3 reels of microfilm

Location of original Central Library, 25B Irongate, Derby DE1 HS, England

Description
1) Catton Papers comprising correspondence of Wilmot Horton, Under-Secretary of State for War and the Colonies 1821–28. The collection is arranged in four series:

   (a) Catton ABC: a series of volumes of letters 1821–37 arranged alphabetically by correspondent. Correspondents include Sir George Arthur, Saxe Bannister, John T. Bigge, Sir Thomas Brisbane, Sir Thomas Fowell Buxton, George Canning, William, John and Richard Carter, Sir William Colebrooke, Sir Francis Forbes, Robert Gouger, Henry Goulburn, Lord Hatherton, Henry Hobhouse; William Huskisson, Rev. John Dunmore Lang, John Macarthur, R. Matheson, W. Norris, Lord Palmerston, Sir Robert Peel, Sir Herbert Taylor, Robert Torrens, and William Wilberforce. Includes a paper (42 p.) by the National Colonization Society, arguing against proposals made by Col. Torrens and Wilmot Horton on a system of emigration and land allocation for South Australia.

   (b) Numbered volumes: a series of volumes of correspondence 1824–37. Correspondents include Sir Richard Bourke, James Busby, Thomas Potter Macqueen, Henry Forbes and H. Dumaresq.

   (c) Unbound letters: letters 1822–34 arranged chronologically. Correspondents include George Villiers, H.B.M. Vavasour, George Galway Mills, G. Watson Taylor, Rev. Edward Stanley, T.H. Scott and Edward Miller Mundy.

   (d) Subject volumes: papers arranged by subject, with a letter from Governor Bourke 1835, and printed papers relating to emigration.

2) Miller Mundy Manuscripts: 27 letters 1835–50 mainly to Alfred Miller Mundy while he was with the 21st North British Fusiliers in Van Diemen's Land and Port Phillip and when he was Colonial Secretary of South Australia 1843–49. There are letters from his father Edward Miller Mundy, his father-in-law Sir John Hindmarsh, Admiral Sir George Mundy and Sir George Grey.

3) Brickhill Hall Collection: journals and correspondence of William Sacheverell Coke. Diary February–September 1827, describing his life in New South Wales and two journals kept on the *Wanstead* from Van Diemen's Land to England. The correspondence 1825–32 consists mainly of letters to Coke's father describing conditions on board the convict ship *Regalia* from Ireland, at the barracks in Sydney and while living at Newcastle in 1827. There is a letter from James Stirling promoting the settlement in Western Australia. Two letters, dated 1877 and 1878, are to Coke from H.H. Hayter, Office of the Government Statistician, thanking him for information on officers in the early colony.

75-page list available for reference.

Name **DERBYSHIRE RECORD OFFICE**

Title Collections

Inclusive dates 1821–1934

Quantity 1 reel of microfilm

Location of original Derbyshire Record Office, County Offices, Matlock, Derbyshire DE4 3AG, England

Description
1) Dickson Family: correspondence 1863–81, mainly from James Dickson and James R. Hamilton to Dr Frank Dickson. The letters from James Dickson to his father relate to his departure from England and prospects of work in Dunedin, New Zealand. Letters from James R. Hamilton concern James Dickson's death and estate and his own business affairs.

2) Derbyshire Archaeological Society: document 1821 on the population of the British Empire with engravings of Lord Liverpool and the Duke of Clarence.

3) Rev. Samuel Hey: document 1880 concerning Mahala Cuthbertson and estates in New Zealand.

4) George Davies: letters 1923, 1934 from George Davies describing economic and political conditions in New Zealand.

5) Spondon Parish: paper, 1838 concerning the rate of emigration to Australia with note regarding payment of £15 to two emigrants to South Australia.

6) Melbourne Parish: correspondence, plans and newspaper cuttings 1880 concerning restoration of the church of the Melbourne Vicarage, Derbyshire, including appeals to the people of Melbourne, Australia, for donations through George C. Levy of the Melbourne International Exhibition Offices.

Seven-page list available for reference.

Name **DEVON RECORD OFFICE**

Title Collections

Inclusive dates 1801–1904

Quantity 4 reels of microfilm

Location of original Devon Record Office, Castle Street, Exeter, Devon EX4 3PU, England

Description
1) Papers 1801–78 of Addington Family. Includes correspondence of Lord Sidmouth, referring to: colonial appointments; land grants; convicts; the administration of Java; journey of George W. Evans over Blue Mountains; logs kept by Francis Addington on HMS *Wolverene* 1876–78 and HMS *Sappho* 1878–79.

2) Papers 1877–1903 of Fortescue Family of Castle Hill, including a diary 1877–80 of S.W. Fortescue recording a voyage from Plymouth to Melbourne on SS *Whampoa*, visiting Australia and New Zealand; visits to stations, mines, libraries and theatres; and a voyage from Sydney to Singapore and China on SS *Bowen*.

3) Papers 1861–65 of Edward Seymour, Duke of Somerset, including journals of D.J. Gamble, Deputy Quartermaster-General in New Zealand, and letters concerning the death of William Wills.

4) Family history records 1870–1904 of Gidley Family compiled by B.C. Gidley, referring to Philip Gidley King.

5) Records 1787–1843 of Exeter Gaol, including transportation orders and papers.

6) Papers 1901 of Sir Roper Lethbridge concerning Devonshire families in the colonies.

7) Journal 1882 of Mrs Thomson on a voyage from Glasgow to Rockhampton on *Selkirkshire*.

16-page list available for reference.

Entry 138   Reel M2596

Name **HMS *DISCOVERY***

Title Logbooks

Inclusive dates 1901–04

Quantity 1 reel of microfilm

Location of original General Library, Natural History Museum, Cromwell Road, South Kensington, London SW7 5BD, England

Description
Logbooks kept during HMS *Discovery* expedition of Antarctic exploration 1901–04. Subjects include: details of bacteria from various specimens,

recorded by first medical officer and Reginald Koettlitz; collections registers; station logs; measurements of crew; and diary 1901–04 kept by Thomas Hodgson.

Three-page list available for reference.

Entry 139 — Reel M1913

Name **DISRAELI, Benjamin, 1st Earl of Beaconsfield (1804–1881)**

Title Papers

Inclusive dates 1847–80

Quantity 1 reel of microfilm

Location of original Bodleian Library, University of Oxford, Broad Street, Oxford OX1 3BG, England

Note
Conservative MP 1837–76. Leader of Conservative Party in the House of Commons 1848–76; Chancellor of Exchequer February–December 1852, 1858–59 and 1866–68; Leader of Conservative Party 1867–81; Prime Minister February–December 1868 and 1874–80.

Description
Political correspondence, including official and semi-official letters. Subjects include: emigration; colonial governorships; Fiji; establishment of Moreton Bay as a separate colony; the Congress of Berlin (1878); military action in Malaya; colonial appointments; affairs of Sir James Brooke; and Fenian prisoners. Major correspondents are Lord Carnarvon, Lord Stanley, Lord Derby, J. Pope Hennessy, Duke of Buckingham and Charles Gavan Duffy.

16-page list available for reference.

Entry 140 — Reels M2980–2982

Name **DONCASTER ARCHIVES DEPARTMENT**

Title Collections

Inclusive dates 1821–1971

Quantity 3 reels of microfilm

Location of original Doncaster Archives Department, King Edward Road, Balby, Doncaster, South Yorkshire DN4 0NA, England

Description
1) Records 1842–1968 of Bridon Plc, formerly British Ropes Ltd, including history of the company, financial records and photographic albums, with references to branches in Australia and New Zealand.

2) Records 1872–76 of solicitors Somerville and Baxter, including annual report and accounts of Bank of South Australia.

Five-page list available for reference.

Entry 141 — Reels M1713–1717

Name **DONNITHORNE FAMILY**

Title Papers

Inclusive dates 1836–81

Quantity 5 reels of microfilm

Location of original Hertfordshire Record Office, County Hall, Hertford SG13 8DE, England

Note
James Donnithorne (d.1852) worked for the East India Co in Mysore. He retired to Sydney in about 1836 where he joined many public movements and invested in real estate in New South Wales and Victoria. His daughter Eliza (c.1826–1886) inherited the bulk of his estate. She was jilted in 1856 and never again left her house.

Description
1) Papers 1836–50 of James Donnithorne relating to his business activities in India and Australia, including accounts, stock returns, bills, receipts and letters. Correspondents include Alexander F. Mollison, James Graham, Stuart A. Donaldson and Charles Ebden.

2) Letters 1846–81 received by Eliza Donnithorne.

Six-page list available for reference.

Entry 142 — Reel M1172

Name **DORSET MILITARY MUSEUM**

Title Manuscripts

Inclusive dates 1830–1930

Quantity 1 reel of microfilm

Location of original Dorset Military Museum, The Keep, Bridport Road, Dorchester, Dorset DT1 1RP, England

Description
Papers relating to the service of the 39th (Dorsetshire) Regiment in New South Wales in 1827–32. They comprise two diaries of expeditions into the interior in 1830 and 1832, and a manuscript and newspaper cuttings on the life of the explorer Capt. Charles Sturt.

Two-page list available for reference.

Entry 143   Reels M1170–1171

Name **DORSET RECORD OFFICE**

Title Collections

Inclusive dates 1727–1975

Quantity 2 reels of microfilm

Location of original Dorset Record Office, 9 Bridport Road, Dorchester, Dorset DT1 1RP, England

Description

1) Selections from parish records 1840–52 referring to emigration of paupers to Australia.

2) Papers 1858–87 of Sir Frederick Weld, colonial governor, and other members of Weld Family relating to property and investments in New Zealand, family history and administration of Straits Settlements.

3) Papers 1727–38 of William and Jocelyn Pickard concerning death and estate of Strange Pickard of Fort Marlborough.

4) Diary and commendations 1860–61 of Lieut. Albert Battiscombe of HMS *Pelorus* serving in New Zealand War.

5) Papers 1885–1915 of Williams Family, including letters of I.T. Simes in Sydney and Condobolin, New South Wales.

6) Journal 1854–55 of Annie Beer on a voyage from London to Melbourne on the *Canaan*.

7) Papers 1871–1918 of Florance Family, including letters from members of the family in New Zealand.

8) Papers and publications 1834–1957 concerning the Tolpuddle Martyrs.

9) Copies of letters 1935–54 concerning Samuel Stephens, surveyor with the New Zealand Company and one of the founders of Nelson.

10) Papers of Hardy Family 1851–72, including diaries of Nathaniel Hardy on voyage to Adelaide on the *Thetis* in 1851 and return voyage to Plymouth in 1862, and a family tree.

11) Manuscript 1975 by P.A. Lewis on the history of Sandpit Farm in Broadwindsor, Dorset, referring to the Hardy Family in South Australia and the winemaking firm of Thomas Hardy & Sons Ltd.

11-page list available for reference.

Entry 144   Reels M995–999

Name **DOWNSIDE ABBEY**

Title Records

Inclusive dates 1819–69

Quantity 5 reels of microfilm

Location of original Downside Abbey, Stratton on the Fosse, Bath BA3 4RH, England

Note

Benedictine abbey in Somerset founded in the late 1700s. Many of the early Catholic priests in New South Wales had trained or taught at Downside, including J.B. Polding, the first Archbishop of Sydney, W.B. Ullathorne and C.H. Davis.

Description

Letters, arranged chronologically, sent to Rev. T. Heptonstall, Abbot Gregory and other members of the Downside community. Correspondents include Polding, Ullathorne, Davis, C. Conolly, Bishop R. Salvado, Bishop R.W. Willson, Bishop F. Murphy, Bishop J.B.F. Pompallier, Bishop J.A. Goold.

Topics include: affairs of the Abbey; the mission in New South Wales; St Mary's Cathedral; travels in rural districts; the establishment of bishoprics in other colonies; the Benedictine convent at Parramatta; financial matters; spread of churches and schools; visit of Polding to Rome; life in the colonies; recruitment of priests and nuns; relations with Irish priests; J.J. Therry; education; and relations with civil authorities, especially Henry Parkes.

71-page list available for reference.

Entry 145   Reel M835

Name **DU CANE, Sir Edmund Frederick (1830–1903)**

Title Letters

Inclusive dates 1851–56

Quantity 1 reel of microfilm

Location of original Mr Anthony Pullan, Berkshire, England

Note

Military officer and prison administrator. Arrived in Western Australia in 1851 to superintend works for the convict establishment. Later he acted as visiting magistrate of convict stations in the colony and became known for his progressive attitude. He returned to England in 1856 and later became Chairman of Directors of Convict Prisons, Inspector General of Military Prisons and Surveyor-General of Prisons.

Description

16 letters from Du Cane in Western Australia to his mother and brothers, Arthur and Richard. The first two letters were written on board the *Anna Robertson,* one describing in detail the passengers, eating and sleeping conditions, and shipboard life. The content of his letters from Western Australia varies from details of social life to sketches and written descriptions of the settlements at Perth and Guildford and discussions of the convict system. Events recorded include the Governor's expedition in February 1852 to Champion Bay, the wreck of the *Eglinton* in September 1852 and rumours of the cessation of transportation in 1853. His letters include sketches of settlers and officials, Aborigines, buildings and animals.

One-page list available for reference.

Entry 146   Reels M672–673

Name **DUFFY, Sir Charles Gavan (1816–1903)**

Title Papers

Inclusive dates 1840–1903

Quantity 2 reels of microfilm

Location of original National Library of Ireland, Kildare Street, Dublin, Republic of Ireland

Note

Journalist, Irish nationalist and Victorian politician. Emigrated to Australia in 1855 and in the following year was elected to the Victorian Legislative Assembly. Between 1857 and 1865 he held various positions, including Minister of Lands, and in 1871–72 was Premier and Chief Secretary. Speaker of the House of Assembly 1877–80.

Description

1) Letters to Duffy, mainly from English and Irish literary and political figures. They are divided into periods 1840–46, 1846–54 and 1855–1902. Correspondents include Thomas O'Shea, W.S. O'Brien, Thomas Carlyle, Robert Lowe, Sir Redmond Barry, Sir Henry Parkes, Sir George Bowen, Lord Carnarvon and J. Henniker Heaton.

2) Miscellaneous correspondence 1842–92 between members of Duffy's circle and an account by Fred Lucas of his visit to Rome in 1855, in letters to Duffy.

3) Various documents relating to the publication of Duffy's works including a cutting with author's amendments to an article by Duffy, 'Half a Century of Boons to Ungrateful Ireland'.

4) Miscellaneous documents concerning Duffy and Young Ireland, including a poem by Charles Kickham and accounts by Richard O'Gorman and T.B. MacManus of the Rising of 1848.

One-page list available for reference.

Entry 147   Reel M1689

Name **DUNN, Edward J. (1844–1937)**

Title Papers

Inclusive dates 1871–1948

Quantity 1 reel of microfilm

Location of original University of Cambridge, West Road, Cambridge CB3 9DR, England

Note

Geologist. Officer of Geological Survey of Victoria 1864–71, worked in South Africa, returned to Australia 1886 as consulting geologist, Director of Geological Survey of Victoria 1904–12.

Papers formerly held by the Royal Commonwealth Society, London.

Description

1) Drafts of autobiography and notes, including notes on Bendigo and Beechworth, Victoria; Mount Morgan, Queensland; and Coolgardie, Western Australia; and Australian explorers and geologists.

2) Cutting books 1871–80, 1886–87, mostly relating to Cape Colony goldfields and diamond fields.

3) Correspondence 1871–1948 dealing with Dunn's geological discoveries and writings, including letters of Sir Joseph Hooker, A. Ramsay, Sir Richard Owen and Baron Ferdinand von Mueller.

4) Photographs of Dunn and his home, Rosemeath, Melbourne.

5) Publications about Dunn and his ethnographical collections.

Two-page list available for reference.

Entry 148   Reel M2493

Name **DUNSTAN, Benjamin (1864–1913)**

Title Papers

Inclusive dates 1913–23

Quantity 1 reel of microfilm

Location of original Palaeontology Library, Natural History Museum, Cromwell Road, South Kensington, London SW7 5BD, England

Note
Geologist. Dunstan joined the Queensland Geological Survey in 1897 and was Acting Government Geologist 1902 and Chief Government Geologist 1915.

Description
1) Notebooks containing lists of fossil collections.
2) Correspondence 1913–23 with R.J. Tillyard. Subjects include Tillyard's work in Nelson, New Zealand, and dispatch of fossil specimens to London.
3) Printed material.

Two-page list available for reference.

Entry 149   Reels M1339, M2836

Name **DURHAM COUNTY RECORD OFFICE**

Title Collections

Inclusive dates 1814–1989

Quantity 2 reels of microfilm

Location of original Durham County Record Office, County Hall, Durham DH1 5UL, England

Description
M1339:
1) Papers 1850–96 of Hodgkin Family, mainly letter-books 1866–68 of Jonathan Hodgkin describing his travels in Australia and New Zealand, and meetings of the Society of Friends.
2) Papers 1848–1927 of Vane–Tempest–Stewart Family, including letters of Capt. R. FitzRoy, Sir Daniel Cooper and J.H. Aldridge of Adelaide to Lady Londonderry.
3) Papers 1842 of John Buddle, colliery engineer, referring to employment of engineers and clerks in Australia and New Zealand.
4) Report (c.1955) of Hugh Mackay, carpet manufacturer, of visit to Australia and New Zealand.

Five-page list available for reference.

M2836:
1) Papers 1898–1960 of Sir Cuthbert Headlam. Subjects include evacuation of Suvla and Anzac Cove.
2) Correspondence 1839–64 of Pease Family of Darlington referring to travels of Joseph Pease in Australia.
3) Papers 1832–1977 of Wallis Family of Darlington. They include a sketchbook of James Backhouse recording his travels in Australia in 1832–38, etchings of Tasmanian birds by Edward Backhouse in 1840, and family letters.
4) Records 1911–51 of Cleveland Bridge Engineering Company. Subjects include New Zealand and Queensland railway bridges.
5) Darlington Library Collection, including diary 1883–84 of John R. Harker kept on a journey from Darlington to New Zealand on *Rangitiki*.

Eight-page list available for reference.

Entry 150   Reel M2799

Name **DURHAM LIGHT INFANTRY (68th Regiment)**

Title Records

Inclusive dates 1863–66

Quantity 1 reel of microfilm

Location of original Durham Light Infantry Museum, Aykley Heads, Durham DH1 5TU, England

Note
The 68th Regiment was based in New Zealand, mainly in Tauranga and Auckland, in 1864–66.

Description
1) Sketchbook and letters 1863–64 of Capt. Hugo S. Light referring to the Maori War.
2) Diaries 1864–65 of Major Charles U. Shuttleworth referring to voyage to New Zealand on the *Light Brigade*, relations with Maoris, and social activities.
3) An ink sketch 1864 of Gate Pa by H.G. Robley.

Two-page list available for reference.

Entry 151   Reel M603

Name **DWYER, Michael (c.1770–1825)**

Title Papers

Inclusive dates 1798–1900

Quantity 1 reel of microfilm

Location of original National Library of Ireland, Kildare Street, Dublin, Ireland

Note
Irish insurgent and New South Wales settler. Participated in the Irish insurrections of 1798 and 1803. In 1805 he was permitted to exile himself for life to New South Wales to avoid being brought to trial. He was granted land at Cabramatta, Sydney, in 1809 and was later appointed Chief Constable at Liverpool.

Description
1) Luke Cullen papers. About 400 p. of notes relating to the life of Dwyer and events in 1798, written by Brother Luke Cullen, a monk of Clondalkin, near Dublin, in a volume which also contains entries for the Clondalkin School roll (c.1816–25).
2) Notes, drafts and cuttings compiled by J. Cyril and M. Weale (c.1900) towards a study of Michael Dwyer.

One-page list available for reference.

Entry 152   Reels M470–535

Name **EAST INDIA COMPANY**

Title Records

Inclusive dates 1769–1830

Quantity 66 reels of microfilm

Location of original India Office Library, 197 Blackfriars Road, London SE1 8NG, England

Note
In 1786 the British East India Co purchased from the King of Quedah the island of Pulo Penang, which it renamed Prince of Wales Island. In 1795 the Dutch surrendered Malacca and its dependencies; it was briefly restored to the Dutch in 1818–25. In 1805 Penang was constituted a Presidency. In 1819 the British Government was permitted to establish a factory at Singapore and in 1826 Penang, Singapore and Malacca were incorporated as the Straits Settlements, the Governor being responsible to the Governor-General of India.

Description
Lengthy reports, letters and dispatches relating to the British East India Co's interests in the Straits Settlements. The main body of factory records are consultations or proceedings of the presidents and councils sent contemporaneously to the company in London. There are Bengal Consultations relating to Prince of Wales Island 1786–95, Prince of Wales Island Public Consultations 1805–30, with indexes 1808–30; Prince of Wales Island Secret and Political Consultations 1806–11, 1813, 1818, 1826–29 with indexes; Prince of Wales Military Consultations 1806–07 with index; Singapore Political and Secret Consultations 1827–28 with index; Malacca Public Consultations 1827; and Malacca Political Consultations 1828. There are also letters and abstracts of letters from Prince of Wales Island 1805–30, and dispatches and their abstracts from the company to the Presidency at Prince of Wales Island 1805–30.

Other records have been grouped under the headings Singapore diary 1827–30 with index, Malacca diary 1826–30 with index, and Malacca journal and ledger 1826–30. There are separate groups of miscellaneous documents and reports 1769–95 and 1805–10.

Five-page list available for reference.

Entry 153   Reels M816–819

Name **EAST SUSSEX RECORD OFFICE**

Title Collections

Inclusive dates 1668–1934

Quantity 4 reels of microfilm

Location of original East Sussex Record Office, The Maltings, Castle Precincts, Lewes, East Sussex BN7 1YT, England

Description
1) Quarter Sessions Records: expenses of criminal prosecutions and transport of convicts 1835–57; return of expenses of conveying convicts 1857–78, for East and West Sussex.
2) Rye Corporation records: returns 1835–51 of expenses of criminal prosecutions and transportation; circulars and papers 1847–52 on expenses of criminal prosecutions and transportation.
3) Boards of Guardians records: Eastbourne Union register of emigrations to Australia and New Zealand 1911–29.
4) Parish records: Ashburnham Parish: poster and notices 1838–40 advertising free passages to New South Wales; Hartfield Parish: 'Information

Respecting the Australian Colonies', Colonial Office (1831); T. Frederick Elliot, Secretary to the Commission, printed circular Colonial Office 1831; printed form to be returned to Colonial Office by 'persons desirous of entering into agreements for their conveyance to the colonies' by the Commissioners for Emigration.

5) Private records: printed reports 1893 of the Wentworth Goldfields Pty Co Ltd, Lucknow, New South Wales; *The Isle of Pines, or, a Late Discovery of a Fourth Island in Terra Australis Incognita* (London, 1668); a copy of *Morning Herald,* London, containing notice of marriage at Scone, New South Wales, of Thomas Tourle of Balala to Helen M. Emma Moise.

6) Papers 1924–34 of Sir William Campion, Governor of Western Australia, including: journals 1921–31; visitors books 1924–31; correspondence and photographs 1925–31 in connection with his activities as Western Australian President of Toc H; photographs and addresses 1929–31; three printed items: *Guildford 1829–1929: A Century of Progress* by L. Gibbons (1929), *The Case of the People of Western Australia in Support of Withdrawal from the Commonwealth of Australia* (489 p.) (1934), signed by members of the Western Australian Secession Delegation of 1933, and *Hints for Speakers* (1933) issued by the Conservative and Unionist Central Office.

Nine-page list available for reference.

Entry 154 Reel M837

Name **EDELSTEN, Frederick A.**
Title Diary
Inclusive dates 1867–68
Quantity 1 reel of microfilm
Location of original Mr C.R. Edelsten, London, England

Note
The firm of Edelsten, Kingsborough and Pearson operated a manchester warehouse in Pirie Street, Adelaide.

Description
Diary recording Edelsten's travels, 24 July 1867–3 October 1868. He arrived in Adelaide from England on 14 October 1867 aboard the *City of Adelaide.* He travelled around the south-eastern district of South Australia and then made a return journey to Perth, travelling by ship from Adelaide to Albany and thence by coach to Perth. In August 1868 Edelsten returned to England via Albany and

Ceylon, where he stayed a short while. The diary includes many observations on, and sketches of, Australian flora and fauna and photographs of Albany, Perth, Mt Eliza, scenes in the outback and the Edelsten warehouse in Adelaide.

One-page list available for reference.

Entry 155 Reel M721

Name **EDGELL, William Henry, Rev.**
Title Diaries
Inclusive dates 1897–1901
Quantity 1 reel of microfilm
Location of original Mrs R. Rowland, Derbyshire, England

Note
Missionary in the Melanesian Mission. From 1897 to 1905 he was stationed in the New Hebrides. He later worked in the Diocese of Auckland.

Description
Five diaries 1897–1901 recording daily events in the missions and including statistics on schools, churches, registers of baptisms, marriages and burials, and Mota words and phrases.

Entry 156 Reel M1676

Name **EDINBURGH UNIVERSITY LIBRARY**
Title Collections
Inclusive dates 1798–1941
Quantity 1 reel of microfilm
Location of original Special Collections Department, Edinburgh University Library, George Square, Edinburgh EH8 9LJ, Scotland
Special conditions Permission to reproduce is required from Edinburgh University Library.

Description
1) Letters 1867–76 of T. Halliwell to J. Halliwell-Phillips describing life as a goldminer, shepherd and schoolteacher in New Zealand.

2) Papers 1837–74 of geologist Sir Charles Lyell, including letters of H. Brown, J. von Haast and Sir James Hector in New Zealand.

3) Papers 1846–70 of Sir Roderick Murchison, mainly relating to the first discovery of Australian gold, and including letters of W.B. Clarke, E.H. Hargraves, P.E. Strzelecki, W.T. Smith and P.P. King.

4) Papers 1879–1900 of Sir Archibald Geikie, comprising letters from Australian and New Zealand geologists, including E.J. Dunn, F.W. Hutton, J. von Haast and E.T. Hardman.

5) Letter 1879 of E. Schulyer to Lord Augustus Loftus on his appointment as Governor of New South Wales.

6) Diary 1914 of Professor J.H. Ashworth describing his voyage to and from Australia, visits to museums and universities, and meetings with Australian scientists.

7) Papers 1937–41 relating to writings of Marnie Bassett.

8) Papers 1830–41 of Professor Robert Jameson referring to fossils from New South Wales, emigration to Australia and appointment of naturalist for HMS *Fly*.

Five-page list available for reference.

Entry 157   Reel M2049

Name **EEDY FAMILY**

Title Papers

Inclusive dates 1841–1932

Quantity 1 reel of microfilm

Location of original Miss R.F. Cuskelly, Sussex, England

Description
1) Letters 1868–88 of Capt. John Eedy of Sydney to his sister Jane Eedy. Subjects include Sydney centennial celebrations, economic depression in colonies, and growth of Sydney.

2) Letters 1926–30 of Charles Eedy of Tanna, New Hebrides, to his cousin May Riley containing family news.

3) Family photographs 1866–1925.

Two-page list available for reference.

Entry 158   Reels M838–840

Name **ESSEX RECORD OFFICE**

Title Collections

Inclusive dates 1782–1903, 1966

Quantity 3 reels of microfilm

Location of original Essex Record Office, County Hall, Chelmsford, Essex CM1 1LX, England

Description
Quarter Sessions Records:
1) Minor functions, miscellaneous: drafts of Orders of Quarter Sessions for transportation May 1845–June 1853, showing name, crime and sentence of each convict.

2) Clerk of the Peace. Parliamentary returns; returns of transportation orders 1844–53, giving name, age, crime and sentence of each convict; expenses of prosecutions and of conveying convicts sentenced to transportation.

3) Process Books of Indictments 1782–1866: 11 volumes giving a note of every indictment session by session supplying name, abode and occupation of defendant, offence, plea, verdict and sentence. With each volume there is an index of defendants.

Private Records:
1) Documents 1868–97 relating to the estate of John Vaughan of Hotham Creek, Pimpara, Queensland.

2) Documents 1848–62 relating to Charles Perry, Bishop of Melbourne, and his family.

3) Letters 1882–98 from Col. Benjamin A. Branfill, Nelson, New Zealand, to T.L. Wilson.

4) Thesis by M.H. Dunwell: 'True Patriots from Essex: An Investigation into Transportation of Convicts from the County of Essex to New South Wales during the Period 1787–1809, with Particular Reference to Transportees of the First Fleet' (1966).

5) Hanslip Ward & Co (solicitors) deposit: letter 1844 of J.S.T. Dowbiggin of Hobart to Miss Cocker concerning religion and education.

6) Letter 1830 of Dr Edward Hawkins, Oriel College, Oxford, to Christopher C. Parker referring to emigration as a means of alleviating agricultural distress.

7) Legal documents, correspondence and newspaper cutting 1839–60, in the Petre Family papers, referring to land in Wellington and Nelson, New Zealand.

8) Sperling Family correspondence 1810, 1816, referring to William Bligh.

9) Power of attorney 1876 to Owen Kemp from George T. Kemp, Richmond River, New South Wales.

10) Letters 1866–1903 to Rose Robertson of South Australia, later Mrs John Player Frowd.

11) Passport 1896 of Herbert W. L. Way to travel on the Continent and in the Philippine Islands.

12) Documents 1899 of Alexander Wallace, concerning various hardwood company interests in Western Australia, and letter from his son Arthur C. Wallace, Deniliquin, New South Wales.

13) Letters 1848 from William Kingston to George Warburton concerning emigration.

14) Letter 1850 from H. Caslake, Union House, to Rev. J. Bullock about emigrants from Radwinter.

11-page list available for reference.

Entry 159   Reel M2565

Name **EUGENICS SOCIETY**

Title Records

Inclusive dates [c.1910]–61

Quantity 1 reel of microfilm

Access conditions Restricted

Location of original Contemporary Medical Archives Centre, Wellcome Institute for the History of Medicine, 183 Euston Road, London NW1 2BE, England

Note
Founded in 1907 to promote public awareness of eugenic problems. Henry Twitchen, a wealthy Australian grazier, left the Society a large legacy in 1930.

Description
1) Records 1950–58 of Migration Council.
2) Correspondence and papers 1930–32 on voluntary sterilisation.
3) Correspondence 1926–61 with eugenics societies in Australia and New Zealand.
4) Papers 1930–38 concerning Henry Twitchen.
5) Correspondence 1922–58, including letters of Henry Twitchen and Edith How-Martyn.

11-page list available for reference.

Entry 160   Reel M841

Name **EVERETT, George (1811–1893)**

Title Papers

Inclusive dates 1838–55, 1949

Quantity 1 reel of microfilm

Location of original Col. G.N. Everett, Sussex, England

Note
George Everett and his brother John (1816–1902) arrived in Sydney in 1838 on the ship *Hope.* They took up a selection, 'Ollera', north of Armidale, New South Wales, and were joined in 1842 by their younger brother Edwin (1822–1909). George returned to England about 1856 but still retained his interest in the station, while John returned in 1858 and managed the sale of 'Ollera' wool in London. Edwin bought the adjacent property and became one of the largest landholders in the district.

Description
1) Letters 1838–55 from George Everett in northern New South Wales to his family in England describing the family selection, mentioning bushrangers, trouble with Chinese employees, gold digging and the expansion of 'Ollera' station.
2) Three photographs of the Everett Family at Tenterfield, New South Wales.
3) Thesis by A.V. Cane entitled 'Ollera 1838 to 1900: A Study of a Sheep Station' (University of Sydney, 1949).

Four-page list available for reference.

Entry 161   Reel M423

Name **AN EX-CANTERBURY RESIDENT**

Title Pamphlet

Inclusive dates c.1865

Quantity 1 reel of microfilm

Location of original Mr K.A. Webster, London, England

Description
Printed pamphlet entitled *Letters from New Zealand* by an ex-Canterbury resident, published in London, and dedicated to John Bull, Esq., Junior. It consists of ten letters and is mainly a philosophical comment on the New Zealand way of life but with important notes on particular features such as the importance of the discovery of gold, the need for railways, and Maori agitation. There is very little personal detail although the last letter on the botanic system of medicine relates his own experiences.

Name **EXHIBITION** *Grands Voiliers Autour
du Monde*

Title Exhibits

Inclusive dates 1801–c.1830

Quantity 1 reel of microfilm and 6 photographs

Location of original Original of report in Archives
Nationales, Ministere de la Marine, 60 rue des
Francs-Bourgeois, Paris 3e, France

Location of originals of photographs noted in
Description.

Note
In March 1962 an exhibition entitled *Grands Voiliers
Autour du Monde: Les Voyages Scientifiques
1760–1850*, was held in the Musee de la Marine,
Paris. Items shown included paintings, drawings,
manuscripts, maps, ethnographical objects and
natural history specimens.

Description
Selection of items shown at the exhibition:
1) 11-page copy of a transcript, in French, of
   a report by a member of Nicholas Baudin's
   expedition in 1801 describing the west coast
   of Australia and containing an account of the
   discovery of the Vlamingh Plate on Dirk Hartog
   Island. The report covers the period 26 July–
   4 August 1801.

2) Six photographs:

   (a) Oil portrait of Louis Antoine de Bougainville.
   Collection of Baronne de Vazehles.

   (b) Watercolour by Ferry, *Tombeau du Père
   Receveur à Botany Bay*. Collection of Musee
   de la Marine.

   (c) Watercolour by Pellion of Bathurst.
   Collection of Baron de Freycinet.

   (d) Watercolour *Vue du Port Jackson prise de
   l'Observatoire*. Collection of Baron de Freycinet.

   (e) Wash drawing *Voyage à Bathurst.
   Une Vue de Prospect Hill. Maison de Camp de
   M. Lawson*. Collection of Baron de Freycinet.

   (f) Watercolour by Edouard Paris, *Etablissement
   Pénitentiaire de Port Arthur*. Collection of Jobbe
   Duval.

One-page list available for reference.

Name **FAIRBRIDGE SOCIETY**

Title Records

Inclusive dates 1912–76

Quantity 5 reels of microfilm

Location of original University of Liverpool, Sydney
Jones Library, PO Box 123, Liverpool L9 3DA,
England

Note
The Fairbridge Society was formed in 1909
following a meeting organised by Kingsley
Fairbridge at Oxford. Fairbridge and his wife
brought the first party of 13 orphan boys to Western
Australia in 1912, with the first Fairbridge Farm
School being established at Pinjarra. Other farm
schools were set up at Molong, New South Wales
(1937), and Bacchus Marsh, Victoria (1937). In
1981 the last farm school at Pinjarra closed down.

Description
1) Minutes 1925–52 of Executive Committee,
   Council and Annual General Meetings.

2) Correspondence, including files on the
   Northcote Trust (1934–70), Commonwealth
   Relations Office (1949–72), extension activities
   to New Zealand (1932–36) and extension
   activities to Queensland (1934–55). Subjects
   include: the selection and passages of boys for
   the Northcote Farm School at Bacchus Marsh;
   the Fairbridge/Northcote Family schemes; and
   farm schools in New Zealand and Queensland.
   Correspondents include Sir Charles Hambro,
   Sir Arthur Coles, L.R. Lumley, W.R. Vaughan,
   E.T. Crutchley and R.L. Dixon.

3) Papers 1913–39 on Pinjarra School, including
   reports, circulars, minutes and notes.

4) Papers 1944–60 on future of Fairbridge Society.

5) Photographs of Australian parties.

Four-page list available for reference.

Entry 164   Reels M2291–2314

Name **FAWCETT LIBRARY**

Title Collections

Inclusive dates 1858–1972

Quantity 24 reels of microfilm

Location of original Fawcett Library, Calcutta House, Old Castle Street, London E1 7NT, England

Note
The Library began in 1926 as the Women's Service Library. In 1977 the Fawcett Society (named after the suffragette Dame Millicent Fawcett) transferred the Fawcett Library to the City of London Polytechnic.

Description
1) Records 1882–1919 of British Women's Emigration Association (for earlier records, see entry 72).
2) Records 1919–51 of Women's Migration and Overseas Appointment Society.
3) Papers 1942–53 of feminist Teresa Billington-Greig. Subjects include: internment of Adela Pankhurst Walsh; federalism in Australia; and growth of Queensland Women's Electoral League.
4) Papers 1885–1902 of Josephine Butler. Subjects include Contagious Diseases Acts, Women and Girls' Protection Ordinance, and Women's Christian Temperance Union.
5) Papers 1937–54 of Dame Kathleen Courtney, founder of Women's International League. Subjects include: Young Women's Christian Association; Australian League of Nations Union; Courtney's visit to Australia and New Zealand in 1938; and Pan-Pacific Women's Association.
6) Papers 1902–19 of Australian feminist Vida Goldstein. Includes: manuscript of a lecture by Goldstein on her visit to United States in 1902; cutting book 1903 relating to Goldstein's campaign in Victoria and women candidates in general; Australian representation at the International Women's Suffrage Conference at Amsterdam; Women's Suffrage Bill in Victoria; 1919 Peace Treaty; and British and European politics.
7) Papers 1872–1951 of Edith How-Martyn, Chairman of Suffrage Fellowship. Subjects include: Australian women at war; women candidates in 1943 Australian federal election; Women for Canberra Movement; and women's issues in New Zealand.
8) Research papers 1958–60 of Norman Mackenzie, assembled while writing his book *Women in Australia*.
9) Papers 1928–53 of writer and preacher Agnes Maude Royden, including letters of Catherine King.
10) Autograph collection 1906–58 relating to female suffrage, emancipation and women's movement in Australia and New Zealand.

22-page list available for reference.

Entry 165   Reel M1134

Name **FEATHERSTON, Beaumont (1839–1918)**

Title Journal

Inclusive dates 1891–94

Quantity 1 reel of microfilm

Location of original Capt. B.A. Featherston-Dilke, Warwickshire, England

Note
Wealthy traveller who spent three years travelling in the South Pacific, generally staying at Government House or clubs in the major cities. A friend of Lord and Lady Hopetoun, he stayed with them at Government House in Melbourne for lengthy periods in 1892–94.

Description
Journal of travels in the South Pacific, New Zealand and Australia by yacht, visiting Samoa, Fiji, Sydney, Melbourne, Brisbane, Adelaide, Hobart, Albany, the Cape of Good Hope, Auckland, Dunedin, Christchurch, Wellington, Napier and Rotorua. They record his attendance at dinner parties, cricket matches and race meetings, plays and concerts. In addition to the journal, there are brief accounts by Featherston of places visited entitled 'Cruise of the White Heather'.

Three-page list available for reference.

Entry 166   Reel M1199–1200

Name **FEILDING, William H.A., General (1836–1895)**

Title Papers

Inclusive dates 1871–1924

Quantity 2 reels of microfilm

Location of original Rt Hon. Earl of Denbigh, Warwickshire, England

Note
As agent of the Emigrants' and Colonists' Aid Corporation, Feilding visited Australia and New Zealand in 1871 and selected 100 000 acres of land

near Palmerston North. The town established at the settlement in 1874 was named Feilding. He again visited Australia in 1881 and New Zealand in 1894.

Description
The collection consists of correspondence, diaries, cuttings and drawings of General Feilding. They deal with his visit to Australia and New Zealand in 1871–72 to select land for the Colonists' Land and Loan Corporation; his visit to Queensland in 1881–82 to advise on a railway from Roma to Point Parker; and the work of the Transcontinental Railway Syndicate. There is also a diary of Charlotte Feilding on a trip to Canada, New Zealand and Singapore in 1894–95.

Two-page list available for reference.

Entry 167   Reel M939

Name **FIELDEN, Thomas Perceval (1882–1974)**
Title Journal
Inclusive dates 1925–26
Quantity 1 reel of microfilm
Location of original Mr R.J. Fielden, Kemsing, Sevenoaks, Kent, England

Note
Music teacher and examiner. Professor of Pianoforte at the Royal College of Music 1921–52. As an examiner in music for the Associated Board of the Royal Academy, London, he toured Australia and New Zealand 1925–26, giving piano recitals as well as examining students.

Description
Journal, 30 April 1925–10 March 1926, describing his journey from London on the *Cormorin*, calling at Fremantle, Adelaide, Melbourne and Sydney; and his travels around eastern Australia and return voyage from Brisbane via Darwin, Batavia, Singapore to London. The 647-page journal has an index at the beginning to places, people, concerts and lectures, and contains a number of photographs of acquaintances, wildflowers and places visited. Some of the people mentioned in the journal are Rev. 'Tubby' Clayton, Dr Harold Davies, Sir Dudley de Chair, Dr A.E. Floyd, Sir Robert Garran, Bernard Heinze, Frank Hutchens and Michael Terry. The typescript contains detailed and lively descriptions of the many centres he visited, including country towns, with candid comments on Australians he met and their attitudes to matters such as industrial strikes and rivalry between State capitals.

Entry 168   Reel M437

Name **FITZSIMMONS, John M. (d.1860)**
Title Letters
Inclusive dates 1841–47, 1871
Quantity Part of 1 reel of microfilm
Location of original National Library of Australia, Canberra ACT 2600

Description
Five letters 1841–47 from John M. Fitzsimmons (d.1860), surgeon, to his brother, written from Hartley, New South Wales, mainly discussing family matters but also commenting on unemployment in the colony. One letter 1871 written by his daughter refers to the death of her father and family matters. Six miscellaneous receipts and small notes including one about James Slattery and another about the burial of Elizabeth Faulks.

Entry 169   Reels M444, M3033–3037

Name **FLINDERS, Matthew, Capt. (1774–1814)**
Title Papers
Inclusive dates 1779–1912
Quantity 6 reels of microfilm
Location of original M444: Public Record Office, Ruskin Avenue, Kew, Richmond-upon-Thames, Surrey TW9 4DU, England;
M3033–3037: National Maritime Museum, Greenwich, London SE10 9NF, England

Note
Naval officer and explorer. In 1798, with George Bass, he circumnavigated Van Diemen's Land. In 1801–02 he circumnavigated Australia in HMS *Investigator*, being the first navigator to chart the southern coast. In 1803, on a voyage to England, he was forced to land on the Ile de France (Mauritius), where he was held prisoner until 1810. On his return to England he completed his book *A Voyage to Terra Australis.*

Description
M444:
Selections from Admiralty 1 and 7 in the Public Record Office relating to Matthew Flinders (Adm. 1/177, 1200, 1800, 1803–4, 1806–9, 2020–1, 3762–3, 4379, 4382, 4689 and Adm. 7/707–8). They include correspondence between Flinders and the Admiralty regarding the outfitting of the *Investigator,* his exploration of the coast of Australia and his time on Mauritius, including his work on magnetism. There is correspondence between the Admiralty and the French Government concerning

Flinders, dispatches from Governor P.G. King and official correspondence from the Transport Board regarding the release of Flinders from Mauritius and the recovery of his journal. Three letters written by Sir Joseph Banks 1806 are concerned with the preservation and transport of the botanical and mineral specimens collected by Robert Brown and the sketches of Ferdinand Bauer.

Also included are two copies of his unpublished manuscript 'Narrative of the Causes that Prevented His Majesty's Ship, the *Investigator,* from Completing the Examination and Discovery of the Coasts of Australia, July 1806' (332 p.)

M3033–3037:

1) Correspondence 1797–1814. Correspondents include Sir Joseph Banks and Thomi Pitot.
2) Journals and narratives 1791–1810. Including journals kept on HMS *Providence* (c.1791) and HMS *Bellerophon* (1793–94), narratives of voyages on HMS *Tom Thumb* (1795–96) and *Investigator* (1814).
3) Manuscript, printed charts, drawings and prints 1792–1812. Includes chart of the passage between New Holland and New Guinea as seen from HMS *Providence* in 1792, and charts published by Alexander Dalrymple and A. Arrowsmith.
4) Other papers, including letters sent to Mrs Flinders by Sir Joseph Banks, Sir John Franklin and Thomi Pitot.
5) Papers 1800–1912 of Sir William Flinders Petrie concerning the life of his grandfather.

Eight-page list available for reference.

Entry 170   Reels M1942–1944

Name **FLOREY, Howard Walter, 1st Baron (1898–1968)**

Title Papers

Inclusive dates 1898–1968

Quantity 3 reels of microfilm

Location of original Royal Society, 6 Carlton House Terrace, London SW1Y 5AG, England

Note
Professor of Pathology, University of Sheffield 1931–35 and University of Oxford 1935–62. Awarded Nobel Prize for Medicine 1945. Provost of Queen's College, Oxford 1962–68. President of Royal Society 1960–65; academic adviser, Australian National University 1946–57; and Chancellor, Australian National University 1965–68.

Description
1) Papers 1942–63 concerning penicillin, including reports, correspondence, notes, broadcasts, talks, bulletins and papers on Florey's visit to Australia in 1944.
2) Pathology correspondence 1951–64. Correspondents include W.J. Cliff, H.M. Doery, J. Casley-Smith, A. Day, S. Faine, Joan Gardner, F. Gibson, G.B. Mackaness, N.P. Markham and Sir Douglas Copland.
3) Papers 1954–67 concerning the Royal Society. Subjects include: election of Fellows of Royal Society from Commonwealth; Anglo-Australian telescope; Island of Niue Expedition 1961–62; and Florey's election as President of the Royal Society in 1960.
4) General correspondence 1945–68. Subjects include: medical schools at Australian universities; Australian Academy of Science and Anglo-Australian telescope. Correspondents include F. Fenner, C.H. Kellaway, R.D. Wright, Sir John Eccles, Sir Leonard Huxley, H.R. Marston, D.L. Wilhelm and Sir Mark Oliphant.
5) Letters of congratulation on award of Copley Medal of the Royal Society in 1957 and elevation to peerage in 1965.
6) Lectures 1944–63.
7) Letters received by Lady (M. Ethel) Florey on death of Lord Florey in 1968.
8) Papers 1948–65 of Lady Florey, including a visit to Australia in 1948.

43-page list available for reference.

Entry 171   Reels M1101–1113

Name **P.W. FLOWER AND COMPANY**

Title Records

Inclusive dates 1836–1916

Quantity 13 reels of microfilm

Location of original Guildhall Library, Guildhall, Aldermanbury, London EC2P 2EJ, England

Note
Marsden and Flower was a firm of general merchants in Sydney. Marsden died in 1841 and his partner Phillip W. Flower was joined by Severin K. Salting and John H. Challis in the new firm of Flower, Salting and Co. A counterpart firm, P.W. Flower and Co, was established in England at the same time. The London firm was for a time the largest importer of Australian wool in Britain.

Description
1) General ledgers 1853–1906.
2) Ledgers 1869–97.
3) Journals 1862–72.
4) Accounts of shipments, shares registers and other miscellaneous papers.
5) Business papers 1836–1906 of Philip Flower and records concerning his estate, including schedules of properties and personal estate, Dunedin Gas Company debentures, deeds, correspondence and accounts.
6) Accounts and other papers 1909–10 concerning estate of George Salting.
7) Records 1908–14 of Cunningham Plains Estates.
8) Deeds of partnerships, will of S.K. Salting, and other miscellaneous papers.

Seven-page list available for reference.

Entry 172   Reel M2843

Name **FLOWER, Sir William (1831–1899)**
Title Papers
Inclusive dates 1886–91
Quantity 1 reel of microfilm
Location of original Archives Section, Natural History Museum, Cromwell Road, South Kensington, London SW7 5BD, England

Note
Director of the British Museum (Natural History) 1884–98.

Description
Correspondence with naturalists relating to Flower's work as Director of the British Museum (Natural History). Subjects include difficulties in obtaining Pacific Islands skulls. Main correspondents are W. Saville Kent of Hobart, Alfred Corrie of HMS *Pelican* and Henry Forbes of Christchurch.

Two-page list available for reference.

Entry 173   Reel M2995–3032

Name **FORD, Harold M.**
Title Papers
Inclusive dates 1926–38
Quantity 38 reels of microfilm
Location of original Strathclyde Regional Archives, Mitchell Library, North Street, Glasgow G3 7DN, Scotland

Note
Commercial Secretary of the Clyde Navigation Trust. Ford visited Australia and New Zealand in 1928.

Description
Cutting books, letter-books and correspondence referring to his tour of Australia and New Zealand in 1928; representation of Glasgow firms in Australia and New Zealand; and marketing of Australian and New Zealand produce in Scotland.
Correspondents include S.M. Bruce, Sir James Parr, Lord Stonehaven and Sir Thomas Wilford.

12-page list available for reference.

Entry 174   Reel M1923

Name **FOREIGN AND COMMONWEALTH OFFICE LIBRARY**
Title Manuscripts of Australian explorers
Inclusive dates 1813–74
Quantity 1 reel of microfilm
Location of original Foreign and Commonwealth Office Library, Sanctuary Buildings, Great Smith Street, London SW1P 2BZ, England

Description
1) Journals of Gregory Blaxland's expeditions across the Blue Mountains in 1813 and 1815.
2) Journals of John Oxley's expeditions into the interior of New South Wales in 1817 and 1818.
3) Journal of an expedition in the vicinity of Mount Harris in 1818 and a sketch of Van Diemen's Land 1820 by George W. Evans.
4) Manuscript entitled 'A Brief View of the Progress of Interior Discovery in New South Wales' by Allan Cunningham (c.1832).
5) Journal 1873–74 of Peter Egerton Warburton on expedition from central Australia to Perth.

One-page list available for reference.

Name **FOSTER AND BRAITHWAITE**

Title Records

Inclusive dates 1896–98

Quantity 1 reel of microfilm

Location of original Foster and Braithwaite, 22 Austin Friars, London EC2N 2BU, England

Note
London stockbrokers.

Description
Papers concerning the raising of capital on the London market for two businesses in Sydney. Farmer and Company were seeking additional capital in 1896 and 1897, and the papers relating to this matter include a statement of assets at 31 July 1896 and a list of people who applied for shares in response to the advertisements placed in English newspapers.

The raising of capital for W. and A. McArthur Ltd was negotiated in 1898. W. and A. McArthur was a warehouse firm with property in the centre of Sydney. Copies of the prospectus and auditor's statement are included among the papers.

Entry 176   Reel M1194

Name **FREE CHURCH OF SCOTLAND**

Title Records

Inclusive dates 1851–54

Quantity 1 reel of microfilm

Location of original National Library of Scotland, George IV Bridge, Edinburgh EH1 1EW, Scotland

Note
The Free Church of Scotland was formed in 1842 following a major conflict within the Church of Scotland.

Description
Letters from ministers and missionaries in Australia and New Zealand mainly written to Rev. J. Bonar, convenor of the Colonial Committee of the Free Church. The letters describe pastoral work, social conditions, and the relationship between the Free Church in the colonies and the mother Church in Scotland.

Four-page list available for reference.

Entry 177   Reels M1672–1675

Name **FREMANTLE FAMILY**

Title Papers

Inclusive dates 1807–60

Quantity 4 reels of microfilm

Location of original Buckinghamshire Record Office, County Hall, Aylesbury, Buckinghamshire HP20 1UA, England

Note
Family of naval officers. Vice-Admiral Sir Charles Fremantle (1800–69) commanded HMS *Challenger* and in 1829 took possession of the western part of New Holland. Capt. Stephen Fremantle (1810–60) was Senior Officer commanding the Australian Squadron 1855–57. Their brother Sir Thomas Fremantle (1797–1890), 1st Baron Cottesloe, was a Conservative politician and Secretary at War 1844–45.

Description
1) Papers 1829–57 of Sir Thomas Fremantle and Lady Fremantle, comprising letters from Capt. C.H. Fremantle and Capt. S. Fremantle; and correspondence 1841–42 between Major John Campbell and Lord Stanley on land claims in New Zealand.

2) Papers 1852–60 of Capt. Stephen Fremantle, including correspondence, legal papers, draft reports, orders and records of HMS *Juno*. They document: the social life of naval officers in Sydney and Hobart; a cruise in the Pacific; the transfer of the Pitcairn Islanders to Norfolk Island; the defence of Sydney and Melbourne; the activities of the surveying ship HMS *Herald;* the annexation of the Cocos Islands in 1857; the possible annexation of Fiji; and Fremantle's disciplinary troubles on HMS *Juno*.

Correspondents include Sir Thomas Fremantle, Capt. H.M. Denham, Sir William Denison, W. Hamilton, Sir James Stirling, Sir Michael Seymour, T.G. Browne, Sir Charles Hotham and Sir James Graham.

3) Journal 1856 of Lieut. G.W. Gregorie describing the removal of the Pitcairn Islanders to Norfolk Island.

11-page list available for reference.

Name **FROME, Edward Charles (1802–1890)**

Title Sketchbooks

Inclusive dates 1835–53

Quantity 1 reel of positive microfilm

Location of original Art Gallery of South Australia, North Terrace, Adelaide SA 5000

Note
Soldier and surveyor. Arrived in South Australia in 1839 as its third Surveyor-General. He made several exploratory trips into the interior of South Australia. Returned to England in 1849, but served later with the Royal Engineers, including a posting in Mauritius in the early 1850s.

Description
Approximately 160 sketches and watercolours, mainly of scenes in South Australia, but including nine watercolours painted by Frome in Mauritius 1852–53, one painting by J. Henderson entitled *View in Van Diemen's Land* and two paintings by Samuel Thomas Gill, one with the title *Horticultural Show 1840*.

Subjects of the paintings include: homes of settlers, such as Major O'Halloran, Capt. Charles Sturt, and Frome himself; topographical drawings; camps set up during the survey trips undertaken by Frome; townships established during the early period of settlement in South Australia, such as Kingscote, Kangaroo Island 1840, Wellington, on the River Murray 1840, and Morunde 1842; Aboriginal sites; and views of many South Australian localities.

Seven-page list available for reference.

Entry 179   Reel M1557

Name **GALLEGO, Hernando**

Title Manuscript

Inclusive dates 1567–69

Quantity 1 reel of microfilm

Location of original British Library, Great Russell Street, London WC1B 3DG, England

Note
Pilot on the Spanish ship *Los Reyes*, commanded by Alvaro de Mendana, on a voyage from Callao to the Western Pacific 1567–69.

Description
A Spanish copy of the account of the Pacific voyage of Mendana and in particular his discovery of the Solomon Islands in 1567.

Name **GARDINER FAMILY**

Title Papers

Inclusive dates 1814–65, 1959

Quantity 2 reels of microfilm

Location of original Mitchell Library, State Library of New South Wales, Macquarie Street, Sydney NSW 2000

Note
John Gardiner (1798–1878) migrated to Van Diemen's Land from Ireland in 1822 with his wife Mary Eagle and her family and received a grant of land on the Macquarie River. He became an official of the Bank of Van Diemen's Land. In 1833 Gardiner moved to New South Wales and acquired land near Yass. In 1836 he drove cattle overland from the Murrumbidgee River to Port Phillip. He settled at Port Phillip and built a house at Gardiner's Creek, near Hawthorn, Victoria. He was for a time the manager of the Bank of Port Phillip. He left Australia in 1853.

Description
1) Typescript draft of the Gardiner family tree and notes on the Gardiner, Eagle and Fletcher Families compiled by Leslie J. Wilmoth.

2) Seven letters 1814–65 from Sarah Gardiner including reference to John Gardiner's proposed journey to Australia, also letters from Miriam Scott, Melbourne 1865, and from John Gardiner's parents, John and Martha Gardiner.

3) Manuscript entitled 'The Gardiners of Gardiner's Creek' by L.J. Wilmoth (1959). It includes portraits of the Gardiner Family and copies of documents; a letter 13 November 1835 from G.F. Storey to Dr Pilkington on the alleged poisoning of Edward Eagle, Mrs Gardiner's brother; Mary Gardiner's account of a voyage from Sydney to Port Phillip, March 1837; copy of original deed granting land in Morven, Van Diemen's Land, to John Smith 30 June 1823.

Eight-page list available for reference.

Name **GELL and FRANKLIN FAMILIES**

Title Papers

Inclusive dates 1800–1955

Quantity 5 reels of microfilm

Location of original Mrs A. Gell, Derbyshire, England

Note

Sir John Franklin (1786–1847), Lieut.-Governor of Van Diemen's land 1836–43. Jane Franklin (1792–1875) was his second wife. Rev. John P. Gell (1816–98) was selected by Dr Thomas Arnold of Rugby to go to Van Diemen's Land in 1839 to be headmaster of the proposed Queen's School at Hobart, in which Franklin took a great interest. In 1846 he was appointed Warden of Christ's College, near Longford, and in 1849 married Eleanor Franklin (1825–60), only child of Sir John Franklin, by his first wife. A younger brother of Gell, Arthur Daniel Gell (1822–48), was Private Secretary to Col. G. Gawler, Governor of South Australia.

Description

The papers of Rev. J.P. Gell and his wife include letters to Eleanor Isabella from Sir John and Lady Franklin, and both original correspondence and copies of correspondence and papers about the Queen's School and Christ's College.

Correspondents include Ronald C. Gunn of Hobart. There are also notebooks and diaries, including a diary describing Gell's voyage to Van Diemen's Land on the convict ship *Runnymede* in 1839–40.

Besides the letters from Franklin to his daughter, there are papers of both Sir John and Lady Franklin. These include a few drafts of official letters written by Franklin while Governor of Van Diemen's Land and some of his private and official correspondence. Among letters to Franklin is one from Matthew Flinders 1812. Includes a series of letters from Franklin to Dr John Richardson, surgeon and naturalist. The original Franklin papers are supplemented by a collection of copies of letters, some handwritten and some typescript, chiefly from Franklin. The copies include typescripts of letters written by Franklin aboard the *Investigator*. M390 consists of only three frames, a note on the contents of the Gell archives.

11-page list available for reference.

Name **GENEALOGICAL OFFICE (OFFICE OF ARMS), Dublin**

Title Collections

Inclusive dates 1842–1961

Quantity 1 reel of microfilm

Location of original Genealogical Office (Office of Arms), Dublin Castle, Dublin, Ireland

Note

The Genealogical Office assumed the functions of the Ulster King of Arms, formerly under British administration, on 1 April 1943.

Description

1) Grants and confirmations of arms 1854–1940, with illustrations of coats of arms, to the following Australians and New Zealanders: Sylvester J. Browne, David H.R. Burtchael, James J. Casey, Austin F. Coghlan, Charles V. Creagh, Sylverius M. Crumpe, Norman L. D'Arcy, Rev. Harry Darling, Seymour G.P. Davies, Richard Day, Frederick J. Eyre, Frederick P.B. Fitzgerald, Lieut. Gen. John Fulton, Patrick J. Garvey, William P.C. Greene, John Winthrop Hackett, Hans Hamilton, Joshua A. Hargrave, George Higinbotham, Sir John Kirwan, Sir Linden M.S.K.L. Macassey, Sir John Madden, Arthur W.C. Martin, Joseph Meek, Charles Moore, Henry P. Moore, John F.L. Mullins, Osborne E. Norris, John B. Payne, Thomas L. Murray Prior, Frederic W.C. Roche, James S. Rowan, Lieut. Frederick P. Rowley, Ralph S. Smith, David Storey, Frederick P. Toler-Rowley, Robert A.B. Vance, William A.W. West.

2) Registered pedigrees compiled 1842–1955 for the following: Agnew (Tasmania); Bagot (Melbourne); Barnewell (Upper Thornton, Australia); Barton (Havelock, Victoria); Browne (New Zealand and Ballarat, Victoria); Carleton (New Zealand); Coghlan (Sydney); Davey (Rockingham, Queensland); Davies (Australia); Deacon (Australia); Denham (Gippsland, Victoria); Dillon (Townsville, Queensland); Dobbin (Sydney); Dowse (Australia); Exshaw (Australia); Eyre (North Adelaide); French (Victoria); Foster (Victoria); Garvey (Wellington and Sydney); Glascott (Richmond River, New South Wales); Goff (Renwicktown, New Zealand); Haly (Tuabinga, Queensland); Hamilton (Melbourne); Hutton (New Zealand); Macgillysacht (Sydney); Mecham (New South Wales); Minnitt (Van Diemen's Land); Molony (Australia); Mulligan (Australia); Newton (Auckland); Nicholson (New Zealand and

Australia); Prior (Queensland); Rathborne (Ngeruawahia, New Zealand); Richardson, later Richardson Bunbury (Australia); Rooke (Sydney and Wellington); Sadlier (Tasmania); St George (Australia); Seaver (New South Wales); Twohig (Sydney); Vance (Balmerino, Victoria); Warburton (Palmerston North, New Zealand); Wentworth, (Sydney); Westropp (New Zealand).

11-page list available for reference.

Entry 183   Reel M1682

Name **GEOLOGICAL SOCIETY OF LONDON**

Title Records

Inclusive dates 1831–70

Quantity 1 reel of microfilm

Location of original Geological Society of London, Burlington House, Piccadilly, London W1V 0JU, England

Note
Founded in 1807, the Society began forming a collection of minerals and a library almost immediately. Publication of its *Transactions* commenced in 1811.

Description
1) Letters 1834 of Allan Cunningham and others to the Secretary concerning Australian rocks and fossils.
2) Letters 1831–69 received by Sir Roderick Murchison relating to exploration, discovery of minerals and fossils, geological surveys and mapping of Australia and New Zealand.
   Correspondents include Sir Henry Barkly, W.B. Clarke, Sir John Franklin, J.J. Hector, P.P. King, C. Sturt and Sir Henry Young.
3) Maps and sketches of districts in Australia, New Zealand, Hawaii and Sarawak, including sketches 1860 by Charles Heaphy of volcanic country of Auckland.
4) Photographs of geologists including J.W. Gregory, R.L. Jack and Sir Edmund Teale.

Four-page list available for reference.

Entry 184   Reels M244–290, M794–801

Name **GERMANY. Ministry of Foreign Affairs**

Title Records

Inclusive dates 1879–1944

Quantity 55 reels of positive microfilm

Location of original Auswartiges Amt Archiv, Bonn, Germany

Note
Selections made after World War II from captured German records, filmed by British and American authorities. The selections relate mainly to Australia, the South Seas, the Indian Ocean, and to colonial possessions of the German, British, French and Dutch governments.

Description
M244–250:
Papers 1920–39 of the German Ministry for Colonies concerning Australia, Japan, China, Siam, Afghanistan, Persia, Egypt, Abyssinia, and other German colonies; papers 1924–30 from the Secretary of State on colonial and mandate territory matters.

M251–264:
Papers 1879–1920, including printed cuttings, leaflets and some official publications. The material deals with affairs in Australia, Hawaii, the Pacific Islands, Fiji, New Guinea, New Caledonia and the New Hebrides. French, Dutch and British interests in the Pacific and Indian Ocean are covered in the file material, which includes declarations 1886 and conventions relating to spheres of influence in the Pacific. These reels also include file material from German embassies in London, Washington and Paris.

M265–290:
File material 1887–1944 on Australia, including documents on politics, industries, shipping, immigration, propaganda, the Australian National Socialist Party (Nazi Party) in Sydney, German churches and schools and German internees. Some material also deals with New Zealand economic affairs.

M794–801:
Records of the German Embassy in London concerning Samoa 1886–1906, being dispatches to and from the Foreign Ministry in Berlin, together with documents supplied for the personal information of the Ambassador. The latter include diplomatic correspondence with the United States and the British Foreign Office, and reports from the German consul in Samoa outlining conditions in the area.

47 pages of lists available for reference.

Entry 185   Reels M291–336A

Name **GERMANY. Navy**

Title Records

Inclusive dates 1854–1944

Quantity 46 reels of microfilm and 14 positive photographs of charts

Location of original Unknown

Note
All these files were filmed selectively in the late 1950s while they were in the custody of the British Admiralty.

Description
M291–294:
Reports and correspondence 1854–85 concerning expeditions in Japanese, Chinese and Southeast Asian waters. The expeditions had commercial and strategic purposes.

M300–304:
Records about expeditions of warships to Australia, the Philippines and South Sea Stations 1880–88, including material on Samoa 1876.

M305:
Scientific marine expeditions 1890–1913; reports on Hawaii, Samoa and Tonga 1891–1900.

M306–312:
File material 1886–1916 concerning German colonies in Africa, Asia and the South Seas.

M313–320:
Reports and correspondence 1905–14 of the East Asia Station, including items on military and political activity.

M320–323:
Reports from and to the Australia Station 1904–14.

M323–331:
Papers 1880–1917 concerning China, including material on the Boxer Rebellion, the merchant navy, civil unrest and politics.

M331–332:
Records concerning Japan, and colonies in Asia administered by France, Holland and Portugal 1894–1914, many annotated 'very secret'.

M333–336A:
Records 1939–44 of the Oberkommando der Marine/Seekriegsleitung relating to the operation of German raiders in the Antarctic and in the Pacific and Indian Oceans, including the *Atlantis, Pinguin,*

Orion, Kormoran and *Komet*. Included are charts of mines laid off the Australian coast.

15 pages of lists available for reference.

Entry 186   Reels M1368–1398

Name **ANTONY GIBBS AND SONS LTD**

Title Records

Inclusive dates 1853–1930

Quantity 31 reels of microfilm

Location of original Guildhall Library, Guildhall, London EC2P 2EJ, England

Note
Antony Gibbs opened his London mercantile house in 1808. His brother George Gibbs was the founder of Gibbs, Bright & Co, a shipping and mercantile firm of Bristol, Liverpool and London. A branch of Gibbs, Bright & Co was established in Melbourne in 1856 by Charles Bright (1829–1915) and branches were later established at Brisbane, Dunedin, Sydney, Adelaide, Newcastle, Kalgoorlie, Fremantle, Perth, Cairns and Hobart. The firm was prominent in Australian shipping, importing, mining, stevedoring, wool, timber and pastoral investment. From 1881 onwards its parent company was Antony Gibbs & Sons.

Description
1) Private letters to partners 1884–1919.
2) Directors' special out–letter-books 1881–1929, including letters of H.C. Gibbs, Alban G.H. Gibbs (later Lord Aldenham) and F.A. Keating.
3) Out–letter-books 1884–1911 of Francis A. Keating, manager of the Australian branch.
4) Records and accounts 1897–98 concerning relations between Gibbs, Bright & Co and New Zealand Exploration Co Ltd.
5) London office confidential information book 1883–1905 referring to British and overseas merchant firms.
6) Records 1884–1909 of Liverpool house, including reports on other banking and merchant firms.
7) Letters and other records 1883–87 of the Melbourne house mainly concerning sheep farming and the wool trade.
8) Papers 1918–20 of F.A. Keating, including letters from the managers of the Melbourne and Sydney houses.
9) Annual accounts 1910–24 of the Australian branches.
10) Australasian private letter-books 1910–30 (12 vols).
11) Private letters 1883–84 of Vicary Gibbs while

serving with Australian branches, chiefly written to his brother Alban G.H. Gibbs.

12) Private out–letter-book 1911–30 of London house concerning Australian branches.

13) Memoranda, minutes, agreements and other records 1903–30 of the London office, mainly referring to minerals and other foreign industrial concerns.

14) Chartering ledgers 1913–30.

89-page list and three-page list available for reference.

Entry 187   Reels M2230–2240

Name **GLADSTONE, William Ewart (1809–1898)**
Title Papers
Inclusive dates 1835–86
Quantity 11 reels of microfilm
Location of original British Library, Great Russell Street, London WC1B 3DG, England

Note
Tory, Peelite and Liberal MP. Gladstone held a number of official posts including Secretary of State for the Colonies 1845–46; Chancellor of the Exchequer 1852–55, 1859–66; and Prime Minister 1868–74, 1880–85, 1886 and 1892–94.

Description
Correspondence, letters, memoranda and official papers extending from Gladstone's first post at the Colonial Office in 1835 until the collapse of his third Ministry in 1886. They deal with: the New Zealand Co; Treaty of Waitangi; Maori affairs; recall of Sir John Eardley Wilmot from Van Diemen's Land in 1846; colonial bishoprics; Australian and New Zealand constitutions; Sydney Mint; colonial tariffs; appointment of governors; establishment of settlement at Canterbury; annexation of Fiji and New Guinea; French and German activities in the Pacific; trade with Dutch East Indies; affairs of Sarawak; and North Borneo Co.

Correspondents include Lord Granville, Lord Kimberley, Lord Derby, Lord Lyttelton, H.C.E Childers, E. Cardwell, Sir Arthur Gordon, Sir George Grey, Rev. E. Coleridge, Bishop G.A. Selwyn, Rev. J.P. Gell, Bishop W.G. Broughton, J.E. Fitzgerald, Sir George Bowen and Sir Henry Parkes.

74-page list available for reference.

Entry 188   Reels M2697–2701

Name **GLASGOW UNIVERSITY ARCHIVES AND BUSINESS RECORD CENTRE**
Title Collections
Inclusive dates 1846–1967
Quantity 5 reels of microfilm
Location of original The Archives and Business Record Centre, Glasgow University, Hillhead Street, Glasgow G12 8QQ, Scotland

Description
1) Correspondence 1911–27 of Professor Frederick Bower. Subjects include: A. Anstruther Lawson; dispatch of ferns and other botanical specimens from Sarawak; Singapore mutiny; Bower's visit to Australia in 1915; article on Australian ferns and botanic gardens at Kuala Lumpur and Singapore.

2) Correspondence 1844–52 of Duncan MacFarlan concerning Presbyterian Church in Australia.

3) Papers 1846–95 of Hamilton Family of Rozelle. Subjects include: cattle prices; a typescript by Hugh Hamilton describing journey to Australia on the *Earl Grey* in 1841; biographical notes by Hugh Hamilton containing description of life in Australia; Bathurst; cattle prices; Morney Plains station in Queensland; and the Victorian goldfields.

4) Letters of Professor Sir William MacEwen, written from the Pacific, New Zealand and Australia in 1923 to his family. Subjects include: description of voyage on the *Tahiti*; social life in Sydney and Melbourne; impressions of Australia; and voyage across the Pacific.

5) Journals of James Allan on voyage to Straits Settlements and China 1872 and to Singapore and Japan 1922–23.

6) Papers 1961 of Professor Thomas F. Rodger concerning Mental Health Conference in Christchurch.

7) Papers 1965–72 of Professor Robert S. Silver, including press statements (many by D.E. Fairbairn) on water resources projects in Australia.

8) Papers 1926–38 of Sir Robert Horn, including speeches and documents on Empire Migration.

9) Papers 1879–1906 of MacFie Family. Subjects include: Sandwich Islands; sugar plantations in Rau; sandalwood trade; journal of J.W. MacFie's trip to Hawaii on the *Auronia*, *Australia* and *Mariposa* in 1884; Hawaiian financial affairs; Kilauea plantation; and visit of Queen of Hawaii to London in 1887.

10) Records 1909–18 of Upper Clyde Shipbuilders.

11) Records 1888–96 of Hardie and Rowan relating to Australian and New Zealand mines.

12) Records 1873–78 of Netherlands India Dry Dock Co.

13) Records 1914–49 of mining company Sir Robert McAlpine & Sons Ltd.

14) Records 1967 of Scotts' Shipbuilding and Engineering Co Ltd concerning a tour of Australia.

28-page list available for reference.

Entry 189   Reel M2798

Name **GLASGOW UNIVERSITY LIBRARY**
Title Collections
Inclusive dates 1861–1961
Quantity 1 reel of microfilm
Location of original Glasgow University Library, Hillhead Street, The University, Glasgow G12 8QQ, Scotland

Description
1) Correspondence 1861–1902 of physicist Sir William Thomson, 1st Baron Kelvin. Subjects include India–Australia cable connection.

2) Papers 1928–61 of James Laver of Albert Museum. Includes Laver's letters to Horace Brodzky and letters of Daryl Lindsay, Lionel Lindsay, A.W. Wheen and David Low.

3) Correspondence 1894–1946 of art critic Dugald MacColl, including correspondence with Charles and Stella Conder; draft of MacColl's article 'Two Summers with Conder'; history of the MacColl Family including Senator James MacColl; and letters of John Rothenstein and William Rothenstein concerning Conder.

4) Correspondence 1885–1903 of James McNeill Whistler, including correspondence with Mortimer Menpes about his book on Whistler, letters of Anna Whistler concerning Harry Haden of Queensland, and copies of Whistler's letters concerning Peter Arthur Studd's visit to the South Seas.

5) Papers 1927–45 of art historian Harold Wright, including an article on Lionel Lindsay's etchings and exhibitions of watercolours in Sydney.

6) Account of Archibald Campbell's voyages to Japan, Aleutian Islands and Sandwich Islands 1806–12, edited by James Smith.

7) Correspondence 1911–13 of Alexander MacCallum Scott referring to racial discrimination in the civil services of Singapore, Federated Malay States and Hong Kong.

8) William Hunter's Museum Ethnographical Collection 1886–1941. Correspondence dealing with dispatch of birds of paradise and Maori mat from Waimate; Aboriginal weapons from North West Australia and Queensland; Aboriginal skulls; Tasmanian Aboriginal artefacts; and the Cook Collection in the Bernice P. Bishop Museum.

14-page list available for reference.

Entry 190   Reel M2290

Name **GLOUCESTERSHIRE RECORD OFFICE**
Title Collections
Inclusive dates 1837–1950
Quantity 1 reel of microfilm
Location of original Gloucestershire Record Office, Clarence Row, Alvin Street, Gloucester GL1 3DW, England

Description
1) Records 1837–40 and 1914 of Parishes of Bisley, Dursley and Dymock. Subjects include emigration to Australia and Canada, Poor Law Commission and World War I.

2) Account 1854 by H. Edwards of a voyage to Australia on the *Ganges*.

3) Journal 1836–38 of George E. Stranger, surgeon on the *Sara and Elizabeth*.

4) Papers 1886–97 of Fijian official Sir John Thurston.

5) Letters 1864–67 of Anne Sherwood written from Richmond River and Casino, New South Wales, to her sister Theodosia Hale, referring to family news, farming, Australian fauna, and Aborigines.

6) Papers 1852–67 of Austin Family, including an account of a voyage to Australia on the *Castle Eden*.

7) Correspondence 1844–79 of Eagles Family. Subjects include estate of Rev. J. Eagles and relations between W.G. Eagles of Melbourne and his family in England.

8) Papers 1846–60 of Col. C. Bridge concerning services in Maori War.

9) Papers 1878–87 of Sir Michael Hicks Beach, Secretary of State for the Colonies 1878–80, referring to defence of Australian colonies; governorships of Victoria and New Zealand; Victorian constitutional crisis; Australian Federation; and reform of the Victorian Constitution. Correspondents include Lord Normanby and Sir George Bowen.

10) Papers 1895–1950 of Newman Family woolbrokers.

11) Papers 1839–40 relating to Joseph Mercer, including extracts from a diary kept by Mercer on a voyage in 1839 from Liverpool to Adelaide on the *Lady Lilford.*

12-page list available for reference.

Entry 191 Reel M1173

Name **GODERICH, Frederick Robinson, 1st Viscount (1782–1859)**

Title Papers

Inclusive dates 1831–33

Quantity 1 reel of microfilm

Location of original British Library, Great Russell Street, London WC1B 3DG, England

Note
Frederick John Robinson, 1st Viscount Goderich (created 1827), 1st Earl of Ripon (created 1833). Chancellor of the Exchequer 1823–27; Secretary of State for the Colonies 1827 and 1830–33; Prime Minister 1827–28.

Description
The papers all date from Goderich's second period at the Colonial Office. They mainly contain requests for appointments in the Australian colonies. Correspondents include Sir Richard Bourke, Ralph Darling, Judge John Stephen and Capt. W. Windeyer.

Six-page list available for reference.

Entry 192 Reels M1628–1637

Name **GORDON, Sir Arthur (1829–1912)**

Title Papers

Inclusive dates 1855–1912

Quantity 14 reels of microfilm

Location of original British Library, Great Russell Street, London WC1B 3DG, England

Note
Sir Arthur Hamilton Gordon, 1st Baron Stanmore (created 1893). Colonial governor, posts including first Governor of Fiji 1875–80, first High Commissioner of Western Pacific 1877–82 and Governor of New Zealand 1880–82.

Description
1) Correspondence, letter-books and papers mostly dating from the period 1875–82. They deal with: Gordon's governorships; the establishment of British rule in Fiji; legislation; land claims; the Pacific labour trade; missionaries; French ambitions in the Pacific; Samoan and Tongan affairs; military and naval defence; establishment of Western Pacific High Commission; New Zealand politics; Maori affairs; German and Queensland annexations in New Guinea; Australasian Federal Council; and church affairs. Correspondents include Sir Michael Hicks Beach, Sir Robert Herbert, Sir William Des Voeux, Sir John Thurston, Bishop J.R. Selwyn, D. Wilkinson, Sir William MacGregor, J. Gorrie, W. Carew, L. Fison and G.W. Rusden.

2) Correspondence 1875–82 of Lady Gordon with her family in England.

11-page list available for reference.

Entry 193 Reels M725–727, M2888–2902

Name **GOULD, John (1804–1881)**

Title Papers

Inclusive dates 1831–86

Quantity 8 reels of microfilm

Location of original M725–727: Newton Library, Department of Zoology, University of Cambridge, Downing Street, Cambridge, England; M2888–2902: Zoology Library, Natural History Museum, Cromwell Road, South Kensington, London SW7 5BD, England

Note
Ornithologist. After writing books on European birds, Gould began a study of the birds of Australia. He published *A Synopsis of the Birds of Australia* (1837) and in the following year he and his wife sailed for Australia. They visited many parts of the country and discovered 300 new species of birds. The first part of *The Birds of Australia* was published soon after their return to England in 1840 and the work was completed, in 36 parts, in 1848.

Description
M725–727:
1) The bulk of the collection consists of the original manuscript notes and sketches collected by Gould for his book *The Birds of Australia.* Each folder (or notebook) has the name of the order or tribe written on the outside, and inside the folder the notes are divided by species. At the top of each sheet there is an illustration of the bird in question, of which some are lithographs from Gould's earlier work *A Synopsis of the Birds of Australia and the Adjacent Islands*

(1837), while others are original watercolour paintings by Gould. In the margin are headings probably written by his secretary, Edward Prince, such as Latin name, English name, diet and locality inhabited, with manuscript notes and occasional rough sketches by Gould.

2) Letters, notes and lists by Gould: letters from Gould to Sir William Jardine 1835–49 and to Alfred Newton 1856–61 describing birds and specimens in Europe and Australia; three lists of Australian birds; a list of Swan River birds; and a list of the drawings by Aylmer B. Lambert in the possession of Lord Derby.

3) Letters of Australian and Pacific interest 1857–76, written to Alfred Newton and chiefly relating to Gould's works on Australian birds. Correspondents include T. Allcock, J.J. Briggs, E. Prince, O. Salvin, P.L. Sclater, H.B. Tristram and A.R. Wallace.

Four-page list available for reference.

M2888–2902:

1) Correspondence arranged in alphabetical order 1831–86. Subjects include: Gould's publication *Birds of Australia*; sighting of birds; introduction of salmon into Tasmanian rivers; discovery of gold in Tasmania; dispatch of specimens; Elizabeth Coxen's drawings; Gould's collection of Australian birds; George French Angas; and expeditions of A.C. Gregory, John Gilbert, E. Kennedy, Ludwig Becker, Ludwig Leichhardt and John MacGillivray. Correspondents include Robert Ball, Charles Coxen, Stephen Coxen, Sir George Gipps, John Edward Gray, William J. Hooker, Sir William Jardine, Alfred Newton, Sir Richard Owen, Robert J. Shuttleworth and Ludwig Becker.

2) Australian collection 1844–64 including notes, letters and drawings pertaining to Australian mammals and birds. Subjects include: cassowary; dugong; drawings of George French Angas; and drawings of Southern hairy-nosed wombats. Correspondents include Johann G. Krefft.

41-page list available for reference.

Entry 194 Reels M2638–2639

Name **GOUROCK ROPEWORK & COMPANY**

Title Records

Inclusive dates 1882–1971

Quantity 2 reels of microfilm

Location of original Archives and Business Record Centre, Glasgow University, Glasgow G12 8QQ, Scotland

Note
Founded in 1736 by Argyllshire fishermen to supply them with reliable ropes. In 1811 the works moved to Port Glasgow and the control passed into the hands of the Campbell and Birkmyre families. In 1903 it became Gourock Rope Works Co Ltd.

Description
The records comprise financial papers, correspondence and legal papers relating to the company's operations in Australia and New Zealand. Correspondents include F.M. Munro, David Fell, George D. Cockburn, J. Matthews and A. Battye.

Four-page list available for reference.

Entry 195 Reels M373–376

Name **GRAHAM, John Benjamin (1813–1876)**

Title Papers

Inclusive dates 1841–1926

Quantity 4 reels of microfilm

Location of original State Library of South Australia, GPO Box 419, Adelaide SA 5001

Note
South Australian merchant and investor. Graham arrived in Adelaide in 1839 and built up a prosperous general store. He was one of the first investors in the Burra Creek Copper Mines and director of the South Australian Mining Association. His mother followed him to Adelaide with her second husband, John Adams. Graham returned to England in 1848 and married Louisa Rymill in 1849. From 1848 to1867 his agent in South Australia was Henry Ayers, who was also secretary and later managing director of the Burra Burra Copper Mines. From 1867 his agents and those of his heirs were his brothers-in-law Henry and Frank Rymill and their successors.

Description
1) Diaries of J.B. Graham 1841–42, 1848–51, 1858 (7 vols), containing references to the

progress of his general store and business difficulties in the new settlement, his journey back to England in 1848, and return visit to Australia in 1858.

2) Diary 1848–49 of John Adams in Adelaide mentioning the prosperous state of the family affairs.

3) Letters 1848–70 from Henry Ayers to J.B. Graham on business matters.

4) Letters 1858–1910 from Henry and Frank Rymill to J.B. Graham and later to his son H.R. Graham both before and while they acted as his agents, especially in the management of his station 'Canowie', near Port Pirie.

5) Correspondence, accounts, financial statements, valuations and returns 1870–1926, concerning the stations 'Canowie' and 'Curnamona'.

6) Small number of letters and reports 1847–68, concerning the South Australian Mining Association and Burra Burra Copper Mines.

7) Printed plan 1889 of 'Glen Warwick' and 'Baratta' stations, at the foot of the North Flinders Ranges, and manuscript sheet giving estimated receipts and expenditure of the stations.

8) Photographs of J.B. Graham in later life.

Six-page list available for reference.

Entry 196   Reel M462

Name **GRANT, John (b.1776)**
Title Papers
Inclusive dates 1769–1810
Quantity 1 reel of microfilm
Location of original National Library of Australia, Canberra ACT 2600

Note
Convict and poet. Grant was transported to New South Wales in 1804. He protested against the convict system and its officials in his 'Bond of Union' of October 1805 although he had himself been granted a ticket-of-leave. This criticism led him to be sentenced to five years hard labour on Norfolk and Phillip Islands. Eventually he was granted a full pardon by Governor Macquarie and returned to England in 1811.

Description
1) Documents 1769–1803, including financial statements and indenture of apprenticeship to his uncle Edward Grant, and petitions after his conviction in 1803.

2) Letters 1803–10 to his mother and sister Matilda, describing the voyage on the *Coromandel,* his acquaintances Major George Johnston, Judge Richard Atkins, Charles Bishop and Sir Henry Hayes, and later involvement with Governors King, Bligh and Macquarie. There is also correspondence with Robert Campbell while John Grant was on Norfolk Island and a copy of his 'Bond of Union'.

3) Five poems written by Grant 1804–05 while he was at Parramatta and Norfolk Island.

4) Journal January 1805–March 1810, with a typewritten transcript by W.S. Hill-Reid, Joan O'Hagan and others, including copies of letters sent by him and detailed descriptions, such as his first impressions of Norfolk Island.

5) Notebook kept January–May 1809 on his return to Sydney from Norfolk Island.

Six-page list available for reference.

Entry 197   Reels M2346–2347

Name **SS GREAT BRITAIN**
Title Records
Inclusive dates 1852–75, 1907–08
Quantity 2 reels of microfilm
Location of original SS *Great Britain* Project, Great Western Dock, Gas Ferry Road, Bristol BS1 6TY, England

Note
SS *Great Britain* was launched at Bristol in 1843. It was severely damaged when it ran aground in 1850 and was later converted into a passenger and cargo ship, plying between Australia and England. Its last voyage from Australia was 1875–76. The Project was established to collect archives concerning the ship, its passengers and crew.

Description
The records include manuscripts, typescripts, diaries and logs kept on board SS *Great Britain* on voyages between England and Australia 1852–1876. They contain accounts of passengers and life on board.

Writers include Allan Gilmour, William Bray, Edward Byrd, Thomas Cawly, John Gifford, Andrew Alexander, James Walter, George Greaves, Rosamund D'Ouseley, Louise Buchan and John Campbell.

Eight-page list available for reference.

Entry 198   Reels M446–458, M418–420, M422

Name **GREAT BRITAIN. Public Record Office**

Part A: Reels M446–458

Title Colonial Office records relating to the Malay States

Inclusive dates 1873–96

Quantity 13 reels of microfilm

Location of original Public Record Office, Ruskin Avenue, Kew, Richmond-upon-Thames, Surrey TW9 4DU, England

Note
In 1874–75, at the direction of the Colonial Office, the Governor of the Straits Settlements, Sir Andrew Clarke, appointed Residents to the four Malay States of Perak, Selangor, Negri Sembilan and Pahang. The agreement with the Perak chiefs of 20 January 1874 specified that the Resident was to be accredited to the Sultan's Court and his advice was to be asked and acted upon on all questions other than those touching Malay religion and customs. In July 1895 the Malay rulers accepted a Treaty of Federation, which provided for a Resident-General responsible to the Governor of the Straits Settlements. Certain departments were unified under federal heads, such as the Judicial Commissioner, Attorney-General, Commandant and Chief Commissioner of Police.

Description
Extracts relating to the protected Malay States (Native States) from the Public Record Office classes CO 273, CO 537 and CO 809. These are confidential and open dispatches from the Governor of the Straits Settlements to the Secretary of State for the Colonies, together with enclosures, Colonial Office minutes, and draft replies from the Colonial Office to the Governor 1874–96. In addition, there is correspondence between the Colonial Office and other government departments (e.g. War Office, Admiralty). Mainly one volume of miscellaneous correspondence for each year, chiefly from individuals or non-official organisations.

M446–448:
CO 273/84–218: Confidential dispatches from the Governor of the Straits Settlements to the Colonial Office including enclosures and Colonial Office minutes relating to the Native States 1876–96.

M449–456:
CO 273/76–223: Selected pieces from CO 273 comprising dispatches from the Governor of Straits Settlements, sometimes with enclosures, and letters from offices and individuals relating to the Native States 1874–96. Almost all these documents are accompanied by the Colonial Office minutes and draft replies to the Governor's dispatch or correspondence.

M457–458:
Tables of contents from each volume CO 273/9–223, CO 537/45–48 and CO 809/1–44. As tables of contents were not available for CO 273/9–74, a typewritten list was compiled showing only confidential and open dispatches relating to the Native States of the Malay Peninsula. CO 537/45–48 'Supplementary Dispatches' from the Governor of the Straits Settlements to the Secretary of State, with enclosures, Colonial Office minutes, and draft replies 1873–96; CO 809/1–44. Confidential prints containing printed copies of correspondence dealing mostly with the Native States, prepared for inclusion in the House of Commons Papers. They contain most, but not all, of the dispatches in the CO 273 series, but without the Colonial Office minutes.

Part B: Reels M418–420, M422

Title Lists of Colonial Office records relating to the AJCP region

Inclusive dates 1961

Quantity 4 reels of microfilm

Location of original Public Record Office, Ruskin Avenue, Kew, Richmond-upon-Thames, Surrey TW9 4DU, England

Note
In 1961 extracts relating to AJCP areas of interest were copied from the ten volumes of a typescript entitled 'Comprehensive List of Colonial Office Records', together with two supplementary volumes, prepared by the Public Record Office. Reels M418, M420 and M422 are also held by the Mitchell Library and the National Library of Australia in hard-copy format, in four volumes familiarly known as 'The Blue Books'.

Description
M418:
Extracts, being class and piece lists with brief description, from the contents lists to the ten volumes of the Comprehensive List of Colonial Office Records. The extracts are arranged, as is the Comprehensive List, alphabetically by colony, bringing together under each colony the different classes within the Colonial Office record group that relate to that colony.

Colonies or territorial units covered are Auckland Islands, Australia, individual Australian States, Borneo, Brunei, East Indies, Fiji, Gilbert and Ellice Islands, Johore, Kedah and Perlis, Labuan, Malay

States, Negri Sembilan, Sungei Ujong, New Guinea, New Hebrides, New Zealand, Western Pacific, Pahang, Perak, Sarawak, Selangor, Solomon Islands, Straits Settlements, Tonga and Trengganu.

M419:
Extracts covering Hong Kong, Mauritius, the Seychelles, Falkland Islands and Wei Hai Wei.

M420:
Extracts, being class and piece lists with tables of contents, from the two typescript supplementary volumes. The major portion of the extracts from Vol. 1 consists of a class and piece list for CO 537, Colonies (General). Confidential Prints and Accounts Branch records are also listed. Extracts from Vol. 2 include class and piece lists on emigration, governors' pensions, honours and Board of Trade records. A contents list precedes the extracts from each volume.

M422 (ten frames only):
Short prefatory note followed by contents list for M418 and M420. The contents list for the supplementary volumes duplicates the two included on reel M420.

Volumes 1–3 contain the entire contents of M418, with the introductory ten pages of Vol. 1 being the entire contents of M422. M420 has been reproduced in its entirety as a fourth volume. All four volumes bear the spine title *PRO Colonial Office Records*.

Entry 199   Reels M581, M3087–3105

Name **GREATER LONDON RECORD OFFICE**
Title Records
Inclusive dates 1774–1853
Quantity 20 reels of microfilm
Location of original Greater London Record Office, 40 Northhampton Road, London EC1R 0HB, England

Note
These records supplement those in HO 26, which commences with 1791.

Description
Records of cases from the County of Middlesex tried in the London Criminal Court (Old Bailey) and detained in Newgate Gaol:
1) Index to persons indicted 1774–1832: under each letter of the alphabet the lists are arranged chronologically. The list gives name and date of session and an abbreviated indication of the offence and sometimes of the sentence.
2) Gaol Delivery Books (Fair Entry Books) 1785–1834: arranged chronologically by date of court of session, each session's record is divided into:

(i) Gaol Delivery, giving names of justices, jurors and those tried, with a note of their offences and sentences;
(ii) Oyer and Terminer trials, where appropriate, giving names of jurors and recognizances brought forward;
(iii) Gaol Calendar giving names of prisoners arranged by sentence.
3) Calendar of prisoners, Newgate 1820–22, 1830–53: arranged chronologically, giving name of each convict, age, trade, by whom and when committed, offence and sentence.

Three-page list available for reference.

Entry 200   Reels M689–690

Name **GREY, Sir George (1812–1898)**
Title Sketches, paintings and diary
Inclusive dates 1845–53
Quantity 2 reels of microfilm
Location of original British Library, Great Russell Street, London WC1B 3DG, England

Note
Governor of South Australia 1841–45, New Zealand 1845–53, 1861–67, and Cape Colony 1853–60; Prime Minister of New Zealand 1877–79.

Description
Papers and pictures collected by Grey in his early years in New Zealand:
1) BM Add MSS 19953: 'New Zealand Pictorial Scrapbook, 1845–53' by Andrew Sinclair, Cuthbert Clarke and J. Merret, containing watercolours and sketches of landscapes and Maoris.
2) BM Add MSS 19954: watercolours, drawings, lithographs and sketches 1848–53, illustrating New Zealand scenery, buildings and Maoris by Charles Heaphy, Cuthbert Clarke, G.F. Swainson, Charles Decimus Barraud, J.O. Hamley, C.J. Bosquet and others. Also sketches of scenery and natives on the Isle of Pines and Loyalty Islands by C. Heaphy, and of ships and view of the coast of the New Hebrides by G.F. Swainson.
3) BM Add MSS 19955: Cuthbert Clarke's diary, 5 December 1849–19 February 1850, of a journey in the party of Sir George Grey from Auckland to Taranaki, including sketches of scenery and natives and a sketch of Bishop G.A. Selwyn, 6 December 1849.

25-page list available for reference.

Entry 201   Reel M2123

Name **GUNTHER, Albert (1830–1914)**

Title Papers

Inclusive dates 1861–1911

Quantity 1 reel of microfilm

Location of original Natural History Museum, Cromwell Road, South Kensington, London SW7 5BD, England

Note
German-born zoologist. In 1862 he joined the staff of the British Museum. Keeper of Zoological Department, British Museum 1875–95; President of Linnean Society 1898–1901; Vice-President of Royal Society 1875–76.

Description
Correspondence with other zoologists and collectors concerning reptiles, birds, fishes and other specimens in Australia and the Pacific. Correspondents include Sir Walter Buller, Sir Philip Egerton, F.W. Hutton, Sir Daniel Cooper, C.M. Woodford, J. von Haast and Gerard Krefft.

Six-page list available for reference.

Entry 202   Reels M2534–2535

Name **HACKNEY ARCHIVES DEPARTMENT**

Title Collections

Inclusive dates 1827–1986

Quantity 2 reels of microfilm

Location of original Hackney Archives Department, 43 De Beauvoir Road, London N1 5SQ, England

Description
1) Records 1886–1962 of Berger Jenson and Nicholson printmakers, concerning their Australian and New Zealand operations. They include extracts from minute-books, reports, agreements and correspondence.
2) Records 1931–43 of British Xylonite (Australia) Pty Ltd referring to the Australian tariff and the company's factory in Melbourne.
3) Records 1827–58 of Refuge for the Destitute at Hackney relating to male and female emigration to Australia.

29-page list available for reference.

Entry 203   Reels M2728–2759

Name **HADDON, Alfred C. (1855–1940)**

Title Papers

Inclusive dates 1879–1940

Quantity 31 reels of microfilm

Location of original Cambridge University Library, West Road, Cambridge CB3 9DR, England

Note
Naturalist and anthropologist. In 1888–89 Haddon visited the Torres Strait to study marine biology and the Torres Strait islanders. He led the Cambridge Anthropology Expedition to Torres Strait in 1898–99. Haddon's published works include the *Report of the Cambridge Anthropology Expedition to Torres Straits* (1901–12) and *Canoes of Oceania* (1936–38).

Description
1) Personal papers and correspondence 1880–1935 mainly referring to ethnography and anthropological field work in Torres Strait and New Guinea. Correspondents include R.F. Fortune, Bronislaw Malinowski, E.W.P. Chinnery, Gregory Bateson, W. Baldwin Spencer, Daisy Bates, Camilla Wedgwood, A.R. Radcliffe-Brown and L. Dudley Buxton.
2) Papers relating to Haddon's first (1888–89) and second (1898–99) expeditions to Torres Strait. Correspondents include J.S. Bruce, Robert Bruce, Charles Myers, Rev. James Chalmers and Charles Hose.
3) Papers 1892–1938 relating to the New Guinea people and their customs. Correspondents include T. Reeves Palmer and C.G. Seligman.
4) Publications, lecture notes and miscellaneous notes, and off-prints of publications by others.

103-page list available for reference.

Entry 204   Reel M851

Name **HALE, Anne (1833–1912)**

Title Diary

Inclusive dates 1865–70

Quantity 1 reel of microfilm

Location of original Mrs M. Birch, Perthshire, Scotland

Special conditions Permission from the owner is required to reproduce any part of the diary.

Note
A relative of Bishop Mathew B. Hale, Anne Hale married Lieut. Thomas Sherwood in 1859.

Sherwood retired from the army in 1863 and they migrated to Australia in 1864 or 1865. They purchased a station at Unumgar in the Richmond River district of New South Wales and lived there for about ten years. See also entry 190.

Description
The diary contains brief entries and refers to daily activities on the station, including visits the family made, visitors to the farm, mustering, weather reports and slaughtering of cattle.

Entry 205   Reel M381

Name **HALE, Mathew Blagden, Bishop (1811–1895)**

Title Papers

Inclusive dates 1849–85

Quantity 1 reel of microfilm

Location of original University of Bristol Library, Tyndall Avenue, Bristol BS8 1TJ, England

Note
Anglican bishop. He became Archdeacon of Adelaide in 1847, and in 1850 founded the Native Institute at Poonindie, South Australia. He was appointed first Anglican Bishop of Perth in 1856 where he remained until 1875, when he was translated to the See of Brisbane. In 1885 he retired and returned to England.

Description
1) Diaries 1851, 1852, 1855, also containing a few entries for 1860 and 1861, and January–April 1876. The earlier diaries 1851–55 describe administration of the Poonindie mission, while the short 1876 diary is mainly concerned with daily routine and Hale's first tour of Queensland.

2) A few extracts from Hale's diaries containing entries for 30–31 December 1851 and 1–8 July 1852.

3) Four letters 1883–84 from Edward Benson, Archbishop of Canterbury, to Hale.

4) Copies of Letters Patent 1857 creating the See of Perth and the act of consecration of Hale as first Bishop.

5) Correspondence, reports and press cuttings 1850–75 relating to the Poonindie Mission including correspondence with the Colonial Secretary's Office in Adelaide and reports on the Mission for 1849, 1850, 1857–59 and 1875.

6) Press cuttings, letters and farewell addresses 1875 and 1885, on Hale's departure from Western Australia and from Australia for England.

7) Addresses 1858–82 by Hale relating to the Elementary Education Bill 1871 in Western Australia, support of Aboriginal children, the responsibility of the Church of England for the welfare of Aborigines, and the transportation of convicts to Western Australia.

Four-page list available for reference.

Entry 206   Reel M1179

Name **HALSEY, Sir Lionel, Admiral (1872–1949)**

Title Papers

Inclusive dates 1905–23

Quantity 1 reel of microfilm

Location of original Hertfordshire Record Office, County Hall, Hertford SG13 8DE, England

Note
Naval officer. Served on Australian Station as flag captain of HMS *Powerful* 1905–08, commanded HMS *New Zealand* on tour round world 1912–13, commanded HMS *Renown* as chief of staff to Prince of Wales on tours of Canada, United States, Australia, New Zealand and West Indies 1919–20.

Description
1) Letters 1905–08 written by Halsey to his parents while serving on Australian Station, referring to: movements of officers; battle practice; Australian defence; federal–State relations; economic conditions; politicians; social and sporting activities.

2) Letters 1913 written by Halsey to his parents while the battle cruiser *New Zealand* was visiting Australia and New Zealand, referring to: Australian naval policy; receptions; speeches; and meetings with Lord Denman and Lord Liverpool.

3) Letters 1918 written by Halsey to his parents while commanding HMAS *Australia*.

4) Letters 1920 written by Halsey to his parents while commanding HMS *Renown*, referring to: receptions for Prince of Wales; press criticisms; and railway accident in Western Australia.

5) Correspondence 1920–23 between Halsey and E. Lee of Masterton, New Zealand.

Three-page list available for reference.

Entry 207   Reels M3059–3060

Name **HAMILTON FAMILY**

Title Papers

Inclusive dates 1839–1954

Quantity 2 reels of microfilm

Location of original National Maritime Museum, Romney Road, Greenwich, London SE10 9NF, England

Note
Sir Henry Keppel, father-in-law of Frederick Hamilton, served on the China Station 1866–69. Henry G. Hamilton emigrated to Australia in 1839. Sir Louis H. Keppel Hamilton served as a member of the Commonwealth Naval Board in Australia 1945–48.

Description
1) Papers 1847–79 of Sir Henry Keppel, including: log of *Meander*, account of voyages in East Indies; labour problem in East Indies; and death of Capt. Owen Stanley.
2) Papers 1839–43 of Henry G. Hamilton, including letters written from Sydney and Clarence River to his family in England.
3) Papers 1945–54 of Sir Louis Hamilton including: account of Mission to Australia; discussions on post-war forces; and visit of American Fleet. Correspondents include Lord Mountbatten and Sir Hugh Binney.

Eight-page list available for reference.

Entry 208   Reel M1912

Name **HAMPSHIRE RECORD OFFICE**

Title Records

Inclusive dates 1834–1974

Quantity 1 reel of microfilm

Location of original Hampshire Record Office, Sussex Street, Winchester SO23 8TH, England

Description
1) Records 1834–1959 of parishes of Hartley Westpall and Rockbourne. Subjects include church matters in Australia and emigrants from Rockbourne to Sydney on the *James* in 1834.
2) Papers 1862–90 relating to the estate of Algernon Lempriere, including property in Queensland.
3) Letters of Lord and Lady Selborne relating to their visit to Jakarta, Bandung and Singapore in 1937.
4) Letters of Gerard Bonham-Carter describing his visit to Australia and New Zealand in 1926–27.

5) Papers 1842–51 of Alexander Waddell referring to his visit to Melbourne in 1851.

Four-page list available for reference.

Entry 209   Reel M674

Name **HARDING, Henry (1829–1899)**

Title Journal

Inclusive dates 1853

Quantity 1 reel of microfilm

Location of original Mr Sidney G. Harding, London, England

Note
Pioneer of the Australian cheese industry. In 1853 Harding accepted a contract with Thomas Mort to establish a cheese factory at Bodalla on the south coast of New South Wales. He was a Wesleyan lay preacher and acted as assistant surgeon on the emigrant vessel *Ida*. He travelled to England in 1856 but returned to Australia and acquired a large property in Victoria.

Description
Journal March–June 1853 of a voyage from London to Melbourne on the immigrant ship *Ida* describing day-to-day events on the ship and weather conditions.

One-page list available for reference.

Entry 210   Reels M367–372

Name **HARGRAVE, Lawrence (1850–1915)**

Title Papers

Inclusive dates 1866–1915

Quantity 6 reels of microfilm

Location of original Powerhouse Museum, Harris Street, Sydney NSW 2000

Note
Aeronautical pioneer and explorer. Participated in a number of expeditions to New Guinea between 1871 and 1889 including a journey up the Fly River in 1876 with the D'Albertis expedition. Worked as Assistant Astronomer at the Sydney Observatory for four years before retiring and spending the rest of his life as an inventor. He designed and built many model flying machines.

Description
Letters, notes, memoranda and drawings together with some printed material, mainly journal articles and newspaper clippings. Hargrave corresponded with fellow researchers all over the world and was

also an avid writer to newspaper editors' columns on current affairs such as temperance, Federation and early Spanish exploration in the South Pacific, as well as being a regular contributor to scientific and technical journals.

1) Notebooks with indexes, containing letters, diagrams, calculations, photographs, newspaper cuttings and journal articles, mainly on Hargrave's aeronautical work, but including drafts and clippings of letters to newspapers and to individuals on other topics. The material is arranged chronologically.

2) Correspondence 1866–91, newspaper cuttings and notes, concerning journeys undertaken by Hargrave, including one as a member of the New Guinea Expedition, formed to prospect for gold. En route to New Guinea in February 1872 the expedition's brig *Maria* was wrecked near Cardwell, Queensland. Correspondence and notes on the D'Albertis and other New Guinea expeditions participated in by Hargrave include dealings with the New South Wales branch of the Royal Geographical Society of Australasia.

3) Newspaper cuttings, notes, calculations and correspondence 1878–83 concerning astronomy, including Hargrave's work at the Sydney Observatory, and correspondence with H.C. Russell.

One-page list available for reference.

Entry 211   Reel M2079

Name **HASSALL FAMILY**

Title Papers

Inclusive dates 1898–1938

Quantity 1 reel of microfilm

Location of original Greater Manchester Record Office, 56 Marshall Street, New Cross, Manchester M4 5FU, England

Note
Members of the Hassall Family included William and Martha Hassall of Ballarat, Victoria, and their son James and daughter-in-law Harriet Hassall of Adelaide.

Description
Correspondence 1901–29 of James Hassall, Harriet Hassall, Nellie Reed and Martha Hamilton of Adelaide with relatives in Manchester. Also legal papers 1923–38 concerning estate of Thomas Hassall of Ballarat.

One-page list available for reference.

Entry 212   Reel M836

Name **HAYWARD FAMILY**

Title Papers

Inclusive dates 1857–c.1872

Quantity 1 reel of microfilm

Location of original Mr M.P.J. Hayward, Gloucestershire, England

Note
Johnson Frederick Hayward (1822–1912) arrived in Adelaide in 1847 from England. He originally settled at Pekina near Burra, South Australia. Martinus Peter Hayward (1817–1904) arrived in Australia as surgeon on the same ship as J.F. Hayward. He too settled in South Australia and was later surgeon on another immigrant ship from England.

Description
1) Typescript copy of Johnson Frederick Hayward's 'Incidents in My Australian Life' (c.1872), being an account of life on a sheep station 1846–56.

2) Three journals kept by J.F. Hayward describing journeys to and from England 1858–59, and in Europe 1859. Also diaries of Martinus Peter Hayward 1863–64 kept on voyages between England and Australia.

3) Testimonial 1857 to M.P. Hayward as candidate for post of South Australian Emigration Agent in England, containing many signatures.

4) A number of portraits of various members of the Hayward Family.

One-page list available for reference.

Entry 213   Reels M2850–2853

Name **HEARNSHAW FAMILY**

Title Papers

Inclusive dates 1939–86

Quantity 4 reels of microfilm

Location of original Mrs S. Wall, Cheshire, England

Note
Psychologist. Hearnshaw was married to Gwenneth Dickens of Perth, Western Australia. He took his family to New Zealand where he was a lecturer in Psychology at Victoria University College, Wellington 1939–47, and Director of the Industrial Psychology Division of Department of Scientific and Industrial Research at Wellington 1942–47. They returned to England in 1947.

Description
1) Letters 1939–47 of Leslie and Gwenneth Hearnshaw to his parents in England. The letters include accounts of their life in New Zealand, New Zealand society and Professor Hearnshaw's work in New Zealand.

2) Letters, written from Perth, 1947–48 of Gwenneth Hearnshaw and her mother, Mrs Dickens, to Leslie Hearnshaw.

3) 'An Englishman in War-time New Zealand', an account by Leslie Hearnshaw while living in New Zealand 1938–47, and on subsequent visits 1964–86.

4) Diaries 30 January–11 February 1940, kept by Leslie and Gwenneth Hearnshaw during a holiday at Mt Egmont, New Zealand.

Five-page list available for reference.

Entry 214   Reel M2254

Name **HENDERSON FAMILY**

Title Papers

Inclusive dates 1854–97

Quantity 1 reel of microfilm

Location of original Sir Edmund Neville, Norfolk, England

Note
The Henderson Family included Sir Edmund Yeamans Henderson (1821–96), his wife Maria and his father Admiral George Henderson. Major Edmund Henderson was Comptroller of Convicts in Western Australia 1850–55, 1858–63.

Description
1) Letters1860–62 of Edmund Yeamans Henderson to his wife Maria while travelling in Western Australia. They refer to visits to Bunbury, Mandurah, Pinjarra, York and Guildford, social events, and Governor Arthur Kennedy.

2) Letters 1854–63 from George Henderson to Edmund and Maria Henderson.

3) Letters from Maria Henderson to Edmund Henderson, written from Fremantle and Rottnest Island, giving family news.

4) Letters 1860–62 from Maria Henderson to George Henderson refering to family news, Perth society and Georgina Kennedy.

5) Letter 1862 from convict P. Hussie at Busselton seeking conditional pardon.

6) Letter 1852 from Jack Henderson at Fremantle describing the wreck of the *Eglinton*.

7) Miscellaneous documents, including an obituary of Edmund Yeamans Walcott Henderson, *Royal Engineer Journal*, February 1897.

One-page list available for reference.

Entry 215   Reels M2085–2087

Name **ALFRED HERBERT LTD**

Title Records

Inclusive dates 1918–61

Quantity 3 reels of microfilm

Location of original Coventry City Record Office, Mandela House, Bayley Lane, Coventry, West Midlands CV1 5RG, England

Note
The firm of Alfred Herbert Ltd of Coventry was founded by Sir Alfred Herbert. Registered in 1894, it became the largest manufacturer of precision tools and machinery in Britain.

Description
Correspondence, memoranda, notes on foundation of Alfred Herbert (Australasia) Pty Ltd, auditors reports and annual accounts. Correspondents include C.E. Young, Sir Alfred Herbert, D. Gimson, and Norton, Smith & Co, Sydney.

Two-page list available for reference.

Entry 216   Reels M1548, M2083–2084

Name **HEREFORD AND WORCESTER RECORD OFFICE**

Title Collections

Inclusive dates 1802–1938

Quantity 3 reels of microfilm

Location of original Hereford and Worcester Record Office, St Helen's, Fish Street, Worcester WR1 2HN, England (M1548) and Hereford and Worcester Record Office, County Hall, Spetchley Road, Worcester WR5 2NA, England (M2083–2084)

Special conditions Further copies of M1548 can be made only by the Hereford and Worcester Record Office.

Description
M1548:
1) Documents 1869–1904 relating to James W. Clulee of Dunedin.

2) Papers 1852–67 of Sir John Pakington, Secretary of State for the Colonies 1852 and First Lord of the Admiralty 1858–59, 1866,

referring to Australian and New Zealand constitutions, cessation of transportation and appointments to HMS *Galatea*. Correspondents include Lord Derby, Duke of Newcastle, C.J. La Trobe, Sir George Grey, J.R. Godley and Duke of Edinburgh.

3) Papers 1876–80 concerning estate of Justice Alfred Cheeke of New South Wales Supreme Court.

4) Letter 1921 of Dame Nellie Melba to Sir Edward Elgar.

5) Cutting book, photograph album and other papers of composer Sir Granville Bantock relating to his tours of Australia and New Zealand 1907, 1938–39.

6) Papers 1863–68 relating to estate of James Nash of Melbourne.

7) Papers 1856–93 concerning properties of Lyttelton Family in New Zealand.

8) Papers 1835–53 referring to properties of Edward Dumaresq and Rev. P.M. Boissier in Van Diemen's Land.

13-page list available for reference.

M2083–2084:

1) Sheriff's Oaths and Appointments 1827–34 referring to transfer of convicts from Hereford Gaol to ships.

2) Letters of Lieut. (later Admiral) Nicholas Pateshall describing voyage around the world on HMS *Calcutta* (under Capt. D. Woodriff), visit to Port Phillip (October–November 1803) and Port Jackson (November 1803–March 1804), and his encounters with Aborigines.

3) Papers 1802–08 of John Biddulph including hydrographical notes on the Pacific Islands and letters about whaling voyages on the *Tom of London*.

4) Financial records 1890–1908 of Maxwelton Station, Hughenden, Queensland.

Five-page list available for reference.

Name **HERTFORDSHIRE RECORD OFFICE**

Title Collections

Inclusive dates 1797–1921

Quantity 1 reel of microfilm

Location of original Hertfordshire Record Office, County Hall, Hertford SG13 8DE, England

Description

1) Quarter Sessions records 1797–1841 including lists of convicts transported from Hertfordshire.

2) Digswell Parish records 1917–21 comprising admission and discharge book and photograph album of Numbers 4 and 5 Australian Auxiliary Hospitals, Welwyn, and minute-book of Digswell Australian War Memorial Committee.

3) Correspondence 1846–58 of Hertford Meeting of Society of Friends concerning work of Society in Australia.

4) Papers 1893 concerning world tour of Mrs F.C. Hanbury.

5) Minutes 1852–54 of Board of New South Wales Gold Mines.

6) Papers 1823–1922 of Leake Family, including letters 1831–36 of H.M. Leake in Sydney, and letters 1900 of Vice-Admiral Francis Leake of HMS *Bramble* in Singapore, Borneo and Sarawak.

7) Letters 1874 of Arthur Giles-Puller describing travels in Australia, including meetings with Bishop A. Short and Charles Pearson, and visit to Queensland sugar plantation.

8) Correspondence 1839–53 of Edenborough Family concerning business activities of Horatio Edenborough of Goulburn and Sydney, and economic conditions in the colony.

9) Letters 1866–68 of W. Rasche in Melbourne.

10) Letters 1860–64 of C.D.R. Ward and Anne Ward of Wellington referring to Maori War and property and financial matters.

Seven-page list available for reference.

Entry 218   Reel M2501

Name **HIGSON, Daniel (1849–1925)**

Title Diary

Inclusive dates 1 January 1868–11 April 1870

Quantity 1 reel of microfilm

Location of original District Central Library, Market Square, Preston PR1 2PP, England

Note
Higson sailed to Australia on SS *Great Britain* in 1869 and returned to England in 1870.

Description
Diary describing Higson's journey from Liverpool to Melbourne on *Great Britain*, life on board the ship, descriptions of Melbourne, gold diggings, and his journey back to England on board the *Lochuwe*.

One-page list available for reference.

Entry 219   Reels M2862–2877

Name **SIR JAMES HILL AND SONS LTD**

Title Papers

Inclusive dates 1799–1986

Quantity 16 reels of microfilm

Location of original West Yorkshire Archive Service, Bradford, 15 Canal Road, Bradford BD1 4AT, England

Note
Wool merchant. In 1891 Hill established his own business and became one of the leading textile magnates. Mayor of Bradford 1908 and MP for Bradford Central 1916–21. Sir James Hill and Sons (Australia) Ltd and Sir James Hill and Sons (New Zealand) Ltd were formed in 1949 to act as buying agents in Australia and New Zealand. The Australian company was amalgamated with Booth Hill and Sons Pty Ltd in 1968.

Description
Correspondence, financial papers, account statements, balance sheets, minutes and reports of various companies including Sir James Hill and Sons (Australia) Ltd and Sir James Hill and Sons (New Zealand) Ltd, Booth Hill and Sons Pty Ltd, Independent Wool Dumpers Pty Ltd, Booth Newman Pty Ltd, and Fred W. Heap Ltd.

Correspondents include David Knight, Price Waterhouse, Hargreaves Felton, Baillieu Bowring Superannuation Services, Bank of New South Wales, Bank of Adelaide, Australian Mutual Provident Society, New Zealand Shipping Co Ltd,

Walter Hill and Sons (New Zealand) Ltd, Harry J. Brigden & Co, and Newcastle Wool Processing Co Ltd.

11-page list available for reference.

Entry 220   Reel M1953

Name **HILL FAMILY**

Title Papers

Inclusive dates 1894–1935

Quantity 1 reel of microfilm

Location of original Mrs Mary Paget, Cheltenham, England

Special conditions The permission of the owner is needed to reproduce or to publish extracts from the papers.

Note
Charles Hill (1823–94) emigrated to New Zealand with his family in 1863. Hill soon left for the East Indies, but his wife remained in Nelson. In 1871 Mrs Hill and her eldest daughter, Cornelia (Cora), went to Batavia. Cora married Wulf von Bultzingslowen in 1873 and spent most of her life in Germany. Annie Hill, who remained in New Zealand with an aunt, married Rev. Fred Chatterton in 1890 in Nelson.

Description
1) Diary 27 March–4 July 1894 kept by Rev. Fred Chatterton on a journey from Nelson, New Zealand, to England. It describes conversations, as well as his travels, activities and general impressions. It refers to: a voyage from Wellington to Sydney on *Hauroto*; his brief stay in Sydney; voyage from Sydney to Brisbane on *Warrego*; visits to Rockhampton and Thursday Island; meeting with Queensland Premier H.M. Nelson and Attorney-General T.J. Byrnes; separation movement of northern Queensland; voyage through Torres Strait and past Timor, Flores and other islands and arrival at Java (30 April); impressions of Batavia; journey from Semarang to Surabaya; voyage to Singapore on *Carpentier*; impressions of Singapore; missionary activities at Singapore; and departure to Hong Kong and Japan.

2) Memoir 1852–1903 (written in 1934–35 for grandchildren) of Cora von Bultzingslowen. It describes: her earliest recollections; voyage to Sydney on *Mauritius* and to Nelson on *Lord Ashley* in 1864; housing and conditions at Nelson; visits to Tauranga and Auckland; social life in Surabaya; marriage to Wulf von Bultzingslowen; visit to Australia and New Zealand and emigration to Germany in 1877;

and a return visit to Australia, New Zealand and Java 1900–03.

11-page list available for reference.

Entry 221   Reel M417

Name **HINE, Janet D. (b.1923)**

Title Index of HM ships employed in areas of interest to the AJCP

Inclusive dates 1955–56

Quantity 1 reel of microfilm

Location of original Australia House, The Strand, London WC2B 4LA, England

Note
Librarian. Public Library of New South Wales London Liaison Officer 1954–57.

Description
Copy of an index compiled on cards 1955–56, listing ships of the British Navy employed on voyages in areas of interest to the AJCP. The index includes ships undertaking survey and discovery, warships, tenders, storeships and others. Entries are arranged alphabetically by ship's name and show dates of various voyages in the area, captain, and route followed. The entries refer the user to the appropriate Admiralty class and piece number, and it should be noted that many of the Admiralty records cited have been copied in the AJCP Public Record Office series.

Entry 222   Reel M405

Name **HOARE, Frederick**

Title Journals

Inclusive dates 1854–56

Quantity 1 reel of microfilm

Location of original Greater London Record Office, 40 Northhampton Road, London EC1R 0HB, England

Note
Gold prospector and builder. Emigrated from Devon to try his luck on the goldfields of Victoria. He is believed to have bought some land outside Melbourne.

Description
1) Journal of a voyage from Liverpool to Melbourne May–July 1854 on the *Red Jacket*. It is a day-to-day record of the voyage, noting events and commenting on passengers and crew as well as weather conditions and distance travelled. The journal also contains notes referring to land sales around Melbourne, costs of buildings, business transactions (especially with George Squiers) and rough sketches of the campsites on the goldfields around Castlemaine, Victoria.

2) Journal of a voyage from Melbourne to England via New Zealand, commencing April 1856, on the *New Great Britain*. It is chiefly concerned with weather conditions and notes as well as the latitude and longitude and the distance covered each day. The journal ends on 26 July as the ship neared England.

Entry 223   Reel M715

Name **HOBHOUSE, Edmund, Bishop (1817–1904)**

Title Papers

Inclusive dates 1858–1905, 1955–62

Quantity 1 reel of microfilm

Location of original Alexander Turnbull Library, Wellington, New Zealand and Miss Dorothy Hobhouse London, England

Note
First Anglican Bishop of Nelson, New Zealand 1858–65. From 1869 to 1881 he was assistant at Lichfield, Staffordshire to Bishop G.A. Selwyn. Mary Elizabeth Hobhouse (*nee* Brodrick), Hobhouse's first wife, died in New Zealand in 1865, shortly before her husband returned to England.

Description
1) Approximately 170 letters 1858–64 written by Hobhouse and his wife to relatives in England, most of them addressed to his sister Eliza but some of those obviously intended for circulation within the family. The letters contain: descriptions of the voyage to New Zealand; the settlement at Nelson; details of domestic and church life; Hobhouse's numerous journeys around his vast diocese and his work among the settlers and the Maoris. Mary Elizabeth Hobhouse sometimes accompanied her husband on his travels and her letters describe the countryside around Nelson and settlers there, as well as her impressions of visitors to the district and of churchmen. Domestic life in New Zealand is outlined in great detail, but the letters also reveal her interest in the provision of schooling for local children. Nearly all the letters are accompanied by typed transcripts.

2) Diaries kept by Hobhouse and journals written for his wife 1859–64 relate details of the voyage in 1859 from Sydney to Nelson to attend the first Provincial Synod at Wellington, news of which is also included.

3) Letters and papers 1864 concerning Hobhouse's resignation, written by G.A. Selwyn, his wife Sarah, M.A. Martin and Edmund Hobhouse.

4) Four letters 1859–64 from Caroline Abraham, wife of Bishop C.J. Abraham, to Eliza Hobhouse.

5) Obituary notices 1904 for Hobhouse from English and New Zealand newspapers.

6) Miscellaneous items, including correspondence, mainly on ecclesiastical matters, between Hobhouse, G.A. Selwyn and C.J. Abraham; photographs and drawings of New Zealand, including several of Nelson; and a typed copy of 'Outline of My Life' by Hobhouse.

Nine-page list available for reference.

Entry 224   Reel M1918

Name **HODGKIN, Thomas (1831–1913)**
Title Journals
Inclusive dates 1909–10
Quantity 1 reel of microfilm
Location of original University Library, University of Newcastle upon Tyne, Newcastle upon Tyne NE2 4HQ, England

Note
Banker. Active member of the Quaker community in Newcastle upon Tyne.

Description
Journals kept by Hodgkin on voyage on the *Orontes* from Tilbury to Melbourne (January–March 1909), and during his trips to Tasmania, New Zealand, New South Wales, Queensland, Victoria, South Australia, Western Australia and journey back to England on the *Orontes* and *Otranto* (November 1909–January 1910). Includes impressions of places he visited, members of the Quaker communities in the main Australian cities, and the General Meeting of Australian Friends in Adelaide.

Three-page list available for reference.

Entry 225   Reels M675–676, M789–790

Name **HODGSON, Sir Arthur (1818–1902)**
Title Papers
Inclusive dates 1838–89
Quantity 4 reels of microfilm
Location of original Mrs F.E. Spurway, Somerset, England

Note
Queensland squatter and politician. He arrived in Australia in 1838 and settled at Eton Vale on the Darling Downs, Queensland. He became a successful farmer and was general superintendent of the Australian Agricultural Co 1856–61. Member of the New South Wales Legislative Assembly 1858–61 and the Queensland Legislative Assembly 1861–74. After settling in England in the 1870s he visited Queensland several times and helped to promote the frozen meat trade. In 1842 he married Eliza Dowling, daughter of Sir James Dowling, Chief Justice of New South Wales.

Description
1) Shipboard journals, noting details of navigation, weather, daily routine of passengers. The journals were kept during the following voyages: London–Sydney on the *Royal George* 1838; Sydney–West Indies aboard the *Walmer Castle* 1848; England–Australia on the *Thomas Arbuthnot* 1849–50.

2) Account books 1853–73; records of financial transactions 1839–47; tallies kept on Queensland properties 1842–47 of killing, shearing and bales of wool produced, and provisions distributed to station workers.

3) Addresses and articles describing various voyages; drafts for addresses on the mutiny on the *Bounty,* the 1878 Paris Exhibition and forests and historic trees of Great Britain; printed item *Australia Revisited 1874–1889* (28 p.) with manuscript amendments and additions, giving Hodgson's impressions of the colony and its agricultural and economic prospects.

4) Newspaper cuttings, mainly on agriculture; biographical notes on Hodgson by Mrs Spurway; map of holdings in the Eton Vale area, Queensland; four pages from a letter-journal of Rev. Edward Hodgson 1840, with several references to members of the Macarthur Family.

Three-page list available for reference.

Entry 226   Reel M729

Name **HODGSON, Francis Henry, Reverend (1848–c.1930)**

Title Papers

Inclusive dates 1841–1926

Quantity 1 reel of microfilm

Location of original Mrs F.E. Spurway, Somerset, England

Note
Clergyman. Son of Sir Arthur and Lady Hodgson. He spent part of his early life in Sydney and on his parents' property, Eton Vale, Queensland. Educated at Trinity College, he was ordained in 1874 and was rector of a number of parishes in England including Abbots Langley and North Kineton.

Description
The main part of the collection is 'Notes on My Life' 23 November 1848–2 July 1924, being detailed recollections of his life and the history of his family. There is also a small journal written in 1860, when he was 12; a newspaper cutting about his brother E.D. Hodgson; a pencil sketch of Head Station, Eton Vale 1841; and a printed map, with manuscript additions, of part of the Balonne and Dawson River basins of south-east Queensland, given by Ludwig Leichhardt to Sir Arthur Hodgson.

Entry 227   Reel M2575

Name **HODKINSON, William**

Title Log and diary

Inclusive dates 26 June–10 October 1860

Quantity 1 reel of microfilm

Location of original Mrs E. Roberts, Cambridge, England

Note
Hodkinson was a passenger on board the *Phoenix* on a journey from Auckland to Liverpool 1860.

Description
Log and diary 26 June–10 October 1860, describing life on board the *Phoenix* and including references to the Maori Wars.

One-page list available for reference.

Entry 228   Reel M1157

Name **HOLDEN, Andrew (b.1886)**

Title Memoirs

Inclusive dates 1887–1966

Quantity 1 reel of microfilm

Location of original Mrs J.N. Campbell, Bristol, England

Note
Holden was born at Circular Head in north-west Tasmania and educated at Hutchins School, Hobart. His wife, Una Montgomery, was the daughter of Henry Montgomery, Anglican Bishop of Tasmania, and sister of Bernard Montgomery (later Field Marshal Montgomery).

Description
Chapters copied from Holden's memoirs describing early years at Circular Head; life in Hobart 1894–1902 and Oxford 1902–07; the Holden, Ware and Farmer Families, and Una Holden's early life, in which there are anecdotes about the young Bernard Montgomery. Also copied are memoirs of Tasmania in 1887–96 written in 1954 by Lettyce Armitage.

One-page list available for reference.

Entry 229   Reels M1945–1948

Name **HOLFORD, William Graham, 1st Baron (1907–1975)**

Title Papers

Inclusive dates 1948–74

Quantity 4 reels of microfilm

Location of original Liverpool University Archives, PO Box 147, Bedford Street South, Liverpool L69 3BX, England

Note
Professor of Civic Design at Liverpool University 1936–48. Professor of Town Planning at University College, London 1948–70. Holford wrote reports for the Australian Government *Observation on the Future Development of Canberra, ACT* (1958) and *The Growth of Canberra 1958–65 and 1965–72: A Review* (1966). He was consultant to the National Capital Development Commission 1958–70.

Description
1) Papers 1951 concerning Holford's visit to Australia, referring to town planning in Australia.
2) Canberra papers 1957–74 referring to: Holford's report on the future of Canberra; appointment

of Sir John Overall; Holford's consultancy agreements with the National Capital Development Commission, Australian Planning Institute, and National Urban and Regional Development Authority; and visits by Holford and R.W. Gray to Canberra between 1959 and 1966. Correspondents include Peter Harrison, Sir Robert Menzies, W.C. Andrews, R.B. Landsdown, G. Stephenson, R.K.H. Johnson, Sir John Overall and Walter Bunning.

3) Papers 1956–64 concerning town planner Grenfell Ruddock.

4) Canberra reports 1957–65, referring to: proposed National Gallery; Parliamentary Triangle; Central Basin area; Lake Burley Griffin; Commonwealth and Kings Avenue bridges; and Capital Hill.

5) Notes, correspondence and drawings 1963–68 on Canberra Carillon.

6) Papers 1956–70 concerning town planning and public buildings in Sydney, Melbourne, Perth, Adelaide and Hobart.

12-page list available for reference.

Entry 230   Reel M1860

Name **HOLMES, Charles**
Title Papers
Inclusive dates 1880–84
Quantity 1 reel of microfilm
Location of original Mrs E. Bumstead, Cornwall, England

Note
Charles Holmes arrived in Australia in 1881. He lived in Rockhampton, Brisbane, Melbourne and Sydney.

Description
Diary kept by Holmes on the journey to Australia on board the *Earl Granville* 13 December 1880– 14 April 1881, and eight letters to his parents in Cambridge. The letters refer to life in Australia and family news.

Two-page list available for reference.

Entry 231   Reel M392

Name **HOLYOAKE, Henry Thomas and Horatio**
Title Letters
Inclusive dates 1854–73
Quantity Portion of 1 reel of microfilm
Location of original Cooperative Union Ltd, Holyoake House, Hanover Street, Manchester M60 0AS, England

Note
Brothers of George Jacob Holyoake (1817–1906), the English social reformer. In 1854 Henry opened a store at Ballarat and later had a bookshop in Melbourne. In 1863 he was working as a master saddler.

Description
Six letters from Horatio and Henry Holyoake to their brother George and to their mother. The letters, written from Ballarat, Blackwood and Melbourne, describe work and life on the Victorian goldfields and comment on Victorian parliamentarians and politics. They refer to the high standing of G.J. Holyoake in Australia and the support that he had received in the *Argus,* and contain news of family matters.

One-page list available for reference.

Entry 232   Reel M604

Name **HOME, Sir Everard, 1st Baronet (1756–1832)**
Title Address
Inclusive dates 1822, 1825
Quantity 1 reel of microfilm
Location of original Royal College of Surgeons of England, 35–43 Lincoln's Inn Fields, London WC2A 3PN, England

Note
Surgeon and lecturer in anatomy. Surgeon at St George's Hospital 1793–1827 and Chelsea Hospital 1821–32. First President of Royal College of Surgeons 1821 and Keeper of Hunterian Collection.

Description
The Hunterian Oration in Honour of Surgery ... Delivered in the Theatre of the Royal College of Surgeons in London, February 14, 1822 by Sir Everard Home (36 p.), London (1822). The subject of the oration was Sir Joseph Banks. A page of typescript notes 'collected in conversation with Sir Everard Home' 10 October 1825 identifies certain events and people referred to in the oration.

One-page list available for reference.

Entry 233   Reel M980

Name **HOPE, Louis (1817–1894)**

Title Journal

Inclusive dates 1843–57

Quantity 1 reel of microfilm

Location of original Mrs P. Hiley, Hampshire, England

Special conditions Permission to reproduce any part of the journal must be obtained from the copyright owner.

Note
Grazier, sugar grower and politician. Son of John Hope, 4th Earl of Hopetoun. He arrived in Australia in 1843 and spent some time travelling before finally settling in Queensland in 1853. He was a major force behind the colony's infant sugar industry. Member of the Queensland Legislative Council 1862–82.

Description
1) Journal of the voyage from England to Sydney March to August 1843. The entries give course and bearing for each day, meteorological observations, sightings of marine life, but few details of shipboard routine or fellow passengers.

2) Diary May 1844–May 1845 containing an account of a voyage on HMS *Thalia,* sailing first to Tahiti, then to Hawaii. At Tahiti it was discovered that the French were in control, and Hope relates native accounts of battles against the French and writes of the treatment of English officials by the French, and the attitude of the Tahitians towards the English. Hope travelled next to Hawaii where he spent some months wandering about the island group, collecting many botanical specimens, visiting places of interest such as the site of Captain James Cook's death, and sugar and coffee plantations. Expenses incurred during his wanderings are listed periodically. From February to May 1845 Hope travelled from Honolulu to Sydney via Tahiti and other Pacific islands. He describes encounters with the natives, and relates some of the mythology of Huahine, in the Society Islands group.

3) Book lists on various topics such as natural history and geography, followed by a note that Hope settled at Molong, New South Wales, in 1846, although there is no record of his time there.

4) Journal January–May 1851 kept during a voyage from Sydney to England on the *General Hewett,* when he took as part of his baggage lizards and small Australian birds to give to the Zoological Gardens, plus three emus to grace the lawns at Hopetoun House.

5) List of over 300 botanical names with location of habitat, noting which plants are peculiar to certain Pacific Islands, or are widely found.

6) Journal February–October 1857 of daily activities on a property near Brisbane, including mustering cattle, shearing sheep, and building.

Entry 234   Reels M936–937, M1154–1156, M1584

Name **HOPETOUN, John Hope, 7th Earl (1860–1908)**

Title Papers

Inclusive dates 1853–1904

Quantity 6 reels of microfilm

Location of original Hopetoun House, Lothian EH30 9SL, Scotland

Note
John Hope, 7th Earl of Hopetoun, 1st Marquess of Linlithgow (created 1902). Governor of Victoria 1889–95 and first Governor-General of Australia 1901–02.

Description
Reels M936–937:
1) Papers and correspondence 1881–1904, dealing with various subjects such as: Federation; Victorian and federal politics; the South African War; programs for the Royal visit 1901; Imperial penny postage; official postings; honours; site of the Governor-General's house and his allowances; Hopetoun's appointments as Governor and Governor-General; and his resignation in 1902. Principal correspondents include Sir Edmund Barton, Thomas Bavin, Rear Admiral Sir Lewis Beaumont, Lord Carrington, Joseph Chamberlain, Alfred Deakin, Sir John Forrest, Sir Samuel Griffith, General Sir Edward Hutton, Sir Francis Knollys, Lord Knutsford, Sir Henry Loch, James Patterson, Lord Ripon, Sir William Robinson, Lord Rosebery, Lord Salisbury, William Shields, William Syme, Lord Tennyson, Sir George Verdon, Capt. E.W. Wallington and Sir Hartley Williams.

2) Miscellaneous items including: a portrait of Sir Henry Parkes; the commission and letters patent appointing Hopetoun Governor of Victoria; printed speeches; a copy of Sir Henry Parkes' Federation Scheme; the program of Hopetoun's farewell banquet in London in 1900; addresses of welcome 1900–01; items relating to the celebration of Federation January 1901; and a copy of *The Landing of Lieutenant James Cook, RN, at Botany Bay* (1901).

3) Correspondence of Hopetoun's private secretary and accountant in Australia, David

W. Brown, containing in-letters 1900–02, copies of out-letters 1902, and accounts and receipts 1902.

17-page list available for reference.

Reels M1154–1156:
1) Correspondence 1853–1901 including letters of congratulation on appointment as Governor of Victoria and letters concerning Capt. Herbert Waterlow. Correspondents include J.F. McCarron, Lord Kintore, Lord Knutsford and the Prince of Wales.
2) Accounts 1889–94 of Government House, Melbourne.
3) Accounts, cheque book stubs and other financial papers 1901–02.
4) Album of cuttings and sketches 1887–91.
5) Sketchbook, including watercolours, 1900–02.
6) Newspaper cuttings 1901–02.

One-page list available for reference.

Reel M1584:
1) Album of photographs of Victoria in the 1890s.
2) Album of photographs of Melbourne waterworks and reservoirs 1895.
3) Scrapbook 1901 containing cuttings, programs, menus and other items relating to the inauguration of the Commonwealth of Australia.

Two-page list available for reference.

Entry 235   Reels M2626–2631

Name **HORNELL, James (1865–1949)**
Title Papers
Inclusive dates 1913–40
Quantity 6 reels of microfilm
Location of original Cambridge University Library, West Road, Cambridge CB3 9DR, England

Note
Marine biologist. Worked in Ceylon and India, and in 1918–24 was Director of the UK Fisheries Department. This appointment led to his interest in boats and the ethnology of fishermen.

Description
The papers include drafts, correspondence, cuttings, diaries and journals relating to the Scientific Expeditionary Association expedition to the South Pacific on the *St George* 1923–24.

Also diaries of visits to Indonesia and New Guinea 1918, and diaries kept during visits to the Pacific 1924–40.

Nine-page list available for reference.

Entry 236   Reels M1120–1122

Name **HOUSE OF LORDS RECORD OFFICE**
Title Records and papers
Inclusive dates 1790–1965
Quantity 3 reels of microfilm
Location of original House of Lords Record Office, Houses of Parliament, Westminster, London SW1A 0PW, England

Description
1) Selections from Main Papers 1790–1909 including reports of Inspector of Convicts, and manuscript and printed Bills including: 1824 Transportation Bill; 1828 New South Wales Administration of Justice Bill; 1834 South Australian Colonization Bill; 1845 Waste Lands (Australia) Bill; 1846 New Zealand Company Bill; 1850 Australian Colonies Government Bill; 1875 Pacific Islanders Protection Bill; 1885 Federal Council of Australasia Bill; and 1890 Borneo Company Bill.
2) Extracts from Committee books 1824–1912, including Committees on Unopposed Private Bills, Committees on Public Petitions and Select Committee on Private Bills.
3) Papers 1872–98 of Sir George Baden-Powell including writings on Australia 1878–79, papers on French interests in the Pacific, and papers on the proposed Canadian–Pacific Shipping Line and Cable Service.
4) Letters 1907–35 of A. Deakin, Sir George Reid and others to Ralph Blumenfeld, editor of the *Daily Express.*
5) Papers 1879–94 of George Cadogan, 5th Earl Cadogan, concerning international exhibitions and travels of Gerry Cadogan in Australia.
6) Papers 1913–33 of Sir Patrick Hannan concerning Navy League.
7) Letters 1914 of Sir Ronald Munro-Ferguson to William Pringle.
8) Papers 1892–1945 of Sir Herbert Samuel, 1st Viscount Samuel, relating to: statue of Capt. James Cook in London; the Imperial Wireless Chain; imperial organisation; and the Joint Select Committee on Colonial Affairs. Correspondents include Sir John Henniker Heaton, Lord Bledisloe and W. Pember Reeves.

9) Papers 1835–41 of Sir John Shaw-Lefevre on South Australian Colonisation Commission, including letters of R. Torrens, Daniel Wakefield and George Fife Angas.

10) Papers 1903–22 of John St L. Strachey, editor of the *Spectator*.

11) Papers 1924–65 of John Loder, 2nd Baron Wakehurst, Governor of New South Wales 1937–46, comprising copies of letters written during a visit to Australia and Southeast Asia in 1924, and his typescript memoirs.

34-page list of parliamentary records and 15-page list of historical collections available for reference.

Entry 237   Reel M820

Name **HOVE CENTRAL LIBRARY**
Title Collections
Inclusive dates 1805–1901
Quantity 1 reel of microfilm
Location of original Central Library, Church Road, Hove, Sussex BN3 2EG, England

Description
1) Autograph collection: letter 1891 concerning Frank Carlton of Newcastle; five letters 1892–1901 to Edward Horace Man (Deputy Superintendent of the Andaman Islands 1891–1901); Henry H. Giglioni concerning Perak stone implements and his diggings in Andaman Islands; photographs of Andamese and Nicobar natives; letter 1892 from Baron Anatole von Hugel, Curator, Museum of Archaeology, Cambridge requesting photographs of Andamese; letter 1818 from Frederick Augustus, Duke of York, to the Duke of Wellington concerning the cases of Corporals John Wilkinson and John Whalley and Privates Robert Mantle and Giles Seddon transported to New South Wales.

2) Papers of Sir Garnet Wolseley, 1st Viscount Wolseley: correspondence 1839–91 concerning defence of the Straits Settlements and Sydney and other military matters, including appointments. Correspondents include Sir George Bowen, Sir Henry Parkes, Sir James Knight and Sir Harry Rawson. Other items include *The New South Wales Contingents to South Africa, October 1899–June 1900* (1900) and *Suggestions for the Improvement of the Military Force of the British Empire* by Brigadier-General Stewart (1805); letter 1886, with reply from Lord Dunraven, concerning the proposal to extend the services of the Canadian Pacific Co

to Hong Kong; tables 1886 showing the state of the British Army at home, in India and in the colonies.

Four-page list available for reference.

Entry 238   Reel M2392

Name **HULL CITY RECORD OFFICE**
Title Collections
Inclusive dates 1786–1977
Quantity 1 reel of microfilm
Location of original City Record Office, 79 Lowgate, Kingston upon Hull, Humberside HU1 2AA, England

Description
1) Quarter Session records 1786–87 regarding the transportation of William Dring, Joseph Robinson and Robert Nettleton to Botany Bay, and the removal of convicts from Hull Gaol to the hulk *Dunkirk*.

2) Records 1977 of Thomas Hamling & Co Ltd concerning New Zealand fishing industry.

3) Petitions and testimony of Sidney Stephen (1840 and 1845) and Edward Abbott of Hobart (c.1838)

4) Correspondence 1853 of Joseph R. Pease relating to the proposed emigration of his son, James, to Australia or Canada.

5) Album of photographs of W.H. Slack of Rickitts of his trip around the world 1924–25, and visit to Australia, Naples, Ceylon, Port Said, Aden and Cairo 1932–33.

6) Letters of attorney 1880–85 by George Urquhart of South Yarra, Melbourne and letter from Urquhart to Jesse Malcolm concerning property in Teignmouth, Devon.

Four-page list available for reference.

Entry 239   Reel M2393

Name **HULL LOCAL STUDIES LIBRARY**
Title Collections
Inclusive dates 1847–98
Quantity 1 reel of microfilm
Location of original Hull Local Studies Library, Central Library, Albion Street, Kingston upon Hull, Humberside HU1 3TF, England

Description
1) Notes 1895 of William Richardson on early history of Missions to South Sea Islands.
2) Life of Tom Blossom (1777–1855), a missionary to South Sea Islands.

Two-page list available for reference.

Entry 240   Reel M2684

Name **HUMBERSIDE ARCHIVE SERVICE**
Title Collections
Inclusive dates 1834–1913
Quantity 1 reel of microfilm
Location of original Humberside Archive Service, County Hall, Beverley, North Humberside HU17 9BA, England

Description
1) Papers 1834–60 of Clark and Co, solicitors, relating to emigration to Australia, including a letter from Samuel Clark of Christchurch to his brother.
2) Papers 1871–97 of Fawcett Family referring to family news, estates of Robert H. Hubie, farmer of Rockhampton, and Thomas K. Hubie, teamster of St Lawrence. Correspondents are Mary and James Fawcett of Ballarat.
3) Letters 1880–81 of Richard Dillicar of Auckland and Waikato concerning business matters.
4) Calendar of prisoners in Hull Gaol 1825 and Beverley House of Correction 1841 containing details of transportees.

Six-page list available for reference.

Entry 241   Reels M2820–2824

Name **HUNTINGFIELD, William C.A. Vanneck, 5th Baron (1883–1969)**
Title Papers
Inclusive dates 1933–41
Quantity 5 reels of microfilm
Location of original Lord Huntingfield, Cambridge, England

Note
Governor of Victoria 1934–39 and Acting Governor-General of Australia March–September 1938.

Description
Correspondence, speeches, photograph albums, albums of press cuttings and other papers relating to Huntingfield's time in Australia.

The correspondence includes copies of Huntingfield's letters relating to his appointments as Governor of Victoria and Governor-General of Australia, and his later governorships of Madras and Rhodesia. Correspondents include Sir Edward Harding, Sir Alexander Hardinge, Lord Gowrie, Sir Winston Dugan, Sir Leslie Wilson, Lord Baden Powell, J.A. Lyons and Lord Galway.

The photograph albums contain family and official photographs, including photographs of Government House, Melbourne. The albums of press cuttings refer to appointments as Governor of Victoria and Acting Governor-General of Australia, opening of Parliament, and State dinners.

Eight-page list available for reference.

Entry 242   Reel M2522

Name **H. HUSBANDS & SONS**
Title Papers
Inclusive dates 1880–85
Quantity 1 reel of microfilm
Location of original Bristol Industrial Museum, Prince's Wharf, Bristol BS1 5TR, England

Description
Papers 1880–85 of opticians and instrument makers H. Husbands & Sons, referring to purchases of Metford theodolites, and papers and affidavits concerning arbitration between Charles Fredrick Husbands and Henry Husbands in Melbourne.
Correspondents are W.J. Conder and W. Metford.

Two-page list available for reference.

Entry 243   Reel M1190

Name **HUSKISSON, William (1770–1830)**

Title Papers

Inclusive dates 1797–1833

Quantity 1 reel of microfilm

Location of original British Library, Great Russell Street, London WC1B 3DG, England

Note
Canningite Tory politician. President of the Board of Trade 1823–27; Secretary of State for the Colonies 1827–28.

Description
Political papers comprising correspondence on naval, financial and colonial matters, including appointments, proposals for settlements in New Zealand, land grants, and activities of Henty Family in Van Diemen's Land. Correspondents include Lord Bathurst, R. Therry and Thomas Henty.

Five-page list available for reference.

Entry 244   Reels M876–916

Name **HUXLEY, Thomas Henry (1825–1895)**

Title Papers

Inclusive dates 1839–1926

Quantity 41 reels of microfilm

Location of original Imperial College of Science and Technology, College Archives, College Block, Imperial College, London SW7 2AZ, England

Note
Zoologist, lecturer and writer. Assistant Surgeon on HMS *Rattlesnake* 1846–50 on voyage surveying the Great Barrier Reef and islands in Torres Strait, the Gulf of Papua and the Louisiade Archipelago. From 1854 to 1885 he taught natural history at the Royal School of Mines. President of the Royal Society 1881–85.

Description
About 4500 letters. Among the 850 correspondents are John Tyndall, Sir Joseph Hooker, Michael Foster, Charles Darwin, Sir Charles Lyell, Alexander Agassiz, Rev. Benjamin Jowett and Herbert Spencer. This general and scientific correspondence has been arranged in alphabetical order of writers with the letters of each writer in chronological order. There is also family correspondence, consisting of nearly all the letters exchanged between Huxley and his wife from their engagement in 1847 until his death in 1895. In addition to the Huxley correspondence, the collection contains considerable numbers of letters written to Mrs Huxley and to his son Dr Leonard Huxley.

Included in the collection are large numbers of notes, drawings and photographs used in the preparation of scientific papers and lectures on various subjects, including diaries and sketchbooks kept on the voyage of the *Rattlesnake*. There are also the manuscripts of a number of his books and contributions to journals, engagement diaries and some newspaper cuttings and other printed material.

Further description
M876–895 described in *The Huxley Papers* by Warren R. Dawson, London (1946).

M896 described in *Thomas Henry Huxley: List of His Correspondence with Miss Henrietta Anne Heathorn, later Mrs Huxley, 1847–54* (1969), compiled by Jeanne Pingree.

M897–916 described in *Thomas Henry Huxley: A List of his Scientific Notebooks, Drawings and Other Papers Preserved in the College Archives* (1969), compiled by Jeanne Pingree.

Entry 245   M406

Name **HYDROGRAPHIC DEPARTMENT**

Title Charts

Inclusive dates 1770–1821

Quantity 144 aperture cards

Location of original Hydrographic Department, Ministry of Defence, Taunton, Somerset TA1 2DN, England

Note
The Hydrographical Office of the Admiralty was created in 1795 to compile and publish charts and collect and distribute information on navigational matters. It first issued detailed instructions to an Australian surveyor in 1837 and was actively involved in Australian surveys, often in cooperation with colonial governments, until 1915.

Description
Manuscript charts and tracings of Australian and New Zealand coastlines by Royal Navy officers including R. Pickersgill and Capt. James Cook (HMS *Endeavour*), J. Hunter (HMS *Sirius*), M. Flinders (HMS *Investigator*), J. Murray (HMS *Lady Nelson*) and P.P. King (HMS *Mermaid* and *Bathurst*).

12-page list available for reference.

Entry 246   Reels M2318–2467

Name **HYDROGRAPHIC DEPARTMENT**

Title Records

Inclusive dates 1779–1946

Quantity 150 reels of microfilm

Location of original Hydrographic Department, Ministry of Defence, Taunton, Somerset TA1 2DN, England

Description
Records relating to surveys carried out by Royal Navy warships and surveying vessels in the Pacific and Indian Oceans, including surveys of the coasts and adjoining islands and reefs of Australia and New Zealand. The bulk of the records filmed date from 1828 to 1855, when Sir Francis Beaufort was Hydrographer, but many later letters, reports and sailing directions have also been copied. Among the records filmed are extracts from journals and logs, remark books, sailing directions, reports, letters and survey data books and also selected items from the minute-books 1825–56 and letter-books 1815–55 of the Hydrographic Department.

There are letters and reports 1800–1909 from a large number of naval officers, and officials and scientists. Among the more prominent are Sir Francis Beaufort, E.F. Bedwell, Sir Edward Belcher, F.P. Blackwood, H.M. Denham, B. Drury, G.W. Earl, A. Field, R. FitzRoy, M. Flinders, Sir John Franklin, J. Gowland, W. Hobson, Sir Everard Home, Sir William Hooker, F. Howard, J.H. Kay, P.P. King, A.I. Krusenstern, J. MacGillivray, G. Richards, J.S. Roe, Sir James C. Ross, F.W. Sidney, O. Stanley, J.L. Stokes, J. Tuckey, W. Whewell, J. Wickham, T. Woore and C. Yule.

170-page list available for reference.

Entry 247   Reels M1620–1627

Name **INDIA OFFICE LIBRARY**

Title Logs

Inclusive dates 1759–1827

Quantity 8 reels of microfilm

Location of original British Library, Oriental and India Office Collections, 197 Blackfriars Road, London SE1 8NG, England

Note
The India Office was set up in 1859 and was disbanded when India, Pakistan and Ceylon gained their independence in 1947. The Library holds the records of the East India Co (from its formation in 1600) and the India Office, as well as many private

collections relating to South and Southeast Asia. It amalgamated with the British Library in 1982.

Description
Logs of the following convict ships: *Coromandel, Royal Admiral, Warren Hastings, Ganges, Sovereign, Bellona, Prince of Wales, Young William, Resolution, Warwick, Ceres, Minerva, Hercules, Canada, Nile, Minorca, Friendship, Duff, Barwell, Atlas I, Atlas II, Marquis of Wellington, Henry Porcher, Guilford, England, Alexander, Providence, William Pitt, Ocean, General Graham, Mary, Rolla, Perseus* and *Indefatigable.*

One-page list available for reference.

Entry 248   Reel M1979

Name **INSTITUTE OF COMMONWEALTH STUDIES**

Title Collections

Inclusive dates 1926–34

Quantity 1 reel of microfilm

Location of original Institute of Commonwealth Studies, University of London, 28 Russell Square, London WC1B 5DS, England

Note
The Institute was founded in 1949 within the University of London to promote advanced study of the Commonwealth and Empire.

Description
1) Papers 1926–34 of Sir Stephen Tallents, Secretary of the Empire Marketing Board. Main correspondents are A.C.D. Rivett and F.L. McDougall.
2) Papers of Edward M. H. Lloyd comprising photographs, letter-diaries and notes relating to an official mission to Java and Malaya, led by W.G.A. Ormsby Gore, in 1928.

Five-page list available for reference.

Entry 249   Reels M1186–1189

Name **INSTITUTE OF GEOLOGICAL SCIENCES**

Title Records

Inclusive dates 1845–1972

Quantity 4 reels of microfilm

Location of original Institute of Geological Sciences Library, Exhibition Road, South Kensington, London SW7 2DE, England

Note
H.T. de la Beche was appointed the first officer of the Geological Ordnance Survey in 1835, and founded the Museum of Economic Geology in 1841. The Geological Survey was separated from the Ordnance Survey in 1845. In 1965 the Institute of Geological Sciences was established, incorporating the Geological Survey, Geological Museum, and Overseas Geological Surveys.

Description
1) Correspondence 1845–1910 of Geological Survey Office referring to: appointment of geologists in colonies; analysis of minerals found in colonies; supply of maps and publications; and mineral discoveries in Australia. Correspondents include Sir Henry de la Beche, Sir Roderick Murchison, J.B. Jukes, Sir William Denison, Sir Saul Samuel and Sir Redmond Barry.

2) Correspondence 1845–1902 of Geological Museum concerning supply of specimens and publications from colonies. Correspondents include P.E. Strzelecki and F.W. Rudler.

3) Papers 1910–24 of Sir John Flett concerning appointments and purchase of microscope for New South Wales Geological Survey.

4) Correspondence 1892–98 of Professor James Geikie referring to glacial deposits in Victoria and mineral discoveries in New Caledonia.

5) Letters 1932–33 of Sir Edgeworth David referring to the discovery of Cambrian fossils at Teatree Gully, South Australia.

6) Correspondence 1966–72 of F.G. Percival referring to visit to Western Australia and developments at Hamersley.

7) Papers 1906–36 of Sir Edmund Teale including field notebooks when a student at Melbourne University, and letters from Africa to his parents in Australia.

8) Extracts from minute-books 1920–33 of Mineral Resources Department of Imperial Institute.

9) Registered files 1876–1946 referring to appointments, requests for information from colonies, assistance to Colonial Geological Surveys and other matters.

32-page list available for reference.

Entry 250   Reel M1907

Name **INSTITUTE OF PHYSICS**

Title Records

Inclusive dates 1918–70

Quantity 1 reel of microfilm

Location of original Institute of Physics, 47 Belgrave Square, London SW1X 8QX, England

Note
The Institute of Physics was founded in 1918. The Australian Branch of the Institute was founded in 1928. In 1962 the Australian Institute of Physics was established as an autonomous body and in 1963 the Australian Branch was dissolved.

Description
1) Minute-books of Board of Institute of Physics 1918–60. Refer to recognition of Australian and New Zealand degrees, resolution of Australian Branch on atomic energy and secrecy, and grant to Australian Branch.

2) Minute-books of Council of Institute of Physics and Physical Society 1960–70 refer to activities of Australian Branch and formation of New Zealand Branch.

3) Correspondence 1960–63 concerning the proposed Australian Institute of Physics. Correspondents include H.R. Lang and A.F.A. Harper.

Five-page list available for reference.

Entry 251   Reel M2394

Name **ISLE OF WIGHT COUNTY RECORD OFFICE**

Title Collections

Inclusive dates 1838–1973

Quantity 1 reel of microfilm

Location of original Isle of Wight County Record Office, 26 Hillside, Newport, Isle of Wight PO30 2EB, England

Description
1) Letters 1879–80 of emigrant and farmer Leonard Blake written in New Zealand to a cousin in England.

2) Papers 1863–64 of Geary Family, emigrants to Melbourne and New Zealand.

3) Records 1901–23 of brewing and malting company Mew Langton & Co Ltd.

Two-page list available for reference.

Entry 252   Reel M2338

Name **JACOMB, Edward**

Title Papers

Inclusive dates 1899–1923

Quantity 1 reel of microfilm

Location of original London University Library, Senate House, Malet Street, London WC1E 7HU, England

Special Conditions Microfilm must be purchased from London University Library.

Note
Jacomb studied law in Oxford and French law in Paris. In 1906 he visited a family property in Australia, then travelled to New Hebrides. He returned to England in 1920.

Description
Autobiography and miscellaneous papers relate to Jacomb's early life in England and his years in Australia and the New Hebrides. The main correspondent is R.J. Fletcher of Makatea.

Five-page list available for reference.

Entry 253   Reels M2241–2253

Name **JEBB, Richard (1874–1953)**

Title Papers

Inclusive dates 1885–1953

Quantity 13 reels of microfilm

Location of original Institute of Commonwealth Studies, 28 Russell Square, London WC1B 5DS, England

Note
Author of *Studies in Colonial Nationalism* (1905) and other works on the British Empire. Jebb visited Australia and New Zealand in 1899–1900 and 1905–06.

Description
1) Correspondence 1885–1953. Correspondents include L. Curtis, R.R. Garran, Sir Samuel Way, A. Atlee Hunt, F. Fox, W. Nelson, B. Kerr-Pearse, Alfred Deakin, S.M. Bruce, R.G. Menzies, Fabian Ware and E.A. Edwards.
2) Journals 1899–1906 containing detailed accounts of Jebb's tours of Australia, New Zealand, Canada and South Africa.
3) Photograph albums of tour of Australia and New Zealand 1899–1900.

4) Scrapbooks 1904–49 containing reviews of Jebb's writings *Studies in Colonial Nationalism*, *Imperial Conference*, *Britannic Question*, *Empire in Eclipse* and *His Britannic Majesty*, and Jebb's articles for the *Morning Post*.
5) Manuscript of 'Studies in Colonial Nationalism', including unpublished third volume.

Five-page list available for reference.

Entry 254   Reel M723

Name **JEFFCOTT and KERMODE FAMILIES**

Title Letters

Inclusive dates 1831–1912

Quantity 1 reel of microfilm

Location of original Miss L.M.M. Wintour, Avon, England

Note
Sir John W. Jeffcott (1796–1837) was appointed judge for South Australia in May 1836. On his way to the new colony he stayed with his kinsman William Kermode (1780–1852) at Mona Vale in Van Diemen's Land and became engaged to Kermode's daughter Anne. Jeffcott spent only a few months in South Australia. His brother Sir William Jeffcott (1800–55) was a judge of the Supreme Court at Port Phillip 1843–45. William Kermode arrived in Van Diemen's Land in 1827 with his son Robert Q. Kermode (1812–70). In 1839 Robert married Martha, daughter of Thomas Archer, a Tasmanian landholder. One of their children was Robert C. Kermode (1847–1927).

Description
Letters of the Jeffcott and Kermode families written chiefly to John M. Jeffcott, Advocate, High Bailiff of Castletown, Isle of Man, by his cousins Sir John Jeffcott, Sir William Jeffcott, William Kermode and Robert Q. Kermode.
1) Three letters 1834–37 from Sir John Jeffcott, describing Kermode's property 'Mona Vale' and describing South Australia as full of dissension.
2) Four letters 1831–53 from Sir William Jeffcott, referring to his own career and that of Sir John Jeffcott.
3) Seven letters 1838–51 from William Kermode, referring to Sir John Jeffcott's papers, and news of friends and acquaintances, such as Sir William Denison.
4) Two letters 1834, 1837 from Anne Kermode regarding the impending trip to England by her son Robert.

5) Two letters 1835, 1853 from Robert Q. Kermode concerning his family, and his efforts in the State Parliament to end transportation. Includes two obituary notices of his death in 1870.

6) Two letters 1911–12 from Robert C. Kermode referring to the potato blight in Northern Tasmania and a visit to Adelaide.

7) Typescript notes (12 p.) on the Kermode Family.

Five-page list available for reference.

Entry 255   Reel M1185

Name **JERVOIS, Sir William F.D. (1821–1897)**
Title Papers
Inclusive dates 1877–78
Quantity 1 reel of microfilm
Location of original Mr John Jervois, London, England

Note
Governor of Straits Settlements 1875–77; carried out survey of Australian and New Zealand defences 1877; Governor of South Australia 1877–82; and Governor of New Zealand 1883–89.

Description
Papers concerning the political crisis in South Australia in October 1877 when the Colton Ministry was defeated in the Legislative Assembly by a no-confidence motion. They include a minute of Cabinet and Jervois' reply and notes by J.P. Boucaut on the formation of a new Ministry.

Three-page list available for reference.

Entry 256   Reels M1822–1824

Name **JERVOIS, Sir William F.D. (1821–1897)**
Title Papers
Inclusive dates 1874–97
Quantity 3 reels of microfilm
Location of original Mr J.W. Jervois, London, England

Note
Governor of Straits Settlements 1875–77; carried out survey of Australian and New Zealand defences 1877; Governor of South Australia 1877–82; and Governor of New Zealand 1883–89.

Description
Official and family correspondence, notebook, letter-books, newspaper cutting books and a journal.

Official correspondence 1875–93 relates to Jervois' activities as Governor of the Straits Settlements, South Australia and New Zealand, and his surveys of Australian and New Zealand defences. Subjects include: political and military affairs; Australian defences; annexation of New Guinea; Imperial Federation; irrigation; taxation; and Jervois' properties in South Australia. Correspondents include Lord Normanby, Sir George Bowen, Sir Hercules Robinson, Sir William Morgan, Sir Samuel Way, H.E. McCallum and Sir Peter Scratchley.

The journal was kept by John Jervois on his voyage from Adelaide to New Zealand and while travelling in New Zealand in 1881.

Three-page list available for reference.

Entry 257   Reel M1195

Name **JEVONS, W.S. (1835–1882)**
Title Photographs
Inclusive dates 1858
Quantity 1 reel of microfilm
Location of original John Rylands University Library, Deansgate, Manchester M3 3EH, England
Special conditions The Keeper of Manuscripts at John Rylands Library wishes to be notified if these photographs are used for major research or if there are requests to reproduce them.

Note
Economist, meteorologist and photographer. Assayer at Sydney Mint 1854–59; Professor of Political Economy, University College, London 1876–80.

Description
Two albums of photographs of Sydney Harbour, Double Bay, Darlinghurst, Lane Cove and other places in Sydney, and of friends and colleagues at the Sydney Mint.

A short list of the records is on the reel.

Entry 258   Reels M2632–2633

Name **JEVONS FAMILY**

Title Papers

Inclusive dates 1852–1925

Quantity 2 reels of microfilm

Location of original John Rylands Library, University of Manchester, Deansgate, Manchester M3 3EH, England

Note
William Stanley Jevons (1835–82) arrived in Sydney in 1854 to take up an appointment as assayer at the Sydney Mint. He returned to England in 1859 and achieved fame as an economist. His brother Herbert Jevons (1831–74) emigrated to Australia in 1862 and later lived in New Zealand.

Description
1) Letters 1854–68 of W.S. Jevons to his family in England describing his voyage to Australia and life in Sydney, including his work at the Mint.

2) Journal 1854–58 and diaries 1856–58 of W.S. Jevons, including a diary kept on a journey to the Sofala diggings in 1856.

3) Notebooks and cashbooks of W.S. Jevons, kept in Australia.

4) Letters 1862–68 of Herbert Jevons to W.S. Jevons describing life in Sydney, Forbes, Nelson and Dunedin, including employment by Bank of New South Wales, and gold diggings.

5) Photographs of Sydney and Braidwood.

Eight-page list available for reference.

Entry 259   Reels M2975–2979

Name **JOHN RYLANDS UNIVERSITY LIBRARY OF MANCHESTER**

Title Collections

Inclusive dates 1793–1978

Quantity 5 reels of microfilm

Location of original John Rylands University Library of Manchester, University of Manchester, Deansgate and Oxford Road, Manchester M3 3EH, England

Description
1) Journal 1793–94 of Lieut. James Colnett kept on whaling and exploring voyages in the Pacific on the *Rattler*.

2) Autograph collection of Thomas Raffles 1815–74, including King Kamehameha IV, Queen Emma, Queen Pomare, William Howe, Rev. Samuel Marsden and Rev. Richard Fletcher.

3) Autobiography of A.H. Gibson, a farmer of Ngaio, New Zealand, 1931.

4) Papers 1930–88 of the philosopher Samuel Alexander, mostly referring to his early life in Australia.

5) Correspondence 1940–45 of Sir Claude Auchinleck. Subjects include: difficulties in relieving Australians at Tobruk; situation in Middle East; change of government in Australia; New Zealand troops in Syria and Egypt; Australian troops in Cyprus; Australian and New Zealand troops in Palestine and Syria; and French and Dutch forces in post-war Indo-China and Indonesia. Correspondents include R.G. Casey, Winston Churchill, Sir John Dill, Sir Alan Brooke and Lieut. Gen. N.M. Ritchie.

6) Records 1943–56 of the *Manchester Guardian*. They include: correspondence on code of ethics of New South Wales District of Australian Journalists' Association; test matches (cricket); emigration to Australia and New Zealand; David Low's coronation cartoons; Australia's Pacific policy; and 1949 election in Australia. Correspondents include Rohan Rivett, Douglas Wilkie, Sir David Low, M.R. Lamshed and Allan Fleming.

7) Papers 1954–65 of Hugh Hunt, Executive Officer of Australian Elizabethan Theatre Trust. Includes a file on a Sydney production of *Peer Gynt*, correspondence and cuttings.

8) Papers 1942–67 of Major General Dorman O'Gowan, referring to Australian and New Zealand troops in North Africa and Middle East.

9) Papers 1912–40 of historian James Tait, including letters of F.L. Wood.

10) Papers 1889–1929 of historian Thomas F. Tout, including letters of A.A. Finch of Dunedin and Francis Johnstone of Perth.

48-page list available for reference.

Entry 260   Reels M2714–2721

Name **JOHNSON, CHRISTOPHER & COMPANY**

Title Records

Inclusive dates 1859–1950

Quantity 8 reels of microfilm

Location of original Sheffield Record Office, 52 Shoreham Street, Sheffield S1 4SP, England

Note
Founded in 1836. The firm traded extensively with Australia and New Zealand, supplying razors, scissors, tongs and blades.

Description
The records comprise letter-books, correspondence and notes. Subjects include: details of Australian orders and shipping procedures; price lists; shipping and insurance of cargoes for Australia and New Zealand; and the state of Australian and New Zealand business.

Recipients of the letters include Paul Rodgers, William Holmshaw, J.W. Bunby, E. Duckett, Thomas Bates, W. & A. Bennetts, Edward Keep and Co, Australian Mortgage Co Ltd, Bank of New South Wales and Union Bank of Australia.

Four-page list available for reference.

Entry 261   Reel M1180

Name **JONES, Richard**

Title Album

Inclusive dates 1840

Quantity 1 reel of microfilm

Location of original Mrs I. Richards, Surrey, England

Note
Richard Jones was the son of the Sydney merchant, landowner and politician Richard Jones (1786–1852).

Description
When Jones left Sydney to study at Cambridge in 1840 his friends presented him with an album of drawings, watercolours, engravings and poems. They depict members of the Jones Family, Sydney Heads, Hyde Park, St Philip's Church, the La Perouse Monument, and other places and people in Sydney.

In addition to the microfilm, colour transparencies have been made of the paintings.

Entry 262   Reels M1586–1614

Name **JUDICIAL COMMITTEE OF THE PRIVY COUNCIL**

Title Records

Inclusive dates 1857–1972

Quantity 29 reels of microfilm

Location of original Judicial Committee of the Privy Council, Downing Street, London SW1A 2AJ, England

Note
The *Judicial Committee Act 1833* transferred the entire appellate jurisdiction of the King in Council to the Judicial Committee, including appeals from judgements of colonial and territorial courts. It originally comprised Privy Councillors holding high judicial office, but since 1876 most of its work has been carried out by Lords of Appeal in ordinary.

Description
1) Special reference cases referring to the dispute between Victoria and New South Wales over Pental Island 1872 and the dispute between the Legislative Council and Legislative Assembly of Queensland over rights and powers of the two Houses 1886.

2) Appeal Cases 1857–1972 comprising papers in appeals against judgements of Australian, New Zealand and Fijian courts. All papers for cases in the period 1857–73 have been filmed, including background papers presented as evidence to the Committee (Records of Proceedings). After 1873 only the printed Cases for Appellants and Cases for Respondents have been filmed, together with judgements and orders of the Privy Council in cases which were not reported.

45-page list available for reference.

Entry 263   Reels M1678–1681

Name **KEITH, Arthur Berriedale, Professor (1879–1944)**

Title Papers

Inclusive dates 1901–40

Quantity 4 reels of microfilm

Location of original Special Collections Department, Edinburgh University Library, George Square, Edinburgh EH8 9LJ, Scotland

Special conditions Permission of the Edinburgh University Library is required to reproduce reels.

Note
Official in Colonial Office 1901–14; Professor of Sanskrit and Comparative Philology, Edinburgh University 1914–44; author of major works on British and imperial constitutional history and theory.

Description
1) Colonial Office correspondence 1910–14 including letters of Sir Charles Lucas, Sir Gerald Strickland, Sir Thomas Carmichael, Lord Chelmsford, Sir William MacGregor, Lord Liverpool, A. Deakin and Sir Joseph Ward.

2) Correspondence 1908–39 on constitutional issues such as: relations between Colonial Office and governors; Imperial federation; conscription referendum; possible abolition of

State governors; industrial disputes; proposed abolition of Legislative Councils; appointment of Sir Isaac Isaacs as Governor-General of Australia; dismissal of J.T. Lang as New South Wales Premier; and Western Australian secession movement.

3) Letters 1911–18 from Keith to A.V. Dicey on constitutional issues, such as: relations between Britain and dominions; appeals to Privy Council; role of monarch in Empire; and interpretation of the Australian Constitution.

4) Literary and general correspondence 1915–40 referring to Keith's publications, thesis by Walter Murdoch on A. Deakin, and general constitutional matters. Correspondents include J.G. Tucker, Sir James Allen, T.L. Buick, Lord Stanley and Arthur Robinson.

5) Typescripts 1911–37 by Keith on Australian and Imperial political and constitutional topics, including Statute of Westminster.

Seven-page list available for reference.

Entry 264   Reels M1901–1903

Name **KENT ARCHIVES OFFICE**
Title Collections
Inclusive dates 1768–1945
Quantity 3 reels of microfilm
Location of original Kent Archives Office, County Hall, Maidstone ME14 1XQ, England

Description
1) Records 1805–53 of Maidstone Gaol: Convict Book 1805–33 and Calendar of prisoners, with details of prisoners sentenced to transportation.

2) Notebook 1773–74 of Rev. J.E. Gambier describing meeting with Omai and customs of South Sea Islanders.

3) Papers 1827–52 of merchant and banker George W. Norman. They refer to: Australian Agricultural Co; abuses of New South Wales courts; Sir Thomas Brisbane; shortage of provisions in the Swan River Colony; Thomas Peel; Maori War; export of Australian wool and wine; Irish economic problems; and Irish emigration. Correspondents include Archdeacon T.H. Scott, James and Edward Macarthur.

4) Papers of Sir Henry E. Dering, concerning his service with Third Australian Division in 1916–17. Correspondents include Sir William Birdwood and General J. Monash.

5) Correspondence 1848–88 of Aretas Akers-Douglas, 1st Viscount of Chilston. Subjects

include governorships in Australia and New Zealand and development of Melbourne. Correspondents include Lord Knutsford and Charles S. Akers.

6) Papers 1795–1805 of Sir John Pratt, 2nd Earl of Camden, including letters of Lord Wellesley and W. Bligh.

7) Papers 1879–86 of Holsworthy Family, including letter-books of J.M. Holsworthy concerning his exporting business, diary of Fred Holsworthy kept on a voyage from London to Christchurch 1881, and failure of J.M. Holsworthy & Co and Robart Jolley of Melbourne.

8) Papers 1768–1872 of Knatchbull Family of Mersham, including copies of the journals of Sir Joseph Banks kept on voyage of HMS *Endeavour* August 1768–July 1771, and correspondence. Correspondents are N. Vansittart, Charles Dickens, Lord Kimberley and C. van Hulthem.

9) Letters 1856–83 sent to Henry Weigall of Kyneton, his wife Lady Rose Weigall and others from Henry Weigall, Selina Weigall and other members of the family in Melbourne and Kyneton, Victoria. Subjects include: Henry Weigall's work as an artist; 1878 political crisis in Victoria; 1881 Melbourne International Exhibition; bushrangers; cricket matches; and Australian churches.

10) Correspondence 1924–43 of the politician James H. Thomas, Secretary of State for the Colonies 1924 and 1935–36, and Secretary of State for the Dominions 1930–35. It refers to the effects of depression on New Zealand, isolation of federal politicians and Imperial rationalisation and trade. Correspondents include Sir Dudley de Chair, Lord Bledisloe, Sir Philip Cunliffe-Lister and Sir Alexander Hore-Ruthven.

14-page list available for reference.

Entry 265   Reel M435

Name **KERSHAW, George (b.1801)**
Title Notebook
Inclusive dates 1840–55
Quantity 1 reel of microfilm
Location of original Mitchell Library, State Library of New South Wales, Macquarie Street, Sydney NSW 2000

Note
Emigrant to New South Wales. Arrived in Sydney from Liverpool in December 1841 on the *Columbine*. He worked as a plasterer, including

work on the new Government House 1842–43. In October 1849 he was sworn in as a constable at Braidwood, New South Wales, where he was still residing when his wife Selina died in 1855.

Description
Memorandum book with short diary entries, lists of income expenditure and family biographical notes. The diary entries August–December 1841 describe weather conditions and daily routine on the voyage to Australia. There are lists of his earnings and places worked while a plasterer in Liverpool 1840–41 and Sydney 1841–50, and the earnings of William A. Kershaw 1841, 1845–46. At the end of the notebook are religious lecture notes, recipes and a list of distances travelled and places visited while constable at Braidwood, and an inventory of pistols, ammunition and other property given to him when sworn in as constable. Finally there are details of the birth and death of his parents, wife and children.

One-page list available for reference.

Entry 266   Reels M1966–1967

Name **KINTORE, Algernon Keith-Falconer, 9th Earl (1852–1930)**

Title Papers
Inclusive dates 1889–1914
Quantity 2 reels of microfilm
Location of original Rt Hon. The Earl of Kintore, Stonehaven, Scotland

Note
Governor of South Australia 1889–95.

Description
1) Albums of newspaper cuttings, photographs, letters, poems, menus, concert, theatre and sport programs kept by Lord and Lady Kintore in South Australia 1890–95. The cuttings are mostly from the *South Australian Register* and the *Advertiser*. Subjects include: Australian governorships; parliamentary proceedings; vice-regal social events; Freemasonry; review of the defence forces; travels in Australia; and departure of Kintore from South Australia.
2) Government House guestbook 1889–1914 containing autographs of guests at Government House, Adelaide.

One-page list available for reference

Entry 267   Reels M1517–1534, M2840–2841

Name **LAMBETH PALACE LIBRARY**

Title Collections
Inclusive dates 1845–1929
Quantity 20 reels of microfilm
Location of original Lambeth Palace Library, Lambeth Palace, Lambeth Palace Road, London SE1 7JU, England

Note
Founded by the Archbishop of Canterbury in 1610, Lambeth Palace Library is the repository of the records of the Archbishops of Canterbury, central institutions of the Anglican Church, and ecclesiastics and other individuals closely associated with the Church.

Description
Reels M1517–1534:
1) Papers 1845–68 of Archbishop Charles Longley including letters of Bishops F. Barker, C. Perry, C.H. Bromby and G.A. Selwyn mainly referring to the first Lambeth Conference in 1867.
2) Papers 1862–82 of Archbishop Archibald Tait, including letters of Bishops C. Perry, Mesac Thomas, W. Tyrrell, F. Barker, James Moorhouse, W.G. Cowie, Henry J.C. Harper, H.L. Jenner and T.N. Staley.
3) Papers 1846–80 of Baroness Angela Burdett-Coutts relating to her endowment of colonial bishoprics, including letters of Bishop A. Short of Adelaide.
4) Papers 1844–82 of Roundell Palmer, 1st Earl of Selborne, including correspondence with Sir Arthur Gordon on Fijian affairs.
5) Correspondence concerning 1867 and 1878 Lambeth Conferences.
6) Orders of ceremonial 1875–1929 for consecration of colonial bishops.
7) Records 1851–81 of Vicar General concerning appointments, ordination and resignations of colonial bishops.
8) Papers 1867–84 of Bishop John Jackson concerning church affairs in Australia, New Zealand, Fiji, Hawaii and Java.
9) Papers 1836–69 of Bishop Christopher Wordsworth including letters of Bishop G.A. Selwyn.
10) Copy of journal and letters 1824–25 of Major T. Kirkwood describing voyage on convict ship *Minerva*, and activities in Sydney.
11) Act Books 1786–1914 of Archbishops of Canterbury.

82-page list and 15-page list available for reference.

Reels M2840–2841:

1) Correspondence 1861–82 of Archbishop A.C. Tait concerning colonial bishoprics, emigration and pastoral care of emigrants. Correspondents include W.T. Bullock, William Gordon, H.L. Jenner, M.B. Hale and Lord Kimberley.

2) Correspondence 1890–92 of Archbishop Randall T. Davidson with Bishop H.H. Montgomery concerning church in Australia and Melanesian Mission.

3) Papers 1817–26 of Bishop William Howley including reports of Auxiliary Bible Society of New South Wales and letters of Rev. Richard Hill and Archdeacon T.H. Scott in Sydney.

4) Records 1861–92 of the Vicar General.

5) Papers 1883–91 of Lord Selborne relating to annexation of New Guinea and Fijian land claims. Correspondents include Sir Henry Parkes and Sir Arthur Gordon.

26-page list available for reference.

Entry 268   Reels M2800–2802

Name **LANCASHIRE RECORD OFFICE**

Title Collections

Inclusive dates 1805–1950

Quantity 3 reels of microfilm

Location of original Lancashire Record Office, Bow Lane, Preston, Lancashire PR1 2RE, England

Description

1) Calendars of prisoners and transportation documents 1782–83, 1805–47 held at Lancaster Castle and the Houses of Correction at Preston, Salford and Liverpool, giving details of names, ages, crimes, sentences and including a list of convicts under sentence of transportation.

2) Diary 1840 of F. Smythe kept on a voyage from Gravesend to Sydney referring to other passengers, entertainments on board, and sighting of other ships. The diary ends 200 miles out from Sydney.

3) Assize papers 1819–42 containing orders for commutation of death sentences to transportation.

4) Papers 1834–40 of Joseph Pedder describing a journey from Liverpool to Batavia. Subjects include life on board the unnamed ship, description of Funchal, life in Java and the journey home on the *Christina*.

5) Papers 1909–45 of R.J.A. Berry of the Faculty of Medicine, University of Melbourne. Subjects include: cricket in Australia; education congress in Melbourne 1912; reform of Melbourne University; Berry's proposal for a new medical school and his lectures on neolithic man; imperialism; Australian politics; the human brain; and mental defectives.

6) Papers 1894–48 of Thomas Floyd, including letters of Mrs Colin King in Penang and Bukit Mertajam.

7) Records 1948–50 of Platt Bros & Co, textile machineries of Oldham, referring to Australian orders.

8) Correspondence 1812–16 relating to the trial and transportation of Thomas Holden of Bolton.

9) Letters 1840–58 of stepbrothers Richard Taylor and Simon Brown, transported to New South Wales and Van Diemen's Land. Subjects include Taylor's employment in the General Hospital in Sydney, description of Sydney, and Brown's employment in the service of a grazier in Van Diemen's Land.

10) Letters 1840–46 of a convict Richard Boothman describing life on the hulk *Justicia* and in Van Diemen's Land.

17-page list available for reference.

Entry 269   Reel M852

Name **LARCOM, Sir Thomas (1801–1879)**

Title Papers

Inclusive dates 1858–65

Quantity 1 reel of microfilm

Location of original National Library of Ireland, Kildare Street, Dublin, Ireland

Note
Irish official. Commissioner for Public Works 1846; Deputy-Chairman of the Board of Works 1850; Under-Secretary for Ireland 1853–68.

Description
Correspondence and newspaper cuttings concerning murders, arson and other crimes committed by members of the Ribbon Society in County Donegal and the government's retaliatory eviction measures, especially in Derryveagh in 1861. Many of the evicted families emigrated to Australia.

One-page list available for reference.

Entry 270   Reel M1123

Name **LAW, Andrew Bonar (1858–1923)**

Title Papers

Inclusive dates 1905–23

Quantity 1 reel of microfilm

Location of original House of Lords Record Office, Houses of Parliament, Westminster, London SW1A 0PW, England

Note
Conservative politician. Leader of the Conservative Party 1911–21; Secretary of State for the Colonies 1915–16; Chancellor of the Exchequer 1916–19; Prime Minister 1922–23.

Description
1) Correspondence with politicians and others on matters including: tariff reform; Imperial defence; representation of the Dominions in London; Irish Home Rule; and the 1915 Dardanelles Campaign. Correspondents include A. Deakin, Sir George Reid, W.M. Hughes, H.H. Asquith, Lord Milner and Sir Walter Long.

2) Papers 1915–16 of J.C.C. Davidson, private secretary to Law, mostly comprising letters of Sir Ronald Munro-Ferguson dealing with: political situation in Australia; Dardanelles Campaign; federal–State relations; former German colonies in the Pacific; public finance; and the 1916 conscription referendum.

13-page list available for reference.

Entry 271   Reel M678

Name **LEE, John (1783–1866)**

Title Correspondence

Inclusive dates 1840–65

Quantity 1 reel of microfilm

Location of original Buckinghamshire Record Office, County Hall, Aylesbury, Buckinghamshire HP20 1UA, England

Note
Lawyer, antiquarian, philanthropist. Interested in all branches of science, Dr Lee belonged to many learned societies and was elected President of the Royal Astronomical Society in 1862. He had an observatory erected in 1830 on his estate at Hartwell, near Aylesbury, Buckinghamshire.

Description
1) Letters 1842–58 from Charles Lee Smith and his brother John Lee Smith to Dr John Lee. Two

replies from Lee 1847–48 are included. The letters concern domestic and financial matters, Charles' voyage to Australia, the dispatch of natural history specimens to Lee, and events and conditions in the colony of Victoria. In 1842 there is mention of Melbourne workers striking for improved wages, and of the practice of boiling down sheep for tallow. John Smith was partner in the Melbourne firm Mason and Smith.

2) Correspondence 1840–43 mainly from Charles Rumker concerning his failure to receive payment for the sale of land acquired in New South Wales in 1827. In several letters, including one from John S. Roberts of Sydney 1842, there is mention of the business activities of A.B. Sparke of Sydney. A letter to Lee from Phillip P. King 1849 concerns the cost of erecting an observatory and residence at Parramatta.

3) Miscellaneous correspondence, including a letter from George Witt, Sydney 1853 on personal matters; a letter from Bessie N. Parkes, London 1861 seeking subscriptions for a fund to assist young ladies emigrating to Australia, mentioning Bishop Frederick Barker; a letter from William Stratford Lee, Fremantle 1865 stating he is now a ticket-of-leave holder and intends leading a reformed life.

Entry 272   Reels M1898–1900

Name **LEEDS DISTRICT ARCHIVES**

Title Collections

Inclusive dates 1822–1934

Quantity 3 reels of microfilm

Location of original Leeds District Archives, West Yorkshire Archives Service, Chapeltown Road, Sheepscar, Leeds LS7 3AP, England

Description
1) Arthington Trust Archive 1906–34 relating to Australian and New Zealand Baptist Mission in India.

2) Papers 1858–94 of George and Louisa Briggs of Allora, Queensland.

3) Records 1915–30 of Greenwood and Batley Ltd concerning small arms factory and Australian and New Zealand factories of Colonial Ammunition Co. Correspondents include G. Hagger, Commander W. Clarkson, T. Muirhead Collins, S.T. Batley and R. Betts.

4) Correspondence 1823–25 of the politician George Canning, Prime Minister in 1827. Subjects include: Irish affairs; New South Wales Bill 1823; the possible annexation of New

Zealand; Maoris; and Dutch East Indies. Correspondents include H. Goulburn and T. Rowescroft.

5) Correspondence 1822–29 of Augustus G. Stapleton, private secretary to George Canning.

6) Papers 1856–61 of Charles Canning, 1st Earl Canning, Governor-General of India, on appointments of Superintendents in Penang and Singapore, the Indian Mutiny, and export of Indian camels to Australia. Correspondents include E. Blundell and Sir William Denison.

7) Correspondence 1850–74 of Sir Joseph and Lady Radcliffe concerning the Tichborne Case.

8) Letters 1853–67 of Robert and Jane Walker of Goulburn to their family in Leeds.

13-page list available for reference.

Entry 273   Reels M938, M974

Name **LEFROY, Sir John Henry (1817–1890)**
Title Papers
Inclusive dates 1877–1954
Quantity 2 reels of microfilm
Location of original Col. J.L. Knyvett, Berkshire, England

Note
Soldier and colonial governor. Inspector-General of Army Schools 1857–60; Governor of Bermuda 1871–77; Administrator of Tasmania 1880–81.

Description
M938:
Documents, speeches and cuttings relating to Lefroy's term in Tasmania and his knighthood (KCMG) in 1877; typescript entitled 'The Lefroy Family in England in 1877: a memoir by C.E.C. Lefroy compiled in the year 1936'; printed item *To Commemorate the Marriage of Henry Maxwell Lefroy and Annette Bate in December 1853 and their Arrival in Western Australia in April 1854*, by A.A. du H. Milne-Robertson (1954).

M974:
1) Four letters 1880 from a volume of autographs and letters relating to his appointment as Administrator of Tasmania. They are from the Duke of Cambridge, Lord Kimberley and John W. Burgon.

2) Extract from *Autobiography of General Sir John Henry Lefroy* edited by Lady Lefroy, printed for private circulation c.1895, covering his Tasmanian appointment and including copies of his letters 1880–82.

Two-page list available for reference.

Entry 274   Reel M2124

Name **LEICESTERSHIRE RECORD OFFICE**
Title Collections
Inclusive dates 1836–1963
Quantity 1 reel of microfilm
Location of original Leicestershire Record Office, Long Street, Wigton Magna, Leicester LE8 2AH, England

Description
1) Papers 1844–45 on the conviction and transportation of Samuel Chambers.

2) Papers 1870–96 of the Higginson Family of Tawonga, Victoria.

3) Letter 1852 of Samuel Coltman and his wife of Duffield, referring to emigration to New Zealand.

4) Records 1922–63 of Standard Engineering Co Ltd, boot and shoe manufacturer, concerning the company's branch in Melbourne.

5) Journal of Arthur Packe on surveying voyages of HMS *Rattlesnake* and *Bramble*, 26 November 1846–2 December 1849. It refers to: surveying operations in Bass Strait; the Great Barrier Reef and Torres Strait; attacks by Aborigines; Edward Kennedy; and relations with Capt. Owen Stanley, Lieut. Charles Yule and John MacGillivray.

6) Records 1903–50 of R. & W.H. Symington & Co, corset manufacturer, concerning its Australian and New Zealand operations.

7) Letters and letter-diary 1873–74 of David Webster of Brisbane. Subjects include his voyage to Queensland; Palmer River goldrush; and misrepresentation of Australia by Anthony Trollope.

Four-page list available for reference.

Entry 275   Reel M1650

Name **LEVER BROTHERS LTD**
Title Records
Inclusive dates 1925–37
Quantity 1 reel of microfilm
Location of original Unilever Ltd, Unilever House, Blackfriars, London EC4P 4BQ, England

Note
Lever Brothers Ltd amalgamated with the Dutch company Margarine Unie in 1929, forming two parent companies: Unilever Ltd (British) and Unilever NV (Dutch). The Australian and New Zealand companies remained subsidiaries of the British company.

Description
Australian and New Zealand weekly sales ledgers arranged by subsidiary companies. They include Lever Brothers (Sydney), W.H. Burford and Sons Ltd (Adelaide) and New Zealand Soap Co (Wellington).

Two-page list available for reference.

Entry 276   Reels M1642–1649

Name **LEVERHULME, William H. Lever, 1st Viscount (1851–1925)**

Title Papers

Inclusive dates 1899–1927

Quantity 8 reels of microfilm

Location of original Unilever Ltd, Unilever House, Blackfriars, London EC4P 4BQ, England

Note
William Lever founded the firm of Lever Brothers in 1885. Based at Port Sunlight, near Liverpool, it soon dominated the British soap market. Lever Brothers opened its Sydney office in 1888. Lever had extensive plantations in the Solomon Islands and was also director of the Pacific Phosphate Co.

Description
Papers relating to the activities of Leverhulme and Levers plantations, including the operations of the Pacific Islands Co and the Pacific Phosphate Co, the activities of J. Kitchen and Sons in Australia, and Lever Brothers (New Zealand). Subjects include: Javanese, Indian or Chinese labour for Solomon Islands; effects of industrial arbitration on manufacturing in Australia; industrial disputes in Australia; activities of the Australian company; Australian taxation; trade unionism in Australia; and Philippines Refining Corporation.

Major correspondents include W. Hulme Lever, R. Barrie, S. Gross, J. Meek, J.T. Arundel, Lord Stanmore, A.R. Dickinson, J.H. Kitchen, J. McDowell, C.M. Woodford, J.M.B. Stubbs, C.E. Tatlow, H.R. Greenhalgh, H.G. Hart, Sir Gilbert Fox and A. McNatty.

30-page list available for reference.

Entry 277   Reel M2344

Name **LEWIS, John (b. c.1825)**

Title Papers

Inclusive dates 1852–60

Quantity 1 reel of microfilm

Location of original Mrs Diana Deason, Gloucestershire, England

Note
Chief steward on SS *Great Britain* 1853–56 and purser on SS *Royal Charter* 1856–59.

Description
Letters of John Lewis to his family written on board SS *Great Britain* and SS *Royal Charter* on a voyage to Australia.

Two-page list available for reference.

Entry 278   Reel M2007

Name **LIEBIG'S EXTRACT OF MEAT COMPANY LTD**

Title Records

Inclusive dates 1898–1900

Quantity 1 reel of microfilm

Location of original Unilever Plc, Unilever House, Blackfriars, London EC4P 4BQ, England

Note
Liebig's Extract of Meat Co Ltd was founded in 1865, with its headquarters in Antwerp. It was a pioneer in the production of concentrated food, including the fluid extract Oxo.

Description
Typescripts, draft agreement and notes concerning the visits of F.H. Meyer, O. Dutting and C.M. Rotter to Australia. They deal with the Australian cattle industry and possible contract with meatworks, including the Broadsound Meat Co and the North Queensland Meat Export Co.

Three-page list available for reference.

Entry 279   Reels M842–843

Name **LINCOLNSHIRE ARCHIVES OFFICE**
Title Collections
Inclusive dates 1667–1929
Quantity 2 reels of microfilm
Location of original Lincolnshire Archives Office, St Rumbold Street, Lincoln LN2 5AB, England

Description
1) Documents 1854–55 relating to the petition of Rev. Michel H. Becker to be sent on a mission to Australia for the British and Foreign Bible Society.
2) Ancaster Papers: two letters 1707–10 relating to the executorship of Thomas Freeman dying in Batavia, from William Proby, Surat, to John Heathcote, London, acting as agent for the executor, and from Elizabeth Freeman to Capt. Thomas Hugben, the executor; papers sent to Governor Macrae of Madras 1726 concerning debt of Colin Campbell; translation of the King of Spain's grant for erecting a South Sea Co at Cadiz to trade with the Philippine Islands.
3) Elwes Papers: letters 1854–55 from Valentine D.H.C. Elwes to his mother, Elinor Elwes, written mainly from Western Australia, with photographs labelled: Sam Burgess 1854, W. Sholl 1854 and D. Ferguson, Colonial Surgeon, 1854; papers 1849–88 of his sister Eleanora, wife of Charles Fitzgerald, Governor of Western Australia; journal 1854–55 of V.C. Elwes describing a journey to Egypt and Australia.
4) Letters 1866–80 from Henry E. Michel and his family to W. D. Fane referring to New Zealand, Arthur Orton and the Tichborne trial, and family matters.
5) Flinders Papers: selections 1791–97 from the diaries of Matthew Flinders, father of Matthew Flinders the explorer, referring to his son's voyage and promotion; correspondence 1800–07 of Matthew Flinders to his family referring to family matters, his circumnavigation of New Holland and his imprisonment on the Ile de France.
6) Jarvis Papers: personal correspondence 1809–17, 1847 of Capt. G.R.P. Jarvis including letters from Lachlan Macquarie, his brother-in-law.
7) Monson Papers: account of customs payable on goods brought from the East Indies; maps 1806–12, being nautical surveys of the China Sea and the Straits of Malacca; certificate 1777 of Military Commission of James Stuart as Major General in the East Indies; printed list 1806 of the directors of the East India Co; letters 1804–05 to Edmund Larken, Canton,

from George Sparks, Robert Welbank, David Ross and E.S. Ellis on voyages in the East Indies.
8) Turnor Papers 1917–25 relating to emigration, land and soldier settlement.
9) Selections from various deposits, including: letters 1899–1929 to Richard and Gertrude Goulding from Rosa Ramsden of Queensland; George and John Marshall, Lena E. Playll commenting on teaching in Australian schools; and description of a voyage to New Zealand by William Newman 1899–1900; two assignments of mortgage 1902 and 1914 naming Dr William S. Cortes and Jane M. Parker of Manly and Alice Weddell Hobbs of Jondalee, New South Wales; a plan 1853 of the Louth Park Estate, Hunter River, New South Wales; financial documents 1667–81 of Capt. William Williams, merchant involved in trade with the East Indies.
10) Business papers 1877–94 of Matthew, Tom and John Moss of South Australia; correspondence 1847 to Charles D'Eynecourt from James M. Conilly of Portland Bay, New South Wales; letter 1867 from C.W. Powell, Secretary P & O Co, to F. Hill, on mail service contracts; Bill 1884 to extend the powers of the Bank of South Australia; paper 1854 regarding the death of John Thompson transported on the *Pestonjee Bomanjee*; declarations 1854 by John and Elizabeth Clay relating to the Tomlinson Family; power of attorney 1875 from John Twigg of Taranaki, New Zealand, and power of attorney 1875 from Charles Twigg of Warwick, Queensland; note from M.E. Dixon to Mary Anne Morris referring to Kaiapoi, New Zealand

28-page detailed list available for reference.

Entry 280   Reels M596–597

Name **LINNEAN SOCIETY OF LONDON**
Title Records
Inclusive dates 1790–1870
Quantity 2 reels of microfilm
Location of original Linnean Society of London, Burlington House, Piccadilly, London W1V OLQ, England

Note
The Society was founded in 1788. In 1822 it took over the records and collections of the Society for Promoting Natural History. Its main objective was to promote the study of the science of natural history and all its branches. In 1874 a Linnean Society of New South Wales was established under the presidency of Sir William Macleay (1820–91).

Description

1) Linnean Society archives: letters received from Sir Joseph Banks 1806, James E. Bicheno 1821, Joshua Brookes 1823, Robert Brown 1821, John Lewis 1836 concerning specimens collected by Alexander Collie, Dr John Lhotsky 1839 on a biographical sketch of Ferdinand Bauer, Sir John Eardley-Wilmot 1846 and Rev. William Woolls 1860.

2) Macleay correspondence and miscellaneous papers 1805–59. Most of the correspondence is with Sir George Macleay and his father Alexander Macleay and concerns the social conditions and people of New South Wales as well as botanical studies: letters from Rev. James Backhouse 1837 and 1843, Sir Joseph Banks 1805–18, Bishop Frederick Barker 1856, Edward Barnard 1824, Capt. Biden 1825, Jean Bory de St Vincent 1825, Vice-Admiral Sir Courtenay Boyle 1825, Robert Brown 1840, Rev. William Buckland 1843 forwarding a report by Professor Owen, Charles Campbell 1846, Rev. W.B. Clarke 1843–52, Allan Cunningham 1827, Charles Darwin 1839 introducing Syms Carrington, Sir William Denison 1855, William H. Fitton 1825 and 1842, G.W.S. Gethethjarte 1844, Sir George Gipps 1846 accepting Macleay's resignation as Speaker in the Legislative Council, Dr J.E. Gray 1841, 1844, Thomas C. Harrington 1842–59 including testimonials from Sir Ralph Darling, Rev. C.J. Hoare 1829 introducing Archdeacon W.G. Broughton, Sir James Everard Home 1825, Sir William Hooker and J.D. Hooker 1816–45, G. Howitt 1844, T.H. Huxley 1850, J. Innes 1825, David Jones 1857, Robert L. King 1857, P.P. King (n.d.), William Lithgow 1859, Robert Lowe, Duncan Macarthur 1825, John Macarthur (n.d.), Mrs Alexander Macleay (n.d. and 1837) discussing the estate and social events in Sydney, William Sharp Macleay to Shuckard 1839, 1845, F.J. McCrae 1846, J.A.I. Pancher 1853, Sir William Parry 1833, Sir James Clark Ross 1844, Phillip S. Sims 1841, Sir John Sinclair 1825, A. Smith 1843, J. de C. Sowerby 1847, Sir Alfred Stephen 1846, Admiral Sir James Stirling 1834–35, Samuel Wilson 1841, and miscellanea including accounts and plan of cabins of the ship *Duncan Dunbar*.

3) Correspondence of William Swainson: letters from Sir Joseph Banks 1816–19, Andrew Bloxam 1825–26, J. Bunting 1840 and D. Coates 1840 concerning missionary work in New Zealand, Allan Cunningham 1821–31, Richard Cunningham 1833, James Drummond 1837, T.J. Ewing 1837, John Gould 1830–37, Sir William Hooker 1816–39, T.J. Lempriere 1829–39, and a manuscript entitled 'On the Botany of Tahiti' (1870).

4) Miscellaneous manuscripts: William Archer drawings of Tasmanian orchideae 1848–56; James Backhouse 'An Enumeration of Plants Noticed on Visits to Moreton Bay and Lake Macquarie in 1836' (39 p.) and a draft list of Australian plants; Sir Joseph Banks 'Hints on the Subject of Gardening Suggested to the Gentlemen who Attend the Embassy to China' (1792); Ferdinand Bauer letters to his brother 1802–04 and drawing; two letters from General Thomas Hardwick to Sir Joseph Banks, Sir William Hooker 'Prince of Wales Island Flora'; George Suttor 'Notes on the Forest Trees of Australia' 1843; Alfred R. Wallace journals 1856–61, notebooks 1855–59, and list of Australian birds.

5) Society for Promoting Natural History records: minutes of meeting 14 December 1795 and transcription of a letter from Capt. W. Paterson 1794; part of a letter from Norfolk Island 1790.

Nine-page list available for reference.

Entry 281   Reel M1399

Name **LIVERPOOL, Charles Jenkinson, 1st Earl (1727–1808)**

Title Papers

Inclusive dates 1785–1803

Quantity 1 reel of microfilm

Location of original British Library, Great Russell Street, London WC1B 3DG, England

Note
Sir Charles Jenkinson, 1st Baron Hawkesbury (created 1786), 1st Earl of Liverpool (created 1796). Tory politician; President of the Board of Trade 1786–1804.

Description
Correspondence and other papers mainly concerning the establishment of the whale industry in the Pacific. Other papers deal with: claims of the East India Co in the Pacific; trade with the East Indies; the cultivation and import of hemp; and the establishment of the colony in New South Wales. Correspondents include W. Pitt, Capt. J. Blankett, Samuel Enderby, G. Chalmers and Capt. A. Phillip.

11-page list available for reference.

Entry 282   Reel M1400

Name **LIVERPOOL, Robert Jenkinson, 2nd Earl
(1770–1828)**

Title Papers

Inclusive dates 1804–26

Quantity 1 reel of microfilm

Location of original British Library, Great Russell
Street, London WC1B 3DG, England

Note
Robert Banks Jenkinson, styled Lord Hawkesbury
1796–1808, 2nd Earl of Liverpool. Tory politician;
Home Secretary 1804–06, 1807–09; Secretary of
State for the Colonies 1809–12; Prime Minister
1812–27.

Description
Selections from correspondence and official papers
referring to: missions in East Indies; southern
whale fishery; appointment of governors and other
officials; land grants in New South Wales and Van
Diemen's Land; and military forces in the colonies.
Correspondents include W. Wilberforce and
J. Foveaux.

Seven-page list available for reference.

Entry 283   Reels M869–870

Name **LIVERPOOL CITY LIBRARIES**

Title Collections

Inclusive dates 1773–1923

Quantity 2 reels of microfilm

Location of original Record Office and Local History
Department, Liverpool City Libraries, William Brown
Street, Liverpool L3 8EW, England

Description
1) Justices Sessions. Gaol and House of
   Correction: index to minutes of meetings and
   selected sections of minutes concerning
   transport of convicts to hulks and treatment
   of female convicts 1837.
2) C.T. Bowring & Co Ltd: papers 1879 concerning
   purchase of New Zealand bonds.
3) Minutes (selected) 1889–1923 of the Liverpool
   Chamber of Commerce, referring to trade with
   the colonies, mail to East Indies and Australia,
   and a visit to Australia and New Zealand by
   Col. Hawkins.
4) Cash books, ledgers, accounts, balance sheets
   and letter-books 1837–60 of Henry E. Symonds
   and his executors, concerning trade with
   Australian firms such as Younghusband and

Co of Adelaide, and Creeth Hicks and Creeth of
Melbourne.
5) Letters 1773–82 to Mathew Gregson, mainly
   from David Samwell, surgeon on HMS
   Resolution during Capt. James Cook's
   third voyage to the Pacific. They describe
   preparations for sailing; disappointment at the
   small number of zoological specimens brought
   home; the visit to Otaheite, Sandwich Islands;
   and the non-existence of the Northwest
   Passage.
6) Accounts and ledger 1850–69 of Henry T. Wilson;
   contract 1855 to John Pilkington and Wilson to
   convey mails to Australia; poster advertising
   White Star vessels for Melbourne. Wilson was
   part-owner of ships engaged on the Liverpool
   to Port Phillip run, including the *Red Jacket.*
7) Sir William B. Forwood journals: journal
   1857–58 of a voyage from Liverpool to
   Melbourne on the *Red Jacket*; journal 1858
   of a voyage from Sydney to Valparaiso in the
   barque *Queen of the Avon*; copy of the first part
   of the journal of the *Red Jacket* voyage with
   meteorological observations and navigation
   details for the two voyages.
8) Letters 1814–25 to William Roscoe from Thomas
   Rushton of Sydney and Sir James Smith of
   Norwich, the latter referring to the departure
   of Alexander Macleay to take up the position
   of Colonial Secretary of New South Wales.

Seven-page list available for reference.

Entry 284   Reel M2060

Name **LIVERPOOL RECORD OFFICE**

Title Collections

Inclusive dates 1850–1924

Quantity 1 reel of microfilm

Location of original Liverpool Record Office,
Liverpool City Libraries, William Brown Street,
Liverpool L3 8EW, England

Description
1) Voyage book 1864–66 of Sea Insurance Co Ltd.
2) Log 1882–83 of E. Turner kept on *John
   Gambles* on voyage from London to Wellington,
   Newcastle, San Francisco and London.
3) Correspondence 1838–41 of George Holt on
   purchase of sheep and cotton cultivation in
   Australia.
4) Papers 1862–99 of Rev. Alfred J. Tomlin
   concerning church affairs in Australia and
   the Pacific. Correspondents include Bishop
   T.N. Staley.

5) Minute-books 1883–1924 of Liverpool Chamber of Commerce referring to: Australian mail arrangements; Australian customs tariffs; New Zealand customs regulations; *Commerce Act*; *Navigation Act*; and New Zealand Patents Bill.

6) Diary 1892–93 of Sir Richard D. Holt describing travels in Malaya and East Indies.

Ten-page list available for reference.

Entry 285   Reel M1585

Name **LIVERPOOL UNIVERSITY LIBRARY**

Title Collections

Inclusive dates 1875–1931

Quantity 1 reel of microfilm

Location of original Sydney Jones Library, Liverpool University, PO Box 123, Liverpool L9 3DA, England

Description
1) Transcripts of records 1873–91 of the shipowners and merchants J. Swire and Son relating to trade with Australia, Straits Settlements and Philippines, including correspondence between John Swire and P. Holt, and a history of the Straits Steamship Co 1890–1965 by K.G. Tregonning.

2) Papers 1927–31 of Prof. M. Roxby on the 4th Conference of the Institute of Pacific Relations at Shanghai in 1931, including reports of research of F.M. Keesing on native peoples of the Pacific, notes on Maoris by H.F. von Haast, and report of the 1927 Wanganui Maori Conference.

Four-page list available for reference.

Entry 286   Reels M1124–1125

Name **LLOYD GEORGE, David, 1st Earl (1863–1945)**

Title Papers

Inclusive dates 1903–44

Quantity 2 reels of microfilm

Location of original House of Lords Record Office, Houses of Parliament, Westminster, London SW1A 0PW, England

Note
Liberal politician. Chancellor of the Exchequer 1908–15; Minister of Munitions 1915–16; Secretary of State for War 1916; Prime Minister 1916–22.

Description
The bulk of the papers filmed comprise correspondence dating from Lloyd George's years as Prime Minister. They deal with: communications between the British and Dominion governments; the status of the Dominions; World War I; Imperial shipping; future control of German colonies in the Pacific; the 1916 conscription referendum in Australia; Japanese territorial claims; the 1919 Peace Conference; the 1921 Washington Disarmament Conference; the 1921 Imperial Conference; reparations; mandates; Nauru; the League of Nations; Anglo–Irish relations; and visit of Prince of Wales to Australia and New Zealand.

Correspondents include L.S. Amery, Sir Robert Borden, W.S. Churchill, Sir Maurice Hankey, W.M. Hughes, Walter Long, W.F. Massey, Lord Milner, Keith Murdoch.

30-page list available for reference.

Entry 287   Reel M1132

Name **LOCH, Sir Henry (1827–1900)**

Title Papers

Inclusive dates 1848–1900

Quantity 1 reel of microfilm

Location of original Lieut. Col. Charles Earle, Somerset, England

Note
Sir Henry Loch, 1st Baron Loch (created 1895). Governor of Victoria 1884–89; Governor of Cape Colony 1889–95.

Description
1) Typescript copy of part of Loch's autobiography written in the 1890s and covering the years 1848–53. It describes his first visit to Australia and New Zealand in 1852–53.

2) Diary 1884–86 kept by Emma Southgate, a maid of Lady Loch, describing the voyage to Australia on the *Coptic*; life at Government House, Melbourne; and visits to Sydney, Adelaide, Hobart and Victorian towns.

Description of contents filmed on the reel.

Entry 288   Reel M1337–1338

Name **LONDON CHAMBER OF COMMERCE**

Title Records

Inclusive dates 1885–1958

Quantity 2 reels of microfilm

Location of original Guildhall Library, Aldermanbury, London EC2P 2EJ, England

Note
The Australasian Trade Section of the London Chamber of Commerce was formed in 1885. A separate Western Australian Trade Section operated in 1896–1905.

Description
1) Minute-books 1885–1957 of the Australian and New Zealand Trade Section, including reports and copies of correspondence. They refer to many aspects of Anglo–Australasian trade, state-assisted emigration, postal rates, import duties, Australian Federation, and railways.
2) Minute-book 1896–1904 of Western Australian Trade Section.
3) Minute-book 1914–16 of Sydney Consignment Committee dealing with storage and distribution of frozen meat and other foodstuffs consigned by Sydney Chamber of Commerce.
4) Minute-book 1924–26 of London branch of New Zealand Warehousemen's Association.

Three-page list available for reference.

Entry 289   Reel M1336

Name **LONDON GUILDHALL LIBRARY**

Title Collections

Inclusive dates 1834–1925

Quantity 1 reel of microfilm

Location of original Guildhall Library, Aldermanbury, London EC2P 2EJ, England

Description
1) Diary 1841–42 of William Fanning, agent of Dent & Co, kept at Macao and on voyage to Manila and Hobart on *Lord Amherst* and to Sydney on *John Byng*.
2) Risk books 1834, 1854 of Marine Department of London Assurance Co referring to voyages to Australia, New Zealand, East Indies and Singapore.
3) Australian share certificates 1893–1902 of William C. Phillips of London.

4) Letter of instructions 18 January 1878 to G.W. Binney, agent of Sun Fire Office in Province of Auckland.

Three-page list available for reference.

Entry 290   Reels M1–116, M608–670

Name **LONDON MISSIONARY SOCIETY**

Title Records

Inclusive dates 1795–1825

Quantity 181 reels of microfilm

Location of original School of Oriental and African Studies, Thornhaugh Street, Russell Square, London WC1H 0XG, England

Special conditions Further copying not permitted. Now available commercially on microfiche from Inter Documentation AG, Poststrasse 14,6300 Zug, Switzerland.

Note
The Missionary Society was founded in 1795 by a group of Anglican and non-conformist clergy in London. It later became known as the London Missionary Society and was supported largely by the Congregational Church, especially after the formation of similar societies, such as the Methodist Missionary Society, diverted funds and manpower away from the LMS. The Society pioneered mission work in many parts of the world, including Australia, the East Indies, the Pacific Islands and Papua.

Description
As well as papers concerned with the religious activities of the missionaries, much of the material in this collection includes writings, and incidental observations, on exploration, anthropology, linguistics, trade and economics, education, publishing, agriculture and social conditions. Political events closely affected the mission stations and are documented in the Society's records, including the proclamation of a British Protectorate in eastern New Guinea in 1884.

Home Office records:
M613–629: Board minutes 1795–1918; M630–632: Committee minutes 1835–1918; M634–637: Home Office letters 1795–1876 and miscellaneous papers; M69–70, M636–637: papers, references, examination questions and answers of candidates seeking appointment 1796–1880; M71: missionary lectures 1817, 1842–52; M670: register of missionaries 1796–1923, with annotations to 1965.

Overseas missions:

a) Australia, M11: journals 1800–42 kept by W. Shelley, R. Hassall, L.E. Threlkeld and R.C. Morgan; M11, M72–90, M638–640: letters 1798–1919 including reports on voyages of the mission ship *John Williams*.

b) South Seas (Pacific Islands), M1–10: journals 1796–1899 kept by missionaries, seamen and native teachers; M15–17, M644–645: reports 1798–1919; M18–68, M102–116, M632–634, M640–644: letters 1796–1919, most written from Australia and many by Rev. Samuel Marsden, dealing with the New Zealand and South Seas missions; M645–660: miscellaneous and personal documents, pictorial material and diaries.

c) Papua, M11: journals 1872–1901; M12, M611: reports 1882–1919; M91–101, M608–611: letters 1872–1919; M612–613, M659–660: miscellaneous papers and pictorial material, including portraits of South Seas missionaries.

d) Ultra Ganges. M667–669: outgoing letters 1822–54, and journals; M660–662: Malacca 1815–59; M662–664: Penang 1805–69; M664–665: Java (Batavia) 1814–43; M665: Rangoon 1809–10 and Amboyna 1814–43; M666–667: Singapore 1819–84.

e) Personal papers and manuscripts. M13: manuscript entitled 'History of the Tahitian Mission' by John Davies, with annotations by Henry Nott (c.1830); M14: manuscript entitled 'A Brief History of the South Sea Mission' by Joseph Mullens (1878); M71: biographical notes on Mrs Alex Chisholm 1842–52; M640: letters of Rev. George J. Williams 1916–19; M652–656: letters, diaries and papers of Rev. James E. Newell 1879–1908; M657–659: papers, many of them typescript, notes and diaries of Rev. John H. Holmes 1893–1915; M659: papers of Rev. Edwin Pryce-Jones 1899–1919, autobiography of Thomas Blossom, c.1847, and recollections of Samuel J. Whitmee; M660: journal 1866–67 of Lillie Saville, manuscript by Robert Thomson 'History of Tahiti' (1857); M668–669: journals kept by missionaries at the Ultra Ganges stations, including Thomas Beighton and John Ince at Penang 1822–23, W.H. Medhurst at Batavia 1825–26, and others.

26-page list available for reference.

Entry 291   Reel M2289

Name **LONDON UNIVERSITY LIBRARY**

Title Collections

Inclusive dates 1815–1972

Quantity 1 reel of microfilm

Location of original London University Library, Senate House, Malet Street, London WC1E 7HU, England

Special Conditions Microfilm must be purchased from London University Library.

Description

1) Autograph letter series, comprising letters of Sir Joseph Banks, William Cobbett and William Wilberforce.

2) Scrapbook of social reformer Robert Owen containing an account by William Pare of a visit to female convicts at Newgate Prison in 1834.

3) Papers 1900–37 of philanthropists Charles and Mary Booth describing tour of Australia and New Zealand in 1906 and colonial tour of Holman Hunt's painting *The Light of the World*.

4) Papers 1946–72 of physicist Samuel Toltansky relating to his research and writings. Correspondents include E. Hills, N. Fisher and C.F. Bruce.

5) Business records 1899–1952 of John Pollitt and Yorkshire Motor Car Manufacturing Co Ltd relating to Australian motor car industry.

6) Papers 1895–1900 concerning various candidates for examinations in Australia.

7) Papers 1891–96 of Frederick R. Simms referring to establishment of Simms Motor Units Ltd branches in Melbourne, Sydney and Wellington.

8) Correspondence 1909–27 between Thomas S. Moore and Alfred H. Fisher concerning Fisher's visit to Australia and plans for Moore's son Daniel to leave for Australia at the end of May 1927.

14-page list available for reference.

Entry 292   Reel M1114–1119

Name **LONG, Walter, 1st Viscount (1854–1924)**
Title Papers
Inclusive dates 1913–23
Quantity 6 reels of microfilm
Location of original Wiltshire County Record Office, County Hall, Trowbridge, Wiltshire BA14 8JG, England

Note
Walter Long, 1st Viscount Long (created 1921). Conservative politician. Secretary of State for the Colonies 1916–19; First Lord of the Admiralty 1919–21.

Description
Correspondence concerning: Imperial relations; recruiting in Australia and New Zealand; campaigns in France; 1918 Imperial War Conference; control of former German colonies in Pacific; split in Australian Labor Party over conscription; communications between Britain and Dominions; appointment of governors; honours; Imperial trade; federal–State relations in Australia; W.M. Hughes; Keith Murdoch; Archbishop D. Mannix; and administration of Straits Settlements.

Correspondents include Sir William Birdwood, Sir Charles Crewe, D. Lloyd George, W.F. Massey, Sir George Reid, Sir Walter Davidson, Lord Liverpool, Sir Henry Galway, Sir William Ellison Macartney, Sir Ronald Munro-Ferguson, Sir Francis Newdegate, Sir Arthur Stanley, Sir Bickham Sweet-Escott, A.J. Balfour and Sir Maurice Hankey.

Ten-page list available for reference.

Entry 293   Reel M1859

Name **LORD, Richard (b.1861)**
Title Journal
Inclusive dates 1882–84
Quantity 1 reel of microfilm
Location of original Mrs Ena Lines, Gloucester, England

Note
Lord, who was born in 1861, came to Australia on board the SS *Austral* in 1882.

Description
Journal describing the voyage to Australia, life on board the SS *Austral*, and Lord's life in Melbourne, Sydney and Newcastle.

One-page list available for reference.

Entry 294   Reel M401

Name **LOVELL, John**
Title Journal
Inclusive dates 1853
Quantity 1 reel of microfilm
Location of original National Maritime Museum, Greenwich, London SE10 9NF, England

Note
Member of the crew of the emigrant ship *Elizabeth* which sailed from Bristol to Melbourne in 1853.

Description
Journal 23 January–3 May 1853 noting weather conditions, land sightings and daily routine of the crew. Lovell also mentioned complaints of the passengers regarding their allowances, conduct of the ship's doctor and the food.

Entry 295   Reels 3055–3058

Name **LUBBOCK, Basil (1876–1944)**
Title Papers
Inclusive dates 1870–1936
Quantity 4 reels of microfilm
Location of original National Maritime Museum, Romney Road, Greenwich, London SE10 9NF, England

Note
Seaman and author of several histories of sailing ships, including *The China Clippers* (1914), *The Colonial Clippers* (1921) and *The Last of the Windjammers* (1927–28).

Description
1) Diary 14 September–27 December 1882 kept by passenger on the *Superb* between Melbourne and London.
2) Captain's logs including logs of *Patriarch* kept by Capt. Henry Plater on voyages from London to Sydney 1877 and 1883, *Thermopylae* by Capt. John Henderson on voyages from between London and Sydney 1881–83, and *Cutty Sark* by Capt. Moodie on voyages between London and Shanghai 1870–72.
3) Correspondence, notes and photographs 1876–1903 concerning the passenger ship *Torrens*.
4) Papers c.1927–29 relating to Bully Hayes, trading in the Pacific, and blackbirding.
5) Papers c.1882–1922 concerning voyages of the *Cutty Sark* between London and Sydney.

6) Correspondence 1928–34 of Basil Lubbock. Correspondents include Capt. R. Hamilton and Henry E. Earp.

7) Log and journal 1881–84 kept on HMS *Beagle* and HMS *Nelson*.

8) Notes and logs of South Seas whaling vessels.

13-page list available for reference.

Entry 296   Reels M1177–1178

Name **LYTTON, Sir Edward Bulwer-Lytton, 1st Baron (1803–1873)**

Title Papers

Inclusive dates 1836–76

Quantity 2 reels of microfilm

Location of original Hertfordshire Record Office, County Hall, Hertford SG13 8DE, England

Note
Sir Edward Bulwer-Lytton, 1st Baron Lytton (created 1866). Novelist, poet, playwright and Conservative politician. Secretary of State for the Colonies 1858–59.

Description
1) Official papers 1858–59, including letters from Sir Henry Barkly, Sir George Bowen, Sir William Denison, Lord Derby, William Howitt and Charles Sturt. They deal with: political and economic position in the colonies; appointments; emigration; exploration; the separation of Moreton Bay from New South Wales; the appointment of Bowen as first Governor of Queensland; the controversy surrounding the visit to Britain of the Mayor of Melbourne; the proposed annexation of Fiji; and activities of Sir James Brooke in Sarawak.

2) Personal correspondence 1836–76 includes papers about Lytton's work on the life of the convict Thomas Wainewright; letters from the poet R. H. Horne; correspondence concerning copyright and the performance of Lytton's plays in Australia in 1866–70; and letters from Sir George Bowen in Brisbane and Melbourne.

20-page list available for reference.

Entry 297   Reel M592

Name **MACARTHUR, Sir Edward (1789–1872)**

Title Correspondence

Inclusive dates 1854–57

Quantity 1 reel of microfilm

Location of original Unknown

Note
Soldier, and Administrator of Victoria. Eldest son of John Macarthur, he was educated in England and joined the army in 1808. In 1851 he was posted to Sydney as Deputy Adjutant-General. On his promotion to colonel in 1854, he moved to Melbourne and after the death of Governor Hotham in December 1855 was Administrator of Victoria for almost 12 months. In 1858 he chaired a Royal Commission on the defence of the colony. In 1860 he returned to England.

Description
Correspondence and dispatches from, or relating to, Sir Edward Macarthur:

1) Two letters 3 August 1854 and 3 November 1854 to Macarthur from London.

2) Letter 18 August 1857 from Sir Henry Barkly to Henry Labouchere forwarding a copy of a dispatch from the War Office, and with enclosures dated 1, 13, 26 May 1857 regarding reductions in provisions and pay of the military forces in Victoria.

3) Dispatches and private letters 1856 from Macarthur, as Administrator of Victoria, to Labouchere referring to: the death of Sir Charles Hotham; pardoning of convicts; proposed renewal of transportation; dissolution of the Legislative Council; the election of the first Victorian Parliament; and the arrival of Sir Henry Barkly.

4) Addresses and replies by Macarthur on his retirement as Administrator January 1857, and correspondence 20 August and 22 October 1857 regarding a proposed honour for himself.

5) Letters April–September 1857 by Macarthur and Barkly regarding medals struck in Victoria for the Queen.

Entry 298   Reel M1184

Name **McCALLUM, Henry E. (1852–1919)**
Title Diary
Inclusive dates 1875
Quantity 1 reel of microfilm
Location of original Brigadier J. Jervois, Sussex, England

Note
Private Secretary to the Governor of the Straits Settlements 1875–77; official in Straits Settlements 1881–97; Governor of Lagos, Natal and other colonies.

Description
Diary 1875 describing tours of Penang, Perak, Pahang and other Malay States by the Governor and other officials and their negotiations (sometimes recorded verbatim) with the Malay rulers. They refer in particular to the murder of J.W. Birch, the British Resident in Perak.

Entry 299   Reel M1976

Name **McCRAKEN FAMILY**
Title Papers
Inclusive dates 1841–1918
Quantity 1 reel of microfilm
Location of original Dr John McCraken, Perthshire, Scotland

Note
Robert McCraken (1815–85) and Peter McCraken (1818–92) emigrated to Melbourne in 1841. Their brother Alexander McCraken and his wife Jane McCraken emigrated to Australia in 1849 but after several years returned to Scotland.

Description
Letters and journals of Alexander McCraken and letters of his wife Jane McCraken. They describe their voyage to Australia on the *William Hyde*; Adelaide and the Adelaide Hills; establishment of a dairy in Melbourne; economic conditions; news from goldfields; Scottish emigrants; social events and family news.

Three-page list available for reference.

Entry 300   Reel M1951

Name **MACINTYRE, James J.**
Title Papers
Inclusive dates 1840–67
Quantity 1 reel of microfilm
Location of original British Library, Great Russell Street, London WC1B 3DG, England

Note
Businessman. In 1835 Macintyre entered into a partnership with Arthur Willis to form a commission and agency business in Sydney. He migrated to Australia in 1835–36. He returned to England in 1840 and published *Thoughts on Population and Starvation* (1841). Macintyre made a brief visit to Australia in 1853.

Description
Autobiographical account of life in Mexico, Scotland, England and New South Wales, and manuscripts of 'The Physical and Historical Geography of Australia' and 'Walks on Deck and Rambles on Shore during a Voyage of Circumnavigation of the Globe'.

Three-page list available for reference.

Entry 301   Reel M460

Name **MACQUARIE FAMILY**
Title Papers
Inclusive dates 1782–1839
Quantity 1 reel of microfilm
Location of original Scottish Record Office, HM General Register House, Princes Street, Edinburgh EH1 3YY, Scotland

Note
Lachlan Macquarie (1762–1824), Governor of New South Wales 1810–22. Upon the early death of his father, his uncle Murdoch Maclaine of Lochbuie became his guardian. In 1807 he married Elizabeth Campbell and a son Lachlan was born in 1814. Murdoch Maclaine also reared Macquarie's younger brother Charles, who died in March 1835.

Description
1) Volume entitled 'Paybook of the Grenadier Company 71st Regiment' containing accounts of payments to soldiers by Macquarie 1782–83, his accounts with sundry people 1784–86, and the roll of the Company and casualties 1782–83.
2) Letters and documents relating to Lachlan Macquarie including letters 1784–1804 from

Lachlan to his uncle Murdoch Maclaine on personal, family and military matters, written mainly from Bombay, Alexandria and London; letters to his brother Charles and to his sister-in-law concerning the death of her son in Ceylon in 1818.

3) Letter 1794 from Jane, first wife of Lachlan Macquarie, to his mother and two letters from Lachlan Macquarie's mother to her brother.

4) Letters 1793–1802 from Charles Macquarie to his uncle Murdoch Maclaine and to his cousin Murdoch Maclaine 1813–34 on personal, family, military and estate matters; miscellaneous letters and copies of letters 1793–1835 to and from Charles Macquarie including two from his son 1835; and documents relating to Charles Macquarie's estate.

5) Selections 1794–1804 relating to the Macquarie Family from the letter-books of Murdoch Maclaine containing very brief notes of letters sent to various correspondents.

6) Correspondence 1835–39 between Lachlan Macquarie, son of Governor Macquarie, and his cousin Murdoch Maclaine including references to interests in New South Wales.

Two-page list available for reference.

Entry 302   Reels M2415–2421

Name **MAKERETI (1872–1930)**

Title Collections

Inclusive dates 1887–1938

Quantity 7 reels of microfilm

Location of original Balfour Library, Pitt Rivers Museum, South Parks Road, Oxford OX1 3PP, England

Note
Makereti, known as Maggie Papakura, was born in Wakarewarewa and achieved fame as the guide to the Rotorua hot springs. Her last years were spent in Oxford and in 1926, assisted by T.K. Penniman, she began to compile a book on Maori life. Edited by Penniman, *The Old-time Maori* was published posthumously in 1938.

Description
1) Drafts, typescripts and research material for *The Old-time Maori*. They include files on social organisation, marriage, children, food, houses, war and weapons, weaving and tattooing, mythology, history, symbolism and the origins of the Maori race.

2) Three volumes of Maori writings c.1893–94.

3) Letters, cuttings, ephemera and photographs 1900–11.

4) Album of cuttings and photographs relating to 1911 Festival of Empire, and later career of 'Princess Iwa'.

Three-page list available for reference.

Entry 303   Reels M2081–2082

Name **MANCHESTER CENTRAL LIBRARY**

Title Collections

Inclusive dates 1850–1959

Quantity 2 reels of microfilm

Location of original Manchester Central Library, St Peter's Square, Manchester M2 5PD, England

Description
1) Manchester Guardians of Poor: register 1914–47 of children who emigrated to Australia and Canada.

2) Manchester Chamber of Commerce: Home and Dominion Committee minute-book 1910–26 referring to Australian and New Zealand tariffs and taxation and Australian legislation.

3) Correspondence 1951–59 between Lord Simon and Sir Richard Boyer, referring to the Beveridge Committee on the BBC, the Paton Royal Commission on Television 1953, party politics and the debate about television, and the wool industry.

4) Papers 1884–1910 of Dame Millicent Fawcett relating to women's suffrage in New Zealand and Australia.

5) Legal documents 1850–55 of William A. Gardner concerning his property in Van Diemen's Land.

6) Papers 1882–1908 of the Chorlton Family. Subjects include appointment of Congregational missionaries and cuttings and photographs of Samoa and New Guinea.

7) Letters 1853–62 of James Hilton and his brothers Michael and John in Australia to family in England, concerning voyage to Australia, Maryborough goldfields, and bushfires.

Eight-page list available for reference.

Entry 304   Reel M2080

Name **MANCHESTER REGIMENT (63rd &
            96th Regiments)**

Title Records

Inclusive dates 1828–1953

Quantity 1 reel of microfilm

Location of original Tameside Local Studies Library,
Stalybridge Library, Trinity Street, Stalybridge,
Cheshire SK15 2BN, England

Note

The Manchester Regiment was formed in 1881
from the 63rd and 96th Regiments, together with
two battalions of the 6th Royal Lancashire Militia.
The 63rd Regiment was based in Australia, mainly
in Van Diemen's Land, in 1829–33. The 96th
Regiment was based in Australia in 1841–48 and
served in the Maori War of 1845–46.

Description

Records of service of 63rd (May 1828–May 1834)
and 96th (June 1839–June 1849) Regiments,
correspondence, and lists of officers and other
men awarded New Zealand medals.

Three-page list available for reference.

Entry 305   Reel M1130

Name **MANISTY, Sir Eldon (1876–1960)**

Title Cutting book

Inclusive dates 1910–14

Quantity 1 reel of microfilm

Location of original Capt. P. Manisty, London
(original subsequently presented to the Royal
Australian Navy)

Note

Secretary of the Henderson Mission on Australian
naval defence 1910–11. Seconded to the Royal
Australian Navy in 1911–14 and was the Finance
and Civil Member and Naval Secretary of the
Australian Naval Board.

Description

The album contains invitations, menus, programs
and a few letters, as well as newspaper cuttings
on both the Henderson Mission and the Royal
Australian Navy.

Entry 306   Reel M720

Name **MANN FAMILY**

Titlle Papers

Inclusive dates 1836–1950

Quantity 1 reel of microfilm

Location of original Bodleian Library, Broad Street,
Oxford OX1 3BG, England

Note

James Saumarez Mann (1820–51) entered the
Royal Navy in 1835 and reached the rank of
lieutenant, but was later transferred to coastguard
duty due to ill health. His cousin Frederick Gother
Mann (b.1848) worked as a surveyor in Western
Australia at the end of the nineteenth century.

Description

1) Journal kept by J.S. Mann September
   1836–January 1837 while serving on HMS
   Victor on a voyage from Sydney to New
   Zealand, Tahiti, Fiji and other Pacific Islands.
   The journal describes conditions on board and
   includes sketches of ports of call. Letter 1836
   to his sister describing Sydney and referring to
   Maoris.

2) Seven letters written by F.G. Mann to his family
   1889–1909 when he was working as a surveyor
   in Western Australia. They describe aspects of
   railway development, the end of the gold rush,
   and the work of local doctors and priests.

3) *The Mann Family: Notes on Some Members of
   the Mann Family and their Connections with the
   Gother, Fyers and Thorold Families,* compiled
   by Hilda Maud Thorold and Violet Mary Mann
   (1950).

Five-page list available for reference.

Entry 307   Reel M2842

Name **MANTON, Sidnie Milana (1902–1979)**

Title Papers

Inclusive dates 1957–77

Quantity 1 reel of microfilm

Location of original Zoology Library, British
Museum (Natural History), Cromwell Road,
South Kensington, London SW7 5BD, England

Note

Authority on arthropods. Manton visited Australia in
1928 and spent four months with the Great Barrier
Reef Expedition at Low Island.

Description
Correspondence with other scientists concerning their work, including R.W. Taylor's appointment as ant taxonomist at CSIRO, and D.T. Anderson's application for Readership at Sydney University. Manton's letters are included. Correspondents include Don T. Anderson and R.W. Taylor.

Four-page list available for reference.

Entry 308   Reels M425–432

Name **MARIST FATHERS (Society of Mary)**
Title Records
Inclusive dates 1844–1926
Quantity 8 reels of microfilm
Location of original Archivio Padri Maristi, via Alessandro Poerio 63, Rome 00152, Italy
Special Conditions Permission to publish is required from the copyright owner.

Note
Catholic missionary order working in the Pacific. The first Marist missionaries were sent out from France in December 1836 and started work on Wallis and Futuna Islands in November 1837. In 1843 Bishop Bataillon was given jurisdiction over Central Oceania which included Tonga, Samoa and Fiji. In the following year two new vicariates of Melanesia and Micronesia were established, extending from the Caroline Islands to the Solomons and including New Guinea.

Description
Letters from missionaries to the general administration of the Society of Mary in France. They are mainly from missionaries in Fiji but some also relate to the Solomon Islands and Rotuma. There is general correspondence from prefects and vicars apostolic, correspondence from other missionaries and reports from the missions. They contain details of the daily activities of the missionaries and the development of their respective stations, as well as the economic, political and spiritual state of the mission organisation.

Entry 309   Reel M1908

Name **MARRIOTT, Fitzherbert, Archdeacon (1811–1890)**
Title Correspondence
Inclusive dates 1841–53
Quantity 1 reel of microfilm
Location of original Mr R.A. Marriott, Cotesbach, Lutterworth, Leicestershire, England

Note
Ordained priest 1835 and appointed rector of Cotesbach, Leicestershire. Emigrated to Van Diemen's Land in 1843 and appointed archdeacon. He became chaplain of New Norfolk in 1847. Returned to England in 1853.

Description
Correspondence of F.A. Marriott, including letters he and his wife Anne wrote to Marriott's mother, Selina. Subjects include: travels in Australia; resolution of the Protestant Association; defections to the Roman Catholic Church in England; dispute between Lady Franklin and the Gell Family; Sir William Denison; Marriott's preaching and work in Diocese; and matters relating to chaplains and bishops in Australia.
Other correspondents include Charles Marriott and Bishop F.R. Nixon.

Three-page list available for reference.

Entry 310   Reel M1619

Name **MARSDEN, Samuel, Rev. (1764–1838)**
Title Papers (Ethel Gaunt Collection)
Inclusive dates 1819–1966
Quantity 1 reel of microfilm
Location of original Pudsey Branch Library, Leeds City Libraries, 20 Church Lane, Pudsey, West Yorkshire LS28 7TY, England

Note
Anglican clergyman and missionary, who arrived in Sydney in 1794.

Description
A collection of photographs, leaflets, cuttings and correspondence assembled by Ethel Gaunt relating to the life of the Rev. Samuel Marsden, particularly his early years in Yorkshire. There is also a copy of Marsden's journal of his journey to New Zealand in 1819.

One-page list available for reference.

Entry 311

Name **MARSDEN FAMILY**

Title Papers

Inclusive dates 1793–1938

Quantity 2 reels of microfilm

Location of original Rev. R.E. Marsden, Cornwall, England

Note

Samuel Marsden (1764–1838) was an Anglican clergyman, missionary, farmer, sheepbreeder and magistrate. He arrived in Australia in 1794 as assistant to the Chaplain of the Colony. He led a mission to New Zealand in 1814–15. Samuel Edward Marsden (1832–1912) was the grandson of Rev. Samuel Marsden. He was consecrated the first Anglican Bishop of Bathurst in 1869, being the first Australian-born bishop. In 1885 he resigned the See and went to live in England, finally settling in Bristol.

Description

M382:

Rev. Samuel Marsden papers: notes concerning a biography of Samuel Marsden, including copies of certificates and notes on his life by his family; correspondence, including letters from Marsden to family and friends 1810–37, from his son Charles S. Marsden to Jane and S.E. Marsden 1851–64, from John Marsden and John H. Challis 1839–64 concerning family estates, and miscellaneous family letters 1819–76; legal documents and accounts 1802–1902, including wills and documents concerning Marsden properties; literary pieces including a manuscript by Marsden and an essay about his work in New Zealand; newspaper cuttings concerning Marsden and monuments to him in Australia and New Zealand; pamphlets and leaflets; personal effects including a diary 1827, possibly by John Marsden; portraits, photographs of Marsden and his family, Bathurst and the Bay of Islands; handwritten drafts of Marsden's sermons.

M383:

Bishop Samuel Edward Marsden papers: correspondence 1842–1906, including letters to Marsden, letters 1842–89 from Marsden to his mother and sister, and miscellaneous letters 1848–55; miscellaneous material 1869–85 including addresses from parishioners and others, cuttings 1869–85 relating to Marsden and his Diocese, letters and papers 1882–86 concerning Dr John T. Marriott, and letters 1882–86 to Marsden from clergymen in Australia.

18-page list available for reference.

Entry 312

Name **MARTIN FAMILY**

Title Papers

Inclusive dates 1793–1860

Quantity 3 reels of microfilm

Location of original British Library, Great Russell Street, London WC1B 3DG, England

Note

Admiral Sir Thomas Byam Martin (1773–1854), Comptroller of the Navy Board 1816–31. His son Sir Henry Martin (1803–1865) commanded HMS *Grampus* in the Pacific 1845–48. Another son, Admiral Sir William Martin, served on an official mission to China 1816–17 and was Commander-in-Chief in the Mediterranean 1860–63.

Description

1) Papers 1793–1831 of Sir Byam Martin referring to transport of convicts to New South Wales, import of timber and hemp from New Zealand, and appointment of surgeons on convict ships.

2) Papers 1816–60 of Sir William Martin including journal 1816–17 kept on voyage of HMS *Alceste* on a voyage to Java, China and Philippines.

3) Journal, correspondence and letter-books 1834–59 of Sir Henry Martin describing: service on HMS *Grampus*; Anglo–French relations in Tahiti; proclamation of Tahiti as a French protectorate; and affairs in Sandwich Islands. Correspondents include Queen Pomare, Sir George Seymour, A.J. Bruat and Governor Lavaud.

Six-page list available for reference.

Entry 313

Name **MARYLEBONE CRICKET CLUB**

Title Collections

Inclusive dates 1861–1987

Quantity 12 reels of microfilm

Location of original Marylebone Cricket Club, Lord's Cricket Ground, St John's Wood, London NW8 8QN, England

Historical note

Private cricket club based at Lord's ground in London. Formed in 1787, it soon revised the laws of cricket and it remains responsible for the laws. From the late nineteenth century until 1969 it set up bodies to administer county and Test cricket and also organised major overseas tours by English players.

Description

1) Archive collection 1861–1955 comprising diaries, notes, lists of matches, cuttings, photographs, correspondence, menus and printed ephemera relating to cricket matches and tours of Australia, New Zealand, Fiji and England. There are diaries of George Anderson (1863–64), Edward Grace (1864), Vernon Royle (1878–79) and Reginald Foster (1903–04).

2) Autograph letter collection 1897–1956, including letters of P.A. McAlister, M.A. Noble, William Ponsford, F.R. Spofforth, G.H. Trott, Hugh Trumble, J.W. Trumble and William Woodfull, many of them written to Ashley Cooper.

3) Score books of Australian tours of England and MCC/England tours of Australia and New Zealand between 1882 and 1987.

16-page list available for reference.

Entry 314   Reel M719

Name **MASSINGBERD, Peregrine Langton (b.1780)**

Title Journal

Inclusive dates 1832–33

Quantity 1 reel of microfilm

Location of original Lincolnshire Archives Office, St Rumbold Street, Lincoln LN2 5AB, England

Note
Massingberd, his daughters Mary and Margaret, Mary's husband, Hastings Neville, and their baby daughter, sailed for Van Diemen's Land on the *Edward Lombe* on 18 June 1832. Although they had originally intended to settle in Van Diemen's Land, the family returned to England on the *Duckenfield*, arriving in London on 22 September 1833.

Description
Journal 29 June 1832–22 September 1833 containing an explanation of the family's decision to emigrate to Van Diemen's Land, detailed descriptions of the voyage out, impressions of the colony and meetings with prominent people, including George Frankland, A.F. Kemp, John Glover, John Batman, Governor George Arthur, Capt. James England and W.J.T. Clarke. The journal concludes with a description of the voyage back to England and recollections of the family's experiences in the colony. Included in the journal are a few pen and ink drawings, among them plans of the ships *Duckenfield* and *Edward Lombe* and a drawing of the home of a settler named Grove, late of the 63rd Regiment.

Two-page list available for reference.

Entry 315   Reel M1954

Name **MAXSE, Leopold James (1864–1932)**

Title Letters

Inclusive dates 1887–1931

Quantity 1 reel of microfilm

Location of original West Sussex Record Office, County Hall, West Street, Chichester PO19 1RN, England

Note
Proprietor and editor of monthly journal *National Review* 1893–1932. Undertook tour of India, Australia, New Zealand, Canada and United States 1887–88.

Description
The letters refer to Maxse's world tour, *National Review*, and Australian politics, including: powers of British Government in relation to colonial legislation and appointment of governors; Sir John Forrest, B.R. Wise, Alfred Deakin; visit of American Fleet; Australian Labor Party; Coalition Government in Britain; and economic policy. Correspondents include Alfred Deakin, W.P. Reeves, A.W. Jose, F. Fox, L.S. Amery, Ivor Maxse and W.M. Hughes.

14-page list available for reference.

Entry 316   Reel M2512

Name **MEEK, Albert S. (b. c.1872)**

Title Correspondence

Inclusive dates 1894–1931

Quantity 1 reel of microfilm

Location of original Archives Department, British Museum (Natural History), Cromwell Road, South Kensington, London SW7 5BD, England

Note
Naturalist. Meek first came to Australia in 1889 with George Bernard of Coomooboolaroo Station, Queensland. After a visit to England, Meek returned to Australia in 1894 and began his collecting career, mainly for Walter Rothschild, in New Guinea, the adjacent islands, and Solomon Islands.

Description
Letters 1894–1931 from Meek to Dr Ernsk Hartert, H.E. Karl Jordan and Lord Rothschild. Subjects include Meek's collecting activities particularly in Trobriand Islands, Woodlark Island, Bougainville, Dutch New Guinea, Goodenough Island, Rook Island and New Hanover. There are also references to the Goodfellow Expedition and death of G.C. Eichhorn.

11-page list available for reference.

Name **MELANESIAN MISSION**

Title Records

Inclusive dates 1847–1965

Quantity 5 reels of microfilm

Location of original Melanesian Mission,
15 Denewood Close, Watford, Hertfordshire,
England

Note
The Anglican Mission to Melanesia was founded by
Bishop George A. Selwyn in 1849. The Mission's
activities extended over the islands west of Fiji,
including the Solomon Islands and the New
Hebrides. The headquarters and training school
were at Auckland 1849–67, then at Norfolk Island
until 1920, when the training school moved to the
Solomon Islands, with the diocesan office being
opened in Auckland. In 1975 the Mission became
the Church of Melanesia, with its headquarters at
Honiara. The London office was mainly concerned
with forwarding supplies and raising finance.

Description
The bulk of the collection consists of the
correspondence 1887–96 and diaries 1889–1908
of Rev. Henry Welchman and the correspondence
1952–53 of C.E. Fox, together with the draft of his
book *Lord of the Southern Isles.*

Other correspondents include J.W. Blencowe
1862–74, Commodore James G. Goodenough
(relating to the annexation of Fiji), Bishop J.C.
Patteson and Bishop Edmund Hobhouse 1868–70
and Miss M. Rice, Oxford 1941–52. There are
also journals of ColeC. Fowler 1889–91, a Mota
phrasebook by Florence E. Coombe, sketches and
articles by Eric Ramsden, drafts of writings by
Rev. George Sarawia, John Still and Roger Ernest
Tempest on the history of the Mission, including the
work of Bishops G.A. and John R. Selwyn. Finally,
there are lists of members of the Mission compiled
in 1895, 1924 and 1964, and a number of
photographs of Melanesia.

11-page list available for reference.

Name **MELLERSH, Thomas**

Title Journal

Inclusive dates 1836–38

Quantity 1 reel of microfilm

Location of original Battye Library, Alexander Library
Building, Perth Cultural Centre, Perth WA 6000

Note
Mellersh arrived in Western Australia in 1834 and
purchased property near York, where he lived for
four years. While in Western Australia he acted as
property agent for Lady Stirling, the wife of the
Governor.

Description
Daybook kept by Thomas Mellersh at 'Woodlands',
York, 12 March 1836–27 January 1838, recording
day-to-day events on the property, such as sales of
stock, visitors, harvesting and gardening. The journal
was continued on board the brigantine *Abercromby*
on a voyage from Swan River to Mauritius
12 February–May 1838, and from Mauritius to
England 10 May–11 July 1838 on the barque
Majestic. It describes weather conditions and
Mellersh's impressions of passengers and crew.

Name **MERSEYSIDE MARITIME MUSEUM**

Title Collections

Inclusive dates 1808–1900

Quantity 2 reels of microfilm

Location of original Merseyside Maritime Museum,
Albert Dock, Liverpool L3 4AA, England

Description
1) Papers 1864–66 of James Baines and Co,
concerning the company's ships *Elizabeth Ann
Bright* and *Netherby.*
2) Journal 23 March–19 July 1867 of J.T. Deighton
kept on a voyage on the *Fred Warren* from
Liverpool to Melbourne.
3) Journal 8 July–21 August 1856 possibly kept
by a Catholic priest on the *Morning Light* on
a journey from Liverpool to Melbourne.
4) Diary and notebook 1878–79 kept by
F.G. Pearson on a voyage to Melbourne on
the *Loch Sloy.*
5) Diary 1876–77 of Sara Stephens kept on
a voyage from London to Lyttelton on the
Cardigan Castle referring to quarantine of
women at Ripa Island.

6) Papers 1899–1900 of William Midgley, including description of a voyage from Liverpool on the *Grasmere* and bill from Chinese store at Brewarrina.

7) Papers 1856–91 of William C. Barker, including accounts of voyage to Sydney on the *Alnwick Castle* and to New Zealand on the *Mataura*.

8) Diary 1884–85 kept by J. Weston Smethurst on a voyage from Liverpool to Melbourne on the *General Roberts* and then on the *Rotomahana* to Auckland.

Five-page list available for reference.

Entry 320   Reels M1955–1958, M2838–2839

Name **MERSEYSIDE RECORD OFFICE**

Title Collections

Inclusive dates 1808–1971

Quantity 6 reels of microfilm

Location of original Merseyside Record Office, 4th floor, Cunard Building, Water Street, Liverpool L3 1EG, England

Description

M1955–1958:

1) Correspondence 1808–50 of Edward Stanley, 13th Earl of Derby. Subjects include: dispatch of Australian and New Zealand birds for Lord Stanley's natural history collection; New Zealand expedition; John MacGillivray; and *Birds of Australia*. Correspondents include J. Gilbert, John Gould, J. Burke, J. Gray and G.W. Earl.

2) Journal 9 March–27 May 1853 kept by passenger on emigrant ship *Marco Polo* on a voyage from Liverpool to Melbourne.

3) Reports and correspondence 1922–71 of Mersey Docks and Harbour Board concerning visit by T.H. Hawkins to Australia and New Zealand 1922–23, Australian wool, and increased railway rates. Correspondents include H.R. Richards, H.R. Young and D.T.R. Bradford.

4) Letters 1852–53 of James Battersby describing conditions on the Victorian goldfields.

5) Letters 1847–90 of Edward Danson in New South Wales to John T. Danson.

6) Papers 1855 of J.G.W. Lockett, including a diary kept on the *Hope* on a voyage from London to Port Phillip and printed items concerning the vessel.

7) Correspondence 1878–1915 of Leyland Family, including references to the Sudan War, effects of war on employment and prices, and return of wounded soldiers from Gallipoli.

8) Diary 1858–59 of John Hedges describing a voyage from Liverpool to Sydney on the *Admiral Lyons*.

Six-page list available for reference.

M2838–2839:
Correspondence 1856–1939 of Archibald Crawford, biscuit manufacturer of Leith, Scotland, mostly concerning his brothers James and William who lived in Australia. The letters of James and William Crawford describe life on board the *Arcadia* 1891 and *Ormuz* 1921; work on a sheep farm in New South Wales; the war and its effect on business; and the effects of drought and depression on rural property. Correspondents include William Crawford, Thomas Crawford, James S.R. Crawford, Doreen Crawford, Margaret Crawford and Victoria Crawford.

Six-page list available for reference.

Entry 321   Reel M595

Name **MERYON, Charles (1821–1868)**

Title Papers

Inclusive dates 1818–92

Quantity 1 reel of microfilm

Location of original British Library, Great Russell Street, London WC1B 3DG, England

Note
Etcher. His father, Dr Charles L. Meryon (1783–1877), published a number of pamphlets and was the biographer of Lady Hester Stanhope. Charles Meryon was an officer in the French Navy and sailed to New Zealand in 1842 on *Le Rhin* which had been sent to protect the French settlement at Akaroa. He spent four years in the South Pacific, making a number of sketches. The rest of his life was spent in Paris where he worked on his famous series of etchings of the city.

Description
1) Letters in French 1821–37 of Meryon's mother, Pierre Narcisse Chaspoux, and Meryon himself to his father.

2) Letters of Meryon written to his father after his mother's death including several from Akaroa and the Pacific 1838–63, in French. Included also are letters of others 1855–69 relating to Charles Meryon's insanity and death.

3) Correspondence 1892 of Lewis Meryon, nephew of Dr Meryon, with Frederick Wedmore about his biography of Charles Meryon.

4) Translations of some of the family's correspondence made by Dr Meryon with a view to publication, followed by a rough index.

5) Fragment of Dr Meryon's diary 1818.

6) Official papers, certificates of birth, baptism and naval service of Charles Meryon.

7) Manuscripts by Charles Meryon: 'Annotations de la Carte', brief hydrographical notes on the New Zealand seas, c.1846; notes on skies, for tropical and southern landscapes; sketches and notes of South Sea canoes; 'Agenda', notes written by Meryon during the last years of his life, with receipts and other papers.

8) The printed sale catalogues (marked) of two collections of his etchings sold in London 1890 and 1891.

Entry 322   Reels M118–172, M172B, M172C, M536–549, M988–991

Name **METHODIST MISSIONARY SOCIETY**

Title Records

Inclusive dates 1798–1916

Quantity 75 reels of microfilm

Location of original School of Oriental and African Studies, Thornhaugh Street, Russell Square, London WC1H 0XG, England (M118–172 and M536–549); Mitchell Library, State Library of New South Wales, Macquarie Street, Sydney NSW 2000 (M988–991)

Note
The General Wesleyan Methodist Missionary Society was formed by the British Methodist Conference in 1818. Methodist missionaries had earlier come under the aegis of the London Missionary Committee and later the Committee of the London Preachers and local societies. The Society's work in Australia commenced in 1815 with the arrival of Rev. Samuel Leigh, who also established a mission in New Zealand in 1822. Tonga, or the Friendly Islands, was ministered to by John Thomas from 1826, but it was not until 1835 that William Cross and David Cargill began work in Fiji, and Peter Turner landed in Samoa. In 1854 formation of the Australasia Connexion of the Methodist Church was approved by the English Conference, and this Connexion assumed responsibility for missions in the Friendly Islands, Fiji and New Zealand, the latter becoming a separate Conference in 1910.

Description
1) M118–120: Committee minutes 1804–65: minutes of Methodist Missionary Society in London. The minutes are preceded by a copy of a typed list of items of Australasian and South Seas interest, prepared in 1957 by Margaret Alington. The early minutes record the appointments of the first Methodist preachers to be sent to New South Wales and Van Diemen's Land, discuss their activities in New Zealand, relations with Rev. Samuel Marsden, and their work amongst the Australian Aborigines. The minutes deal also with the Society's work in Tonga, Fiji and at the Swan River settlement in Western Australia, and record political events in all the Society's areas of influence.

2) M121–123: District minutes 1822–55: minutes of meetings of committees in the overseas districts, namely New South Wales, New Zealand and Van Diemen's Land, 1822–55. In 1841 the district 'Australia' meeting in Sydney first appears, with committees meeting in the various States to deal with local affairs.

M123–124: minutes of meetings of the committee for the district of Fiji 1835–54 (M988–991 include Fiji district minutes and reports 1835–52, copied from the originals held by the Mitchell Library); minutes of meetings of the committee for the Friendly Islands 1833–55. No minutes appear to be extant for the period 1829–32.

3) M124–148: Inward correspondence 1812–89 arranged by the following areas: Australia 1812–89; Tasmania 1823–76; New Zealand 1819–82; Friendly Islands 1822–75; Samoa 1834–70; New Britain (two letters only) 1878–81. (Incoming letters from Fiji are included on M988–991.) Enclosures with correspondence often include printed matter.

4) Outward correspondence 1814–67. Some outgoing correspondence 1814–19 is included on reel M118, as well as M149, as it was included in the minute-books.

M149–151: correspondence out 1814–54. M149–150 contain indexes to this correspondence.

5) Personal papers. M149: letter-book 1834–61 of Elijah Hoole.

M152–157: James Calvert 1838–1916, notebooks, journals, papers, letters, sermon notes, newspaper clippings, mainly about Fiji.

M157–158: John Hunt 1838–48, journals, letters.

M158–159: Richard B. Lyth 1836–56, letters, including family letters, journal extracts and sermon notes.

M159: manuscript (118 p.) by Henry H. Turton on the first voyage of the *Triton* from England to New Zealand 1889–40; extracts from the 1829 journal kept by Nathaniel Turner; journals and notebooks 1794–1832 of Joseph Orton; letters of John Bumby 1836–57.

M159–166: papers and journals, letters and pictorial material of John Thomas and his wife Sarah 1825–67.

6) M166: candidates' papers 1829–55: minutes of the Candidates Committee, and the Discipline Committee 1843–64, together with biographical information on the candidates, preceded by an index. Retirements and suspensions are recorded, as well as proposed destinations of appointees.

7) M167–171: ship records 1838–61: deeds, logbooks and other papers associated with the *Triton* and the *John Wesley I* and *John Wesley II*. Papers include lists of stores, crew lists, cargo manifests, accounts connected with construction of the ships, and with supplies obtained for them from tradesmen in London, Sydney and Auckland.

8) M171: property and land 1829–95: deeds and letters concerning land and church property, mainly in New Zealand.

9) M171–172: miscellaneous papers and letters 1823–85: correspondence, principally with government departments, including lengthy letters about ownership of land in New Zealand and the effect of Governor Grey's policies; letters concerning the formation of the Australasian Conference in 1855; and miscellaneous correspondence from New Zealand, the Friendly Islands, Fiji and Tasmania.

10) M172B: Pictorial material: copies of engravings and drawings of mission scenes, *Macquarie Harbour, Van Diemen's Land* by T.J. Lempriere; Maori chiefs; map of Fiji; and watercolour of the *Triton* sailing from Bristol 1839, by J. Walter.

11) M172C: search list compiled in 1957 by Margaret H. Alington of New Zealand. This list serves as a guide to the contents of the Society's records.

12) M536–545: printed matter: *Wesleyan Missionary Notices*, volumes 1–31, 1816–1903.

M546–548: *Wesleyan Juvenile Offering*, volumes 1–23, 1844–66, and new series volumes 1–12, 1867–78.

M549: books and printed papers, including annual reports of the Society 1804–06, 1809, 1811–12, 1814.

73–page list available for reference.

Entry 323   Reels M2971–2974

Name **METHODIST ARCHIVES AND RESEARCH CENTRE**

Title Records

Inclusive dates 1817–1948

Quantity 4 reels of microfilm

Location of original John Rylands University Library of Manchester, University of Manchester, Deansgate, Manchester M3 3EH, England

Note
The Centre was established at Epworth House, London, in 1961 to collect books and manuscripts relating to Methodism. It was transferred to Manchester in 1977 but remains the property of the Methodist Church.

Description
1) Correspondence 1903–28 of A.S. Peake concerning his work in New Zealand.
2) Papers 1914–48 of Rev. Tom Dent relating to his work in New Zealand and Solomon Islands.
3) Journal 1818 of Methodist missionary Walter Lawry on a voyage to Sydney.
4) Minute-books 1859–93 of Primitive Methodist Itinerant Preachers' Friendly Society of the yearly meeting referring to appointment of colonial agents in Australia and New Zealand.
5) Individual collections 1817–1933 comprising correspondence and other papers relating to the Society's work in Australia and New Zealand. They include letters of Rev. Thomas Adams, Rev. James Calvert, Rev. John Hunt, Rev. Walter Lawry, Rev. Samuel Leigh, Rev. John Thomas and Rev. Peter Turner.

23-page list available for reference.

Entry 324   Reels M2515–2518

Name **MINISTRY OF DEFENCE. Library**

Title Collections

Inclusive dates 1718–1918

Quantity 4 reels of microfilm

Location of original Library, Ministry of Defence, 3–5 Great Scotland Yard, London SW1A 2HW, England; Hydrographic Office, Taunton, Somerset, England

Note
List of collections transferred to the Hydrographic Office, Taunton, is available from the Manuscript Section, National Library of Australia, Canberra ACT 2600.

Description

1) Correspondence 1915–18 between Sir Alexander Godley and his wife Louisa. Subjects include ANZAC landing at Gallipoli, visit to trenches, comments on Australian and New Zealand troops, and Keith Murdoch.

2) Copy of Capt. James Cook's *A Voyage to the Pacific Ocean* owned and annotated by William Bligh.

3) Journal of a voyage to South Seas kept by Capt. George Shelvocke of the *Speedwell* 1718–21.

4) Journal February–July 1818 and log September 1817–January 1821 of HM cutter *Mermaid*.

5) Journal 28 May–11 September 1793 of Capt. William Bampton of the *Shaw Hormuzcar*.

6) Log 1821–22 of the proceedings of HMS *Bathurst*.

7) Extracts from journal February–March 1779 of Capt. Charles Clerke of HMS *Resolution*, including account of death of Capt. James Cook.

8) Log 1849–51 of HMS *Herald* under Capt. Sir Henry Kellett.

9) Log and proceedings of HMS *Terror* for 1840.

10) Logs 1818–21 of HMS *Mermaid* and *Bathurst* under Lieut. P.P. King.

11) Logs 1849–50 of HMS *Amazon*, *Cambrian*, *Victory* and *Reynard* under William Dawson.

12) Lists of officials of Admiralty Courts overseas.

13) Papers 1789–1842 of Admiral Edward Edwards relating to HMS Pandora.

15-page list available for reference

Entry 325   Reel M1677

Name **MITCHELL, James (c.1793–1858)**
Title Journals
Inclusive dates 1820–23
Quantity 1 reel of microfilm
Location of original Edinburgh University Library, George Square, Edinburgh EH8 9LJ, Scotland
Special conditions Permission of the Edinburgh University Library is required before the reel can be reproduced.

Note
Surgeon on the convict ships *Neptune* and *Guildford* on three voyages to New South Wales.

Description
Two journals covering the voyages to Australia, and Mitchell's travels in New South Wales and Java in 1820 and 1822.

Two-page list available for reference.

Entry 326   Reels M2760–2761

Name **MITCHELL FAMILY**
Title Papers
Inclusive dates 1885–1967
Quantity 2 reels of microfilm
Location of original Mrs Olive Wilkinson, West Yorkshire, England

Note
Oliver Mitchell (d.1929), his wife Eliza Lund (1852–1923) and their children Alice (b.1882) and Ernest (1876–1959) travelled to Australia in 1885. Ernest Mitchell became the official photographer to the Governor of Western Australia.

Description
1) Letters of Eliza Lund and Oliver Mitchell to their family. They refer to mining disaster at Bulli in April 1887, clearing of bushland in New South Wales, and family news.

2) Papers 1888–1958 of Ernest Lund Mitchell, describing his life in Australia as a photographer, economic problems in Western Australia, opposition to Ben Chifley, and oil exploration at Exmouth Gulf.

3) Letters of Lena Mitchell (wife of Ernest Mitchell) to family in England.

4) Family letters 1957–67 sent to Olive Wilkinson (grand-daughter of Oliver and Eliza Mitchell).

Five-page list available for reference.

Entry 327   Reels M2912–2923, M2847–2849

Name **MITCHELL LIBRARY, GLASGOW**
Title Collections
Inclusive dates 1835–1972
Quantity 15 reels of microfilm
Location of original Mitchell Library, North Street, Glasgow G3 7DN, Scotland

Description
M2912–2923:
List of cases for trial at Glasgow circuit between 1827 and 1845. It gives name, crime, date of trial,

indictment, list of witnesses, verdict and sentence, including transportation.

Two-page list available for reference.

M2847–2849:
1) Correspondence 1948–49 between Charles Duguid and R.H. Small concerning Sir Henry Campbell-Bannerman and refering to Duguid's work with Aborigines and as a surgeon.

2) Letter-book 24 April–30 December 1852 of Chairman of Highland and Island Emigration Society, Sir John McNeill, concerning selection and shipment of emigrants to Australia.

3) Journal kept on board the *Artimisia* on a voyage to Australia 22 July–13 December 1848.

4) Journal of R.W. McKellar on the *John Bell* on a journey from Greenock to Sydney 26 July–14 November 1854.

5) Journal of John Edward Stegall kept on his trip to Australia 13 July–16 October 1914, includes war news and defence in Gibraltar.

6) Posters and handbills of New Zealand Campaign 1925, 1928, 1935 and 1938.

7) Papers 1946–61 of a beekeeper Ray Hansen of Taupiri, New Zealand relating to his 450 hives of bees.

Nine-page list available for reference.

Entry 328   Reel M2013

Name **MOLINEUX, Robert (d.1771)**
Title Log of HMS *Dolphin*
Inclusive dates 1766–68
Quantity 1 reel of microfilm
Location of original British Library, Great Russell Street, London WC1B 3DG, England

Note
Master's mate on HMS *Dolphin*, under the command of Samuel Wallis, on voyage around the world 1766–68.

Description
The log contains hourly entries giving speed, courses, winds and remarks, with daily entries for course, distance, latitude, longitude and bearings. There are charts of Port Praja Bay (St Jago), Lucipara Shoal, Banca Straits, Pulo Tato and other islands in the East Indies.

Two-page list available for reference.

Entry 329   Reel M976

Name **MONTEAGLE, Thomas Spring-Rice, 1st Baron (1790–1866)**
Title Papers
Inclusive dates 1833–57
Quantity 1 reel of microfilm
Location of original National Library of Ireland, Kildare Street, Dublin, Ireland

Note
Whig politician. Represented Limerick, Ireland 1820–32 and Cambridge 1832–39 in the House of Commons. Parliamentary Under-Secretary of the Home Office 1827, Secretary of the Treasury 1830–34, Secretary of State for War and the Colonies 1834, Chancellor of the Exchequer 1835–39. Created Baron Monteagle in 1839.

Description
About 300 documents, mainly letters to Lord and Lady Monteagle, dealing with emigration from Ireland to Australia.

1) Letters 1850–53 to Lady Monteagle from emigrants she had assisted, describing life in Australia, requesting similar assistance for relatives and returning money borrowed. Also receipts and three emigrants' forms and letters from the Colonial Land and Emigration Office.

2) Papers and correspondence of Lord Monteagle 1836–48: correspondence of Monteagle with various politicians and government officials such as Sir Robert Peel and Lord Clarendon, including reference to the potato famine in Ireland in 1845 and the work of the Select Committee of the House of Lords on Emigration. There are also letters 1848–49 from Caroline Chisholm containing information collected by her from Irish emigrants relating their success in Australia, and letters 1851 from the New South Wales Association for Preventing the Revival of Transportation.

3) Handwritten drafts of reports including notes on Colonial Emigration Agents, Emigration Commissioners, duties of the Boards of Guardians in Ireland and drafts of forms used by emigrants, their agents and officials, with explanations of their use.

4) Printed material includes some newspaper cuttings, a pamphlet *Proposal to Erect Shelters for Emigrants at Melbourne and Elsewhere* (1853), a circular on the Spiritual Aid Fund, and an abstract from the return furnished by the Commissioners for Emigration containing a table of exports to Australia 1831–40. There is also a list of emigrant ships to Australia in 1848

noting the number of emigrants, date of embarkation and captain and surgeon of each vessel.

Entry 330 Reel M677

Name **MOORE, John, Archbishop (1730–1805)**

Title Papers

Inclusive dates 1793–94

Quantity 1 reel of microfilm

Location of original Lambeth Palace Library, Lambeth Palace Road, London SE1 7JU, England

Note
John Moore was Archbishop of Canterbury 1783–1805. Richard Johnson (1753–1827) was the first clergyman to come to Australia. He arrived with the First Fleet in 1788 and stayed until 1800.

Description
The Moore Papers include the letters and other papers of the first two clergymen in Australia, Richard Johnson and Samuel Marsden.

1) Memoirs dated 16 April 1794, unsigned but written by Rev. Richard Johnson. They begin with Johnson's appointment as chaplain to the proposed colony of New South Wales in 1786, and describe his voyage to Australia and subsequent experiences in Sydney.

2) Copies by Johnson of his letters 1793–94 to Henry Dundas, Major Francis Grose and Capt. David Collins, the Judge Advocate, concerning Johnson's plans for a church and his quarrels with Grose.

3) Further memoirs by Johnson dated 6 August 1794, describing events in the colony since April 1794 and including copies of letters sent by him during that period.

4) Letter 4 May 1794 from Rev. Samuel Marsden, Sydney, to William Wilberforce describing his uncomfortable voyage to Australia, relations with Governor King and agricultural developments in the colony.

5) Letter (n.d.) to William Wilberforce relating to the erection of a church in Sydney. Unsigned but endorsed with Johnson's name.

6) Letter 8 May 1793 from Johnson, Port Jackson, to 'Your Lordship' describing difficulties regarding church services and his quarrels with Grose. With cover addressed to Archbishop Moore.

7) Plan and elevation of the first church in Australia, built by Johnson in 1793, on a site close to the corner of Castlereagh and Hunter Streets, Sydney.

Entry 331 Reel M598

Name **MORRIS, Patrick (1789–1849)**

Title Pamphlets

Inclusive dates 1823, 1828

Quantity 1 reel of microfilm

Location of original Foreign and Commonwealth Office Library, Sanctuary Buildings, Great Smith Street, London SW1P 3BZ, England

Note
Merchant of St John's, Newfoundland. Leader of the fight for representative institutions in that colony. He was an important contributor to the literature of colonial emancipation, and later a member of the Executive Council in Newfoundland.

Description
Printed pamphlets by Patrick Morris:

1) Observations on the present state of Newfoundland in reference to its courts of justice, local government and trade in a letter addressed to the Right Honourable Henry Earl Bathurst by an inhabitant of the colony (1823).

2) Arguments to prove the policy and necessity of granting to Newfoundland a constitutional government in a letter 1828 to the Right Honourable W. Huskisson, Principal Secretary of State for the Colonies by P. Morris, an inhabitant of the colony at Newfoundland. Morris considered the new form of government for New South Wales, of Governor and Council nominated by the Governor, as 'more objectionable than any other for the colonies'.

3) *Report of the Select Committee Appointed to Inquire into the Present State of Agriculture in this Colony* (Chairman: Patrick Morris), Parliamentary Paper.

The material on this reel complements material on the same subject in CO194, Newfoundland: Original correspondence (AJCP reels PRO 3139–3146). CO194/75 contains material written by Morris.

Entry 332   Reel M1686

Name **MURCHISON, Sir Roderick, 1st Baronet
    (1792–1871)**

Title Papers

Inclusive dates 1832–70

Quantity 1 reel of microfilm

Location of original British Library, Great Russell
Street, London WC1B 3DG, England

Note
Geologist and geographer. President of the
Geological Society 1831–33, 1841–43, the British
Association 1846, and the Royal Geographical
Society 1843–45, 1851–53, 1856–59, 1862–71.
Also Director-General of the Geological Survey,
Museum of Practical Geology and Royal School
of Mines 1855–71.

Description
Correspondence dealing with Australian exploration,
gold and other mineral discoveries, collecting
of fossils and appointment of geologists.

Correspondents include Sir William Denison,
Sir Redmond Barry, Charles Sturt, W.S. Macleay,
Sir George Bowen, J.L. Stokes, J. Crawfurd and
Sir Ferdinand von Mueller.

Three-page list available for reference.

Entry 333   Reels M1893–1895

Name **MURRAY, Sir George, Major General
    (1772–1846)**

Title Papers

Inclusive dates 1813–45

Quantity 3 reels of microfilm

Location of original National Library of Scotland,
George IV Bridge, Edinburgh EH1 1EW, Scotland

Note
Soldier and Tory MP 1823–32, 1834. Secretary
of State for War and Colonies 1828–30; Master-
General of Ordnance 1834–35, 1841–46.

Description
1) Letters 1813–45 of Sir Thomas Brisbane and
    Sir Thomas Mitchell. Subjects include: affairs
    of New South Wales Surveyor-General's
    Department; colonial finances; Governor Ralph
    Darling; plans for exploration of interior of New
    South Wales; and Maori War of 1845.

2) General papers 1826–45 comprising
    correspondence, Colonial Office letter-books,
    ordnance letters and private letter-books.

Subjects include: reform of transportation
system; establishment of colony at Swan River;
colonial patronage; revenues from Australia;
defence of Sydney Harbour; Australian
exploring expeditions and New South Wales
governorship. Correspondents include Sir
Thomas Mitchell, Sir Thomas Brisbane, William
Huskisson, Sir Ralph Darling and Lord Stanley.

12-page list available for reference

Entry 334   Reel M833

Name **MURRAY, Sir John (1841–1914)**

Title Album

Inclusive dates 1914

Quantity 1 reel of microfilm

Location of original Mr J.A.J. Murray, London,
England

Note
Marine biologist and oceanographer. Naturalist in
charge of collections on the *Challenger* expedition
of 1872–75 which explored the world's great ocean
basins. Editor of the 50-volume report of the results
of the *Challenger* expedition, and author of many
scientific books and papers. He financed scientific
expeditions to Christmas Island and advocated the
exploration of Antarctica.

Description
Newspaper cuttings concerning the death of
Sir John Murray on 13 March 1914. They are taken
from English as well as French, German, Canadian,
American and Australian newspapers and describe
his death in a car accident, the execution of his
will and the establishment of a bequest to
commemorate his work.

Entry 335   Reel M412

Name **MUSGRAVE, Sir Anthony (1828–1888)**
Title Papers

Inclusive dates 1862–1916

Quantity 1 reel of microfilm

Location of original Duke University, Durham,
North Carolina 27706, USA

Note
Lieut.–Governor of South Australia 1873–77;
Governor of Queensland 1883–88. He held similar
positions in the Leeward Islands, Newfoundland,
British Columbia and Jamaica. His second wife,
Jeannie Lucinda, was the daughter of David
D. Field of New York.

Description

1) Letters of commission and associated instructions 1862–83, appointing Musgrave to his various official positions.

2) Memorial 1883 signed by J.I. Wigham and all the 'principal ladies' of Portland, Jamaica.

3) Correspondence including letters from Sir Alfred Stephen to Dudley Field; 15 personal letters 1890–1901 from Sir Samuel Griffith to Lady Musgrave, with references to Federation and Australian political and public figures; correspondence 1888 between Col. G.A. French and W.A.B. Musgrave, concerning a Capt. Draper; correspondence 1870–1916 concerning journal articles on economic topics by Sir Anthony Musgrave, together with personal and family matters.

4) Schedule of petitions and telegrams presented to Musgrave in December 1884 asking for the reprieve of Bernard Williams and Neil McNeil. McNeil had been found guilty in November 1884 of the shooting of a native of the Solomon Islands. Included is portion of a draft letter by Musgrave on the McNeil case.

5) Diary 1888 kept by Lady Musgrave; book containing items relating to the death of her husband in 1888, including press cuttings, letters of condolence, photographs of Musgrave, photographs of memorials; probate of the will of Musgrave.

6) Correspondence 1910–12 concerning memorials to Musgrave with photographs of the memorials.

One-page list available for reference.

Entry 336   Reels M2125–2229

Name **NATIONAL ARCHIVES OF IRELAND**

Title Transportation records

Inclusive dates 1788–1868

Quantity 105 reels of microfilm

Location of original National Archives of Ireland, Bishop Street, Dublin 8, Ireland

Note

The records, relating to transported convicts and some free settlers who applied to accompany convicts to Australia, were microfilmed by the Irish Government and presented as a bicentennial gift to Australia in 1988.

Description

1) Transportation Registers 1836–57 (TR). Each register is divided into male and female convicts, and each section is subdivided by county. The registers give details of each convict, including age, crime and sentence.

2) Prisoners' Petitions and Cases 1788–1836 (PPC) comprising petitions to the Lord Lieutenant of Ireland requesting commutation or remission of sentences.

3) State Prisoners' Petitions 1798–99 (SPP) comprising petitions to the Lord Lieutenant submitted by those arrested for their involvement in the 1798 Rebellion, for which many were sentenced to transportation.

4) Convict Reference Files 1836–56, 1865–68 (CRF). The Convict Reference Files take over from the petitions series. In addition to petitions, they contain a variety of documents relating to individual convicts, including summaries of the evidence produced at trial, judges' reports and letters from officials and other persons. Files of some of the Fenian prisoners transported in 1868, including Fenian photographs (FP), have been filmed on reel M2225.

5) Free Settlers' Papers 1828–52 (FS). Male convicts who served a minimum of four years of their sentence were entitled to request a free passage for a dependent wife and family to join them in the colony. The series include some lists of convicts who requested this privilege, giving details of date of transportation, name of ship, and name and address of wife. There are also some letters written by convicts to their wives.

6) Male Convict Register 1842–47. A volume listing all male convicts sentenced to transportation in that period.

7) Register of Convicts on Convict Ships 1851–53. A volume listing names of convicts, with date and county of trial, who embarked on ships sailing to Van Diemen's Land and Western Australia.

Nine-page list and computerised index available for reference.

Entry 337   Reels M1905–1906

Name **NATIONAL ARMY MUSEUM**

Title Collections

Inclusive dates 1836–1966

Quantity 2 reels of microfilm

Location of original National Army Museum, Royal Hospital Road, Chelsea, London SW3 4HT, England

Description

1) Diaries and commonplace book 1854–55 of Francis M. Lind (b.1822). The diary describes

the voyage from Calcutta to Sydney via Singapore, Adelaide and Melbourne. The commonplace book contains notes and cuttings concerning the meetings of New Zealand chiefs at Auckland following the murder of Te Kopi.

2) Letter 7 August 1957 from H.D. London to J. Crisp concerning the Maori War 1865–70.

3) Diary June–November 1836 kept by Col. W. Harry Christie on a voyage from Gravesend to Sydney on the *Captain Cook*.

4) Diary 1863 kept by Lieut. Col. R.H. Russell, describing military and social activities in New Zealand including fighting in Tartairaimaika, Wairan and Kataki.

5) Sketch map showing action at Mahoetahi, New Zealand on 6 November 1860.

6) Papers 1880–1966 of C.C.P. Lawson concerning military forces in Australia and New Zealand and his research on uniforms.

7) Journals 1841–54 of Surgeon C. Pine, describing service of the 58th Regiment in New South Wales and New Zealand.

8) Diary April 1900–May 1901 of Nurse D.L. Harris of the New Zealand Contingent kept while serving as a nursing sister at the General Hospitals in Cape Town and Bloemfontein.

9) Diary 1910 of General Francis Maxwell describing visit to Australia and service as Instructor of Light Horse.

Seven-page list available for reference.

Entry 338   Reels M2657–2661

Name **NATIONAL COUNCIL FOR CIVIL LIBERTIES**

Title Records

Inclusive dates 1911–73

Quantity 5 reels of microfilm

Location of original Archive Department, Brynmor Jones Library, University of Hull, Cottingham Road, Kingston upon Hull, Humberside HU6 7RX, England

Note
Founded in 1934 to promote the rights of the individuals, and oppose racial, political, religious and other forms of discrimination and abuse of power.

Description
Correspondence, cuttings, printed material, memoranda and notes relating to civil rights in Australia, New Zealand, Malaya and Singapore; and relations with Australian Council for Civil Liberties,

New Zealand Council for Civil Liberties, Democratic Rights Council, Queensland Civil Liberties League and other organisations. Main correspondents are Brian Fitzpatrick, S.J. Dempsey, Harold Rich, Charles Duguid and Gordon Jackson.

11-page list available for reference.

Entry 339   Reels M2025–2048

Name **NATIONAL LIBRARY OF IRELAND**

Title Collections

Inclusive dates 1769–1964

Quantity 24 reels of microfilm

Location of original National Library of Ireland, Kildare Street, Dublin 2, Ireland

Description
1) Journal 1853–55 of Rochefort Maguire on a voyage from San Francisco to Honolulu on the *Emily*, from Honolulu to Pt Clarence on HMS *Amphitrite*, and to Point Barrow and the Behring Straits on HMS *Plover*.

2) Correspondence 1834–48 of Thomas Spring-Rice, 1st Baron Monteagle. Subjects include transportation; Molesworth Committee; Sir Richard Bourke; Spring-Rice's appointment to Colonial Office; poor Irish emigrants; and Antarctic expedition. Correspondents include G. Arthur, Prof. G. Peacock, Lord John Russell, Sir John Barrow and Sir Wilmot Horton.

3) Letters 1895–1924 from Michael Davitt and Archbishop M. Kelly to William O'Brien.

4) Papers 1842–91 of Sir Charles Gavan Duffy, including commonplace book and letters of W.S. O'Brien.

5) Papers 1797–98 concerning United Irishmen sentenced to transportation.

6) Register of prisoners at an Irish gaol, possibly Spike Island Government Prison, April 1849–October 1850.

7) Papers 1848–1911 of Rev. W. Hickey, comprising typescript copies of letters of Young Irelanders referring to transportation to Van Diemen's Land, W.S. O'Brien, Eva O'Doherty, Australian gold discoveries, and Irish affairs.

8) Papers 1831–38 of Sir Richard Bourke on administration of New South Wales. Main correspondents are D. Perceval, J.J. Therry and R. Therry.

9) Notes and cuttings 1859–71 of Sir Thomas Larcom on Irish emigration to Australia and Fenian convicts in Western Australia.

10) Papers 1957–64 of Alan Queale concerning Irish in Australia.

11) Journal August 1806–October 1810 kept by Lieut. I. Farqueson on voyage round the world, referring to the overthrow of Governor Bligh and arrival of Governor Lachlan Macquarie in Sydney.

12) Correspondence 1882–1914 of John Redmond, mostly relating to the visit of the Irish delegation to Australia in 1906. Correspondents include John Devlin, Cardinal P. Moran, H.B. Higgins and Hugh Mahon.

13) Correspondence 1871–74 between J.C. Hoey and Lord O'Hagan concerning C. Gavan Duffy and W.E. Gladstone.

14) Correspondence 1946–53 between T.J. Kiernan and F. Gallagher concerning Archbishop D. Mannix, H.V. Evatt, Sir Keith Murdoch and Irish Embassy in Canberra.

15) Letters 1950–60 of missionary Rev. Michael Minihan concerning his work in the Philippines.

16) Records 1916–20 of Irish National Aid Association and Volunteer Dependants Fund relating to their fund-raising activities in Australia and New Zealand.

30-page list available for reference.

Entry 340   Reels M1158–1168, M1961–1965

Name **NATIONAL LIBRARY OF SCOTLAND**
Title Collections
Inclusive dates 1739–1964
Quantity 16 reels of microfilm
Location of original National Library of Scotland, George IV Bridge, Edinburgh EH1 1EW, Scotland

Description
M1158–1168:
1) Papers 1785–1817 of Henry and Robert Dundas, Viscounts Melville, referring to Thomas Muir, T.F. Palmer and other Scottish political prisoners, transportation of convicts, trade in Far East, and Prince of Wales Island.

2) Papers 1849–92 of writer Thomas Carlyle, including letters of Charles Gavan Duffy, Sir Henry Parkes and G.W. Rusden.

3) Papers 1805–12 of John Leyden of Penang.

4) Letters 1846–56 of Lieut. Col. Robert Wynyard in Australia and New Zealand.

5) Papers 1824–56 of Admiral Sir Alexander Cochrane and Admiral Sir Thomas Cochrane, including letters of Sir James Brooke.

6) Journals and logs 1794–1819 of William Scott in Penang.

7) Papers 1803–31 of Sir Walter Scott, including letters of John Leyden, Lachlan Macquarie, Ebernezer Knox, Sir Thomas Brisbane and Andrew Murray.

8) Records 1822–95 of Blackwoods, Publishers, including letters of Sir David Munro of Nelson and Sir Edward Braddon.

9) Journals and papers 1800–38 of Lieut. Col. William Mackenzie on HMS *Calcutta*.

10) Papers 1836–58 of George Combe, including letters of Alexander and Mary Maconochie.

11) Papers 1817–28 of Lord Stuart referring to Matthew Flinders and French interest in Australia.

53-page list available for reference.

M1961–1965:
1) Papers 1911–15 of Alexander Murray, Baron Murray, concerning discussion with Keith Murdoch on the Dardanelles Campaign and Murdoch's Gallipoli letter.

2) Letter-books 1845–51 of Admiral Charles Graham written from Java, Auckland, Kawakawa River, Wellington and Sydney dealing with the operations of HMS *Castor* against Maori chiefs in the Bay of Islands.

3) Papers 1910–32 of Robert L. Turner, regarding tribal fighting in New Guinea, and paper entitled 'The Ethnology of Papua'.

4) Papers 1856–61 of Sir Charles W. Pasley referring to Maori War, and Australian railways.

5) Correspondence 1808–47 of Earls of Minto. Subjects include: return of William Bligh and 102nd Regiment to England; expedition to Java; Dutch in Borneo and Sumatra; fighting among the Chinese in Singapore; Stamford Raffles; journey by Lady Franklin and H. Elliot from Port Phillip to Sydney; work of Hobart Observatory; and J.C. Ross' Antarctic expedition.

6) Papers 1915–50 of Rear Admiral Robert K. Dickson, including account of the landing of Allied troops at Gallipoli in April 1915 and Dickson's travels in the Pacific in 1921–23.

25-page list available for reference.

Entry 341   Reels M1653–1658

Name **NATIONAL LIBRARY OF WALES**

Title Collections

Inclusive dates 1778–1972

Quantity 6 reels of microfilm

Location of original Department of Manuscripts, National Library of Wales, Aberystwyth, Dyfed SY23 3BU, Wales

Description

1) Black Books 1785–1830 of Brecon Circuit (Glamorganshire, Breconshire and Radnorshire) of Court of Great Sessions in Wales.

2) Correspondence 1778–1850 of Thomas Pennant referring to association with Lord Sandwich, G. Forster, John R. Forster and Daines Barrington.

3) Papers 1913–15 of David Owen of Brisbane concerning Welsh translations of Latin works and manuscripts of his novels.

4) Papers 1898–1927 of William Hobley concerning Australian bush travellers.

5) Journal April–November 1861 of William Davies, midshipman on *Champion of the Seas*, on a voyage to and from Melbourne.

6) Journal November 1865–February 1866 of J. Davies kept on a voyage from Liverpool to Sydney on the *Agamemnon*.

7) Draft poems of T.H. Jones (d.1965) of Newcastle, New South Wales.

8) Papers 1831–38 of the economist Nassau W. Senior concerning Irish emigration and transportation, including letters of Archbishop R. Whately.

9) Typescript in Welsh (c.1950) of Rev. J. Oliver Stephen entitled 'Ymysg Cymry Awstralia' describing visit to Australia 1927–28.

10) Papers of R.O. Jenkins comprising reports compiled in 1945 on Japanese occupation of Malaya 1942–45.

11) Diary 1887 in Welsh of Griffith Jones kept on a voyage from London to Melbourne on the *Iberia*.

12) Log 1890–91 kept by Thomas Davies and C.H. Bowes on the *Red Cross Knight* on a voyage from Swansea to Melbourne.

13) Papers 1903–25 of Robert J. Griffith concerning his voyage to and life in Australia.

14) Diary–letter 1894–95 of Rev. J.D. Jones describing his voyage from Liverpool to Sydney on the *Amazon*.

15) Reminiscences of Frances Purcell (d.1931) describing life of Welsh immigrant in Sydney.

16) Typescript account by Robert Evans of his voyage to Australia in 1883.

17) Account by Griffith Parry of his voyage to Australia on SS *Arabic* in 1866.

18) Correspondence 1886–1912 of Ellis Edwards referring to goldmining at Maryborough, Victoria.

19) Papers 1859–99 of Baker–Gabb Family including documents relating to estate of Stackpole Gabb of Melbourne.

20) Papers 1800–03 of Edward Clive, 1st Earl of Powis, Governor of Madras, concerning the Dutch East Indies and conduct of R. Farquhar at Moluccas.

21) Papers 1854–61 concerning the estate of Sir Francis Drummond and affairs of the Royal Bank of Australia.

22) Papers 1830–92 of Humphreys–Owen Family including letters of Edward Humphreys, Alice Humphreys, J. Macfarlane and other relatives and friends in New Zealand.

23) Diary August 1871–December 1872 of James Brogden on a visit to New Zealand.

24) Papers 1901–09 of anthropologist E.S. Hartland relating to Australian Aborigines.

25) Papers 1851–1950 of J. Glyn Davies referring to land sales in Melbourne, visit to New Zealand in 1897–98, music, and political events. Correspondents include Peggy Jones, Ray Clarke and Frank Davies.

26) Correspondence 1887–1919 of Sir James and Lady Hills-Johnes, including letters of J.C. Davies of Collie, Western Australia.

27) Papers 1914–49 of economist H.S. Jevons including letters of Walter Nash.

28) Papers 1932–65 of Sir David Parry referring to Committee of Enquiry on the New Zealand University in 1959.

29) Papers 1961–72 of Rev. J.P. Stevenson of Melbourne.

45-page list available for reference.

Entry 342   Reels M2831–2835, M3038–3047,
M3073–3086

Name **NATIONAL MARITIME MUSEUM**

Title Collections

Inclusive dates 1766–1938

Quantity 29 reels of microfilm

Location of original National Maritime Museum, Romney Road, Greenwich, London SE10 9NF, England

Description
M3076–3086:
Section 4: Personal A–L.
(*Note*: Files M–Z were not filmed.)

1) Letter-book 1843–48 of Sir Edward Belcher written on HMS *Samarang*, including surveying in East Indies, and French activities at Sooloo.

2) Log and journal 1883–86 of Lieut. Henry Bethune on HMS *Constance* on voyage to Easter Island, Hawaii and Tahiti.

3) Papers 1860–70 of Capt. William H. Blake, including diary and letter-book kept on HMS *Falcon* on Australian Station.

4) Notes collected by Louis de Bougainville.

5) Logs and other papers 1837–41 of Capt. William Chambers concerning HMS *Alligator* and *Pelorus* at Port Essington.

6) Logs 1868–71 of Sir Assheton Curzon-Howe on voyage of HMS *Galatea*.

7) Papers 1843–66 of Capt. Edmund Fremantle on HMS *Eclipse* on Australian Station.

8) Papers 1847–57 of Capt. Stephen Fremantle on HMS *Juno* on Australian Station.

9) Records relating to Blackwall Yard, including log of *Vansittart* 1825–26, accounts of voyages of East India ships 1836–60, and logs of *Newcastle* 1874–77, *Star of Devon* 1877 and *Lord Warden* 1879–83.

10) Correspondence 1875–1913 of Vice-Admiral William H. Henderson, including letters written while serving on board HMS *Peterel*, *Nelson* and *Liverpool* to his family.

11) Correspondence 1844–45 of Capt. Charles Hope written while in command of HMS *Thalia* on East Indies and Pacific Station.

46-page list available for reference

M3038–3040:
Section 5: Artificial collections:
1) Letters 1775–77 of Capt. James Cook to Sir Joseph Banks, Lord Sandwich and others.

2) Logs of J.M.R. Ince on HMS *Challenger* 1828–29 and *Fly* 1842–46.

3) Journal 1856 of G.W. Gregorie on board HMS *Morayshire* on voyage to Pitcairn and Norfolk Islands

4) Papers 1776–1801 of Capt. Edward Riou, including logs of HMS *Discovery* and *Guardian*.

5) John Fryer: narrative of mutiny on HMS *Bounty*.

11-page list available for reference

M2831–2835:
Section 6: Ships' logs, journals and diaries:
1) Journal 1913–14 kept by Alfred F. Duprey on the *Port Jackson* on a voyage from Rotterdam to Australia.

2) Journal 1873–74 kept in Indian Ocean on HMS *Challenger*.

3) Diary 1833–40 kept by Capt. Henry Gifford on HMS *Volage* and *Cruizer*.

4) Journals 1844–52 kept by Lieut. Thomas Davies on the *America* and *Cygnet* on Pacific Station.

5) Diary 1877 of John Rorke kept on board the *Loch Vennachar* on a journey to Australia.

6) Narrative account 1772–73 of Richard Pickersgill of a voyage on the *Resolution* and log of proceedings 1766–67 of HMS *Dolphin*.

7) Journals 1828–42 kept by W.T. Brookes on board the *Active*, *Recovery* and *Matilda*.

8) Journals 1935–38 of Winifred Lloyd on the *Herzogin Cecile*, *Viking* and *Olivebank* on voyages between England and South Australia.

9) Log 1879–84 of Richard Cotten on HMS *Comus* in East Indies and Pacific.

10) Diary 1869–70 kept by passengers on the *Walmer Castle* from Gravesend to Melbourne and Hobart and return voyage on the *Lady Jocelyn*.

20-page list is available for reference.

M3041–3047:
Section 6: Ships' logs:
1) Logs 1775–1836 of East India Co Ships on voyages to Australia and East Indies, including log of *Dover Castle* 1801–03 kept by Thomas Hamilton; *Tigris* 1836 by Commander William Inglesden; *Ternate*, *Star* and *Duke of Clarence* 1795–1801 by Robert Scott; and *Lord Holland* 1775–77.

2) Log 1803–06 of French vessel *Le Marengo* on a voyage to East Indies kept by Duslos Legris.

3) Logs 1803–1905 of merchant ships on voyages to Australia, including *Clarence* by midshipman

Ralph G. Huggup 1870–72; *City of Poonah* 1852–53 by J.B. Hodgson; *Kelso* 1849–55 by Second Mate William Lock; *Quilpue* 1905 by Oscar W. Lin; SS *Great Britain* 1854–56, *Carlisle Castle* 1880–84 by Midshipman C.R. Longden; *Alsager* 1872–73 by Mate James Watters; and *Parramatta* 1866–67.

4) Logs 1854–97 of Royal Navy ships, including HMS *Crescent*, *Katoomba*, *Orlando*, *Karrakatta* and *Royalist* 1894–96 by Leslie J.L. Hammond; HMS *Flora* and *Orlando* 1896–97 by Leslie J.L. Hammond; HMS *Barracouta*, *Cyclops* and *Penguin* 1874–81 by Lieut. E.D. Ommanney; HMS *Clio* 1870–73 by Midshipman F.H. Boyer; HMS *Champion* and *Duke of Wellington* 1894–95 by Midshipman Humphrey H. Smith; HMS *Encounter*, *Barracouta* and *Assistance* 1873–80 by Lieut. Angus MacLeod; HMS *Garnet* 1891–93 by Midshipman J.D. Allen; HMS *Curacoa* 1890–91 by A.W. Richmond; HMS *Nelson*, *Tamar* and *Espiegle* 1881–85 by Midshipman C.E. Hunter; HMS *Victory*, *Pique* and *Amphitrite* 1854–56, HMS *Rosario* 1872–75 by James Daly; HMS *Royal Arthur* 1899–1902 by Allan R.A. MacDonald; and Master's remark book of HMS *Curacoa* 1865.

18-page list available for reference.

M3073–3075:
Sections 6 and 7: Volumes and documents acquired singly:
1) Memoir 1805 of James Trevenen, including account of his voyage with Capt. James Cook on HMS *Resolution*.

2) Memoir of J.C.H. Nelson, containing details of Japanese attack on Singapore, sinking of HMS *Repulse* and *Prince of Wales* in 1942 and retaking of Malaya.

3) Account of Capt. Christopher Cole of capture of Banda Islands in 1810.

4) Letter-book 1842–44 kept by Commodore J. Toup Nicolas of HMS *Vindictive*, referring to activities of French at Tahiti.

5) Drafts of Capt. James Cook's narrative of his second voyage in 1772–75.

6) Corrected typescripts and galley proofs of *Canoes of Oceania* by A.C. Haddon and James Hornell.

7) Letters 1791–92 of Peter Heywood to his mother concerning mutiny on HMS *Bounty* and his death sentence.

8) Diaries 1880–83 of Capt. Henry Berridge of HMS *Superb* on the Australian Station.

20-page list available for reference.

Name **NATIONAL WESTMINSTER BANK LTD**

Title Deeds

Inclusive dates 1838–63

Quantity 1 reel of microfilm

Location of original National Westminster Bank Ltd, 41 Lothbury, London EC2, England

Note
William Kent (1799–1870), a wine merchant of Cheltenham, England, was the son of William Kent (1751–1812), captain of HMS *Supply*. He visited Sydney 12 December 1838–2 January 1839. Property referred to in the documents may have been several farms which his father owned near Kissing Point, Sydney, and which were sold between 1835 and 1841.

Description
1) Assignments and notice of assignment 1836 and 1838 by William Kent to John Miller of Lambeth, Surrey, bookseller, relating to a share in property in New South Wales. Capt. Philip P. King acted in New South Wales as agent in the sale of the property. The documents were drawn up and signed in Cheltenham and bear receipts for moneys received.

2) Power of Attorney 14 March 1863 from Rev. Henry Tingcombe of Camden, New South Wales, to John P. Stilwell relating to premises in George Street, Sydney.

One-page list available for reference.

Name **NEW ZEALAND AND AUSTRALIAN LAND COMPANY**

Title Records

Inclusive dates 1862–1963

Quantity 93 reels of microfilm

Location of original Scottish Record Office, HM General Register House, Princes Street, Edinburgh EH1 3YY, Scotland

Note
The company, which was based in Glasgow, was formed in 1866 to take over control of about 15 private syndicates which had acquired pastoral property in Australia and New Zealand. By 1877, when it amalgamated with the Canterbury and Otago Association, it owned eight properties in Australia and ten in the Otago region of New Zealand. The company played a leading part in the

establishment of the frozen meat industry. After 1900 it sold many of its New Zealand estates and acquired new properties in New South Wales, Queensland and Western Australia.

Description
M1000–1003:
Minute-books, balance sheets and balance account records of the New Zealand and Otago Agricultural and Land Investment Association Ltd 1862–68, the Canterbury and Otago Association Ltd 1865–76, the New Zealand and Australian Land Co Ltd 1866–1962.

M1003–1046:
Letter-books 1864–1945 of the New Zealand and Australian Land Co. The letters are arranged in chronological order, with each volume prefaced by a nominal index. M1003 begins with the letter-book of Douglas Alderson & Co of Dunedin, New Zealand.

M1046–1056:
Outward Australian correspondence 1882–1912, arranged chronologically.

M1056–1061:
Outward New Zealand correspondence 1882–1912, arranged chronologically.

M1061–1069:
Letter-books containing outward colonial correspondence 1879–1939, arranged chronologically.

M1070–1071:
Australian and New Zealand correspondence 1939–45; foreign letter-book, Australia 1882–1934; foreign letter-book, New Zealand 1882–1924.
M1071–1072:
Letters inwards book 1932–62 giving name and address of sender, with a brief indication of the contents; letter-book of correspondence with HM Inspector of Taxes and Inland Revenue 1945.

M1073–1074:
David Murray correspondence 1881–84; 'Kawarau' letter-book 1884–89; private letter-book 1887–1907.

M1075–1076:
Colonial cablegrams 1888–1963, being copies of cables received and sent to both Australia and New Zealand. Many of the cables deal with financial arrangements, but the majority contain brief reports on rainfall and pastoral conditions; private reports by William S. Davidson, the General Manager, to the Directors concerning New Zealand and Australian properties, 1882 and 1886.

M1077–1079:
Balance sheets, reports and circulars 1865–1926.

M1079–1082:
Miscellaneous papers, including memoranda and articles of association.

M1082–1083:
Reports on estates 1909–30.

M1083–1084:
Taxation files 1926–47.

M1084–1088:
Land and wool sale files 1935–49.

M1088–1092:
Miscellaneous legal and financial documents, pamphlets, maps and plans.

47 pages of lists available for reference.

Entry 345   Reels M1575–1577

Name **NEWCASTLE, Henry Pelham Clinton, 5th Duke (1811–1864)**

Title Papers

Inclusive dates 1841–65

Quantity 3 reels of microfilm

Location of original University of Nottingham Library, University Park, Nottingham NG7 2RD England

Note
Tory, Peelite and Liberal politician. Secretary of State for the Colonies 1852–54, 1859–64.

Description
Letter-books, correspondence and official papers documenting such subjects as: colonial appointments; honours; constitutional difficulties in New South Wales; inter-colonial relations; Victorian goldfields; the New Zealand Company; church in the colonies; introduction of coloured labour; colonial defences; transportation to Western Australia; the Maori Wars; confiscation of Maori lands; and American claims to Fiji.

Correspondents include Queen Victoria, Sir George Grey, W.E. Gladstone, Sir Frederic Rogers, Sir Edward Bulwer Lytton, Sir Charles Fitzroy, Sir William Denison, Sir John Young, C.J. La Trobe, Sir Charles Hotham, T.G. Browne and Governor Sir George Grey.

Seven-page list available for reference.

Entry 346   Reel M1683

Name **NEWCASTLE UPON TYNE UNIVERSITY LIBRARY**

Title Collections

Inclusive dates 1839–1956

Quantity 1 reel of microfilm

Location of original University Library, Newcastle upon Tyne University, Newcastle upon Tyne NE2 4HQ, England

Description

1) Papers 1839–55 of Sir Walter Trevelyan mainly relating to penal reform and the work of Alexander Maconochie at Van Diemen's Land and Norfolk Island. Correspondents include Mary Maconochie.

2) Papers 1897–1956 of the Liberal and Labour politician Sir Charles Trevelyan, in particular dealing with his tour of Australia and New Zealand with Sidney and Beatrice Webb 1898–99 and his interest in industrial arbitration. Correspondents include G. Essex Evans, B.R. Wise, J. Gavan Duffy, E.E. Morris, J.L. Bonython, A. Weigall, R.R. Garran, W.P. Reeves and Ursula Weinmann.

3) Papers 1907–36 of the shipowner and Liberal politician Walter Runciman on a wide range of subjects including shipping, Imperial trade, and the 1932 Ottawa Conference. Correspondents include W.F. Massey, T.A. Coghlan, Malcolm MacDonald and Lord Bledisloe.

Seven-page list available for reference.

Entry 347   Reels M1539–1542

Name **NEWDEGATE, Sir Francis (1862–1936)**

Title Papers

Inclusive dates 1916–26

Quantity 4 reels of microfilm

Location of original Warwick County Record Office, Priory Park, Cape Road, Warwick CV34 4JS, England

Note

Conservative politician. Governor of Tasmania 1917–20; Governor of Western Australia 1920–24.

Description

Extensive collection of personal correspondence documenting his life and official activities in both Tasmania and Western Australia, and subjects including: honours; industrial development in Tasmania; Australian political leaders; the 1917 conscription referendum; federal–State relations; possible abolition of State Governors; and the visit of the Prince of Wales to Australia in 1920. Correspondents include Sir Ronald Munro-Ferguson, Lord Forster, Lord Stamfordham, L.S. Amery, Sir William Irvine, Sir Arthur Stanley, Lord Stradbroke, Sir Walter Davidson, Sir Henry Galway, Sir Elliott Lewis and Sir James Mitchell.

There are also photographs and a diary of official engagements 1917–22.

25-page list available for reference.

Entry 348   Reels M2010–2012

Name **NIGHTINGALE, Florence (1820–1910)**

Title Papers

Inclusive dates 1857–85

Quantity 3 reels of microfilm

Location of original British Library, Great Russell Street, London WC1B 3DG, England

Note

Superintendent of Female Nurses in Hospitals in the East, based at Scutari, Crimea 1854–56. The Nightingale Fund was set up in 1855 and financed the establishment of the Nightingale School for Nurses at St Thomas' Hospital in 1860.

Description

Correspondence concerning the selection of nurses for the Sydney Infirmary, the arrival of Lucy Osburn and her party in 1868, relations between sisters and medical officers, and attempted assassination of Duke of Edinburgh. Correspondents include Henry Bonham Carter, Sarah Wardroper, Richard Whitfield, Sir Henry Parkes, Lucy Osburn and A. Roberts.

Nine-page list available for reference.

Entry 349   Reels M981, M2315–2317

Name **NORFOLK RECORD OFFICE**

Title Collections

Inclusive dates 1786–1965

Quantity 4 reels of microfilm

Location of original Norfolk Record Office, Central Library, Gildengate House, Anglia Square, Norwich, Norfolk NR3 1EB, England

Description

M981:

1) Extracts from the Barton Collection, comprising a copy of the will of Rev. Robert Knopwood of Van Diemen's Land 1834, and notes on the Hoyle and Wall Families of Gloucestershire and New Zealand, written in 1965.

2) Rolfe Family papers. Letters 1877–88 of Charles W.N. Rolfe of Alpha Station, near Beaufort, Queensland, to his family in Norfolk.

3) Rolfe (Heacham) manuscripts. Three printed items about emigration to Australia, especially by females, 1834–35.

4) Petre Papers 1812–73 concerning land and dwellings at Swanton Abbott, Norfolk, formerly owned by Thomas Freeman. His grand-daughter Eliza Graver (nee Eglington) was living in Adelaide in 1862. Papers include certificates of baptism and marriage at Reepham, Norfolk of Freeman's descendants, and letters and documents 1849–74 relating to money paid to Charles Edward Wodehouse of Rockhampton, Queensland.

5) Freeman correspondence. Letters 1875–1907 to William P.B. Freeman, Norwich artist and photographer, and his family from relatives in Victoria. Correspondents include Ellen Bryant of Castlemaine, Alfred Freeman of Carlton, David G. Freeman of South Yarra, and Ellen de Carle Freeman.

6) Yarmouth Borough records 1839–44. Death certificate of Priscilla Tubby of Hobart and papers relating to her estate.

7) Norwich. Town Clerk. Deeds 1900–01. Papers, including birth and marriage certificates, connected with sale of land in Norwich owned by Rose Allison of Brewarrina, New South Wales, Alice Crotch and John Rout, both of Norwich.

8) G. Colman Green's typescript account of a journey to Australia on the *Afric* December 1912–February 1913.

9) Document from the Cubitt Collection, being a petition dated October 1786 requesting that prisoners from the Great Yarmouth gaol be sent to Botany Bay. Personal details of eight prisoners are given.

10) Two letters 1873, one from Christchurch, concerning sale of property in New Zealand belonging to Mr Howes.

11) Printed pamphlet containing letters from emigrants in Canada and South Australia, collected in the Parish of Banham, Norfolk.

13-page list available for reference.

M2315–2317:

1) Papers 1833–37 of William Henry Bulwer relating to his appointment as Parliamentary Agent for Australian Colonies. Includes a petition by inhabitants of Van Diemen's Land against Lieut.-Governor G. Arthur and papers on jury system in Van Diemen's Land and New South Wales.

2) Papers 1872–77 of Press Family of Great Yarmouth, including logbooks, correspondence and other business papers relating to voyage of barque *Frederica* from Yarmouth to Melbourne.

3) Travel diaries 1898–1908 of Edward E. Field covering his travels to Australia and New Zealand on the *Oruba, Wodonga, Talune, Waikaro, Hauroto, Moaua, Corinthe, Taiynan* and *China*.

4) Papers 1914–18 of Sir Henry Rider Haggard referring to his visit to Australia and Empire Settlement Scheme.

12-page list available for reference.

Entry 350   Reel M2678

Name **NORTH DEVON RECORD OFFICE**

Title Collections

Inclusive dates 1787–1966

Quantity 1 reel of microfilm

Location of original North Devon Record Office, North Devon Library, Tuly Street, Barnstaple, Devon EX32 7EJ, England

Description

1) Notes and correspondence 1902–66 concerning Capt. Roger Turpie who commanded the London Missionary Society's ship *John Williams*.

2) Accounts relating to the emigration of the Cavinett Family to South Australia in 1840.

Two-page list available for reference.

Entry 351   Reels M2112–2115

Name **NORTH YORKSHIRE RECORD OFFICE**

Title Collections

Inclusive dates 1785–1965

Quantity 4 reels of microfilm

Location of original North Yorkshire Record Office, County Hall, Northallerton, North Yorkshire DL7 8AF, England

Description
1) Records of Northallerton Quarter Sessions 1785–1853 and York Quarter Sessions 1827–54, including calendars of prisoners.
2) Papers 1867–74 of Pulleine and Cowell Families of Clifton Castle, including correspondence relating to Frederick Pulleine's sheep farm in New Zealand.
3) Papers 1863–65 of Sir Henry Havelock-Allen concerning his service in New Zealand and the Maori War.
4) Papers 1823–33 of William Gowan on colonisation in Australia.
5) Papers 1853–56 of Frederick and Arthington Worsley relating to shipping and New Zealand wool trade.
6) Correspondence 1873 of Sir John Lawson on the Tichborne case.
7) Correspondence 1964–65 of County Archivist concerning identification of First Fleet convicts from Yorkshire.

13-page list available for reference.

Entry 352   Reels M2061–2063

Name **NORTHAMPTONSHIRE RECORD OFFICE**

Title Collections

Inclusive dates 1832–1982

Quantity 3 reels of microfilm

Location of original Northamptonshire Record Office, Wootton Hall Park, Northampton NN4 8BQ, England

Description
1) Papers 1849–59 of Charles Fitzgerald relating to his governorship of Western Australia, and of Valentine Cary Elwes concerning amateur theatricals in Perth.
2) Papers 1888–95 of Lord Winchilsea on Queensland properties of Weinhalt Estate Co.
3) Letters 1839–91 of Edward Holthouse and Thomas Le Gay Holthouse written from Adelaide, Ballarat and Auckland.

4) Papers 1837–50 of Rev. Abner Brown concerning emigration of rural poor to Australia and New Zealand.
5) Diary 1848–52 of Philip Wake kept on a voyage from Portsmouth to Melbourne and on a sheep station on Loddon River, Victoria.
6) Journal 1852–53 of Thomas V. Dickins on voyage from Liverpool to Melbourne on *Albatross*.

Ten-page list available for reference.

Entry 353   Reel M1641

Name **NORTHCLIFFE, Alfred Harmsworth, 1st Viscount (1865–1922)**

Title Correspondence

Inclusive dates 1915–22

Quantity 1 reel of microfilm

Location of original British Library, Great Russell Street, London WC1B 3DG, England

Note
Journalist and newspaper publisher. Proprietor of *Evening News* 1894, *Daily Mail* 1896, *Observer* 1905 and *Times* 1908; Chairman of British War Mission to United States 1917.

Description
Correspondence 1915–22 with Keith Murdoch. It refers to Murdoch's letter to the Australian Prime Minister on conditions at Gallipoli 1915; articles by Northcliffe for Australian and New Zealand newspapers; visits of Australian and New Zealand politicians and generals to England; Murdoch's bid to gain control of Sydney *Evening News*, management of Melbourne *Herald*; H.S. Gullett and W.M. Hughes.

Three-page list available for reference.

Entry 354   Reel M1652

Name **NORTHUMBERLAND RECORD OFFICE**

Title Collections

Inclusive dates 1766–1982

Quantity 1 reel of microfilm

Location of original Northumberland Record Office, Melton Park, North Gosforth, Newcastle upon Tyne NE3 5QX, England

Special conditions Permission to reproduce is required from the County Archivist.

Description
1) Autograph collection 1788–1891 of F.J. Brooks, including letters, engravings and photographs of Australian and New Zealand bishops.

2) Papers 1822–1948 of Ridley Family of Northumberland referring to Dr H. Douglas and other magistrates in New South Wales 1825–26, and property in Canterbury district of New Zealand.

3) Records 1875–85 of mining engineers William Armstrong and Sons concerning mining activities of Australian Agricultural Company.

4) Journal January–April 1849 of A. McCracken kept on the *William Hyde* on voyage to Auckland and Port Phillip.

Eight-page list available for reference.

Entry 355   Reel M1578

Name **NOTTINGHAM UNIVERSITY LIBRARY**

Title Collections

Inclusive dates 1792–1942

Quantity 1 reel of microfilm

Location of original University of Nottingham Library, University Park, Nottingham NG7 2RD, England

Description
1) Papers of Vernon Family, comprising journal 1857–60 of HMS *Cordelia*, captained by C.E.H. Vernon, on voyage to Australia and the Western Pacific and correspondence book 1856–61 of HMS *Iris*.

2) Papers 1933–42 of George Arundell, 8th Viscount Galway, Governor-General of New Zealand, referring to his appointment as a Privy Councillor, the abdication of King Edward VIII, New Zealand public affairs, and Galway's return to England in 1941.

3) Letters 1907 from Lieut. H.D.H. Willoughby to his mother while serving on HMS *Powerful* on the Australian Station.

4) Papers 1840–1907 of J.E. Denison, 1st Viscount Ossington, including extracts from letters of Henry and Alfred Denison in New South Wales and letters of Sir William Denison referring to public affairs in Van Diemen's Land, education, churches, Irish political exiles, and cessation of transportation.

5) Papers 1792–94 of William Cavendish Bentinck, 3rd Duke of Portland, comprising a list of convicts and petitions of convicts sentenced to transportation.

Five-page list available for reference.

Entry 356   Reel M1617

Name **NOTTINGHAMSHIRE ARCHIVES OFFICE**

Title Collections

Inclusive dates 1723–1936

Quantity 1 reel of microfilm

Location of original Nottinghamshire Archives Office, Castle Meadow Road, Nottingham NG2 1AG, England

Description
1) Card index to transportations recorded in the Nottingham Borough Quarter Sessions records 1723–1858.

2) Correspondence 1936 of Sir Albert and Lady Atkey on a tour of New Zealand.

3) Letters 1852 of Thomas Ross describing voyage to Melbourne and life on Bendigo goldfields.

4) Letter 1855 of J. and R. Turner in Melbourne referring to depressed economic conditions.

5) Letters 1922–29 of D.H. Lawrence referring to plans to visit Australia and his assessment of P.R. Stephensen.

6) Papers of Dame Laura Knight comprising typescript biography of acrobat and trapeze artist Joe Bert who toured Southeast Asia and Australia about 1914.

7) Papers 1891–1902 concerning Buck Family in New Zealand.

8) Notes 1868 of voyage of ship *William Davie* from Greenock to Port Otago.

9) Papers 1888–93 of Foster Family referring to management of property in New South Wales and financial matters.

Six-page list available for reference.

Entry 357   Reels M2498–2499

Name **NUFFIELD COLLEGE, OXFORD**

Title Collections

Inclusive dates 1896–1971

Quantity 2 reels of microfilm

Location of original Nuffield College Library, Nuffield College, Oxford OX1 1NF, England

Description
1) Papers 1942–57 of Frederick A. Lindemann, 1st Viscount Cherwell. Subjects include: supply of uranium to British industry; allied forces in New Guinea; British atomic bomb tests in Maralinga; and Australian economic conditions.
2) Papers 1931–49 of politician and diplomat Sir Stafford Cripps, including letters of H.V. Evatt and John Fisher.
3) Papers 1907–14 of the politician Sir Alfred Emmott, 1st Baron Emmott. Subjects include: indentured labour scheme in Solomon Islands; tour of Empire Parliamentary Association; and precedence of Australian and New Zealand Governors.
4) Records 1896–1965 of the Fabian Society, including letters of Sidney Webb, James Jupp and Race Mathews.
5) Papers c.1918–25 of J.P. Bedford relating to guild socialism and trade unionism in Australia and New Zealand.
6) Papers 1937–51 of William Morris, 1st Viscount Nuffield, referring to activities of Morris Motors Ltd in Australia and visits to Australia 1946–47.

13-page list is available for reference.

Entry 358   Reels M1980–2003

Name **O'BRIEN, William Smith (1803–1864)**

Title Papers

Inclusive dates 1829–1864

Quantity 24 reels of microfilm

Location of original National Library of Ireland, Kildare Street, Dublin 2, Ireland

Note
Irish MP 1828–48 and leader of Young Irelanders. In 1848 O'Brien was convicted of high treason. His death sentence was commuted to transportation for life to Van Diemen's Land. He was granted an unconditional pardon in 1856 and returned to Ireland.

Description
1) Journals and diaries 1849–53 kept in Tasmania, including a description of part of his voyage from Ireland to Australia in 1849 on the *Swift*.
2) Notes and speeches on such subjects as emigration to colonies, land sales, wages, and transportation.
3) Letters written from Tasmania describing: his voyage to Australia; imprisonment; Australian goldrushes; Irish affairs; education; and appearance of the wombat and kangaroo rat. Recipients include Lucy O'Brien, Lady O'Brien and William O'Brien.
4) Correspondence 1832–59 including letters of W. Hutt, Sir Wilmot Horton, C. Gavan Duffy, K. O'Doherty, T.F. Meagher, W. Carter and J. Motherwell. They refer to: Limerick Emigration Society; E.G. Wakefield; Irish emigration to Australia; Land Emigration Board; and the activities of Irish political prisoners in Tasmania.

15-page list available for reference.

Entry 359   Reels M2271–2288

Name **OWEN, Sir Richard (1804–1892)**

Title Papers

Inclusive dates 1796–1889

Quantity 18 reels of microfilm

Location of original British Museum (Natural History), Cromwell Road, South Kensington, London SW7 5BD, England

Note
Comparative anatomist and palaeontologist. Superintendent of Natural History Departments of British Museum 1856–83. His publications included *Researches on the Fossile Remains of the Extinct Mammala of Australia* (1877–78) and *Memoirs on the Extinct Wingless Birds of New Zealand* (1879).

Description
1) Correspondence 1836–83. Subjects include: discovery of fossils in Australia; observations of Tasmanian Aborigines; self-government in New South Wales; research on Australian and New Zealand fauna including platypus and moa; dispatch of Australian specimens and skulls of Maoris and Aborigines. Correspondents include W. Clift, G. Bennett, Sir Walter Buller, R. Etheridge, W.B. Clarke, Sir Julius von Haast, J.L.G. Krefft, Sir Ferdinand von Mueller, E.P. Ramsay, T.H.C. Hood and H. Woodward.
2) Notebooks 1830–39 containing Owen's notes on kangaroo, dingo, possum, wombat, echidna,

platypus, orang utan, emu, koala, kiwi, black swan, nautilus and astacus Murrumbidgee.

3) Papers 1804–32 of Sir Everard Home concerning platypus, dugong, cassowary, ostrich, ornithorhynchus and *Dinornis gravis*. Correspondents include G. Busby and H. Dumaresq.

30-page list available for reference.

Entry 360   Reels M1638–1639

Name **OXFORDSHIRE COUNTY RECORD OFFICE**

Title Collections

Inclusive dates 1775–1924

Quantity 2 reels of microfilm

Location of original Oxfordshire County Record Office, County Hall, New Road, Oxford OX1 1ND, England

Description
1) Calendars 1775–1853 of prisoners tried at Oxford Quarter Sessions and Assizes.
2) Letters 1863 concerning plan of Sarah Charles to emigrate to New Zealand on *Captain Cook*.
3) Letters 1922–23 of Bernard and Norman Badger of Katanning, Western Australia.
4) Register of convicts 1815–32 transported to Maria Island, Van Diemen's Land.

Three-page list available for reference.

Entry 361   Reels M1559–1574

Name **PACIFIC JOURNALS AND LOGBOOKS**

Title Ships Logs

Inclusive dates 1664–1833

Quantity 16 reels of microfilm

Location of original British Library, Great Russell Street, London WC1B 3DG, England

Description
Journals and logs recording several major exploring expeditions in the Pacific:

M1559:
Log 1664–67 of B. Verwey.

M1560:
Journal 1766–67 of Capt. Samuel Wallis and charts of G. Pinnock, HMS *Dolphin*.

M1651:
Log 1768–71 of HMS *Endeavour*.

M1562:
Journal 1772–74 of Capt. Tobias Furneaux, HMS *Adventure*.

M1563:
Drawings 1772–74 of William Hodges on voyage of HMS *Resolution*.

M1564:
Log 1772–75 of Lieut. Charles Clerke, HMS *Resolution*.

M1565:
Journal 1776–79 of Lieut. James Burney, HMS *Discovery*.

M1566:
Journal 1776–78 of Thomas Edgar, HMS *Discovery*.

M1567:
Log 1786–87 of Joseph Woodcock, HMS *King George*.

M1568:
Log 1791–95 of Lieut. W.R. Broughton, HMS *Chatham*.

M1569:
Log 1794–95 of Lieut. P. Puget, HMS *Chatham*.

M1570:
Journal 1790–94 of naturalist Archibald Menzies, HMS *Discovery*.

M1571:
Journal 1793–94 of Lieut. James Colnett, merchant ship *Rattler*.

M1572:
Journal 1825–28 of Lieut. George Peard, HMS *Blossom*.

M1573:
Journal 1830–33 of Capt. John Biscoe, whaler *Tula*.

M1574:
Journal 1798–1800 of John Price, transport *Minerva*.

Entry 362   Reel M2727

Name **PAINE, Ronald Wood**

Title Albums of photographs

Inclusive dates 1924–51

Quantity 1 reel of microfilm

Location of original Cambridge University Library, West Road, Cambridge CB5 9DR, England

Note
Entomologist and co-author of *The Coconut Moth of Fiji: A History of its Control by Means of Parasites* (1930).

Description
The albums include photographs of scenery, people, coconut and pineapple plantations, native craft, native ceremonies and villages in Hawaii and Fiji.

Two-page list available for reference.

Entry 363   Reel M391

Name **PALMER, Thomas Fyshe, Rev. (1747–1802)**

Title Letters

Inclusive dates 1794–96, 1804–62

Quantity Portion of 1 reel of microfilm

Location of original Manchester College, Mansfield Road, Oxford OX1 3TD, England

Note
Political reformer. In 1793 he was sentenced to seven years transportation for publishing an address to the people on the subject of parliamentary reform. He sailed to New South Wales on the transport *Surprize* which also carried his fellow Scottish martyrs Thomas Muir, William Skirving and Maurice Margarot. While in Sydney Palmer engaged in various commercial activities and was very interested in natural history and exploration.

Description
1) Handwritten notes concerning the life of Palmer compiled by Mrs Ridyard from official records and published sources.
2) Copies of letters and extracts of letters by Palmer 1794–96, referring to his fellow Scottish martyrs, describing conditions on board the *Surprize,* his health, the climate, minerals and agriculture of Sydney, and enclosing a copy of the inscription for the tomb of Joseph Gerrald.

One-page list available for reference.

Entry 364   Reel M979

Name **PEARSON, George Robert (1858–1908)**

Title Diary

Inclusive dates 1880

Quantity 1 reel of microfilm

Location of original Mr Nelson V. Pearson, Birmingham, England

Note
Accountant, native of Bristol, England.

Description
Diary September 1880–January 1881, kept while Pearson was a passenger aboard the *Lady Jocelyn,* travelling from Portsmouth to Auckland, and June–August 1881 on his return trip to England on the SS *Chimborazo.* The journal gives a detailed account of shipboard life, including domestic arrangements and entertainment arranged by the passengers. Pearson gives brief descriptions of Auckland and Melbourne. A typescript of the diary is included transcribed by Pearson's son.

Entry 365   Reel M1857

Name **PEDLEY FAMILY**

Title Papers

Inclusive dates 1856–1911

Quantity 1 reel of microfilm

Location of original Mrs Margaret Fair, Chester, England

Note
William Pedley of Sandbach, Chester, emigrated to Adelaide in 1856.

Description
The papers comprise genealogical papers 1872, and letters of William, Thomas and Edward Pedley, and other members of the family in Victoria and South Australia.

Three-page list available for reference.

Entry 366   Reels M1878–1886

Name **PEEL, Sir Robert, 2nd Baronet (1788–1850)**
Title Papers
Inclusive dates 1813–50
Quantity 9 reels of microfilm
Location of original British Library, Great Russell Street, London WC1B 3DG, England

Note
Tory MP 1809–50. Home Secretary 1822–27, 1828–30; Prime Minister and Chancellor of the Exchequer 1834–35; Prime Minister 1841–46.

Description
Correspondence and official papers. Subjects include: transportation of convicts to Australia; assisted emigration to Australia; shortage of labour in New South Wales; Maori War; Javanese sugar; New Zealand Company; Borneo; French activities in the Pacific; and expulsion of missionaries from Tahiti. Correspondents include J.W. Crocker, W. Gregory, Lord Aberdeen, H. Goulburn, R. Wilmot Horton, Sir James Graham, Lord Haddington, Lord Stanley, C. Buller, G. Hope, E.G. Wakefield, H. Wise and W.E. Gladstone.

46-page list available for reference.

Entry 367   Reel M1685

Name **PELHAM, Thomas, 2nd Earl of Chichester (1756–1826)**
Title Papers
Inclusive dates 1797–1803
Quantity 1 reel of microfilm
Location of original British Library, Great Russell Street, London WC1B 3DG, England

Note
Tory politician. Home Secretary 1801–03.

Description
A small group of letters referring to the convict hulks, transportation, the case of Sir Henry Hayes, and the separation of the Colonial and Home Offices in 1801. Correspondents include H. Addington, Sir Jerome Fitzpatrick, Sir Charles Bunbury and J. Hunter.

Five-page list available for reference.

Entry 368   Reels M1340–1362

Name **PENNINGTON OF MUNCASTER**
Title Papers
Inclusive dates 1869–1952
Quantity 23 reels of microfilm
Location of original Cumbria Record Office, The Castle, Carlisle, Cumbria CA3 8UR, England
Special conditions Permission of the Cumbria Record Office required before copies of the reels can be supplied.

Note
Liberal politician Edward Horsman (1807–1876) had extensive property and business interests in the Straits Settlements. After his death they were acquired and extended by his brother-in-law Sir John W. Ramsden (1831–1914), chairman of a number of sugar and rubber companies. His son Sir John F. Ramsden (1877–1958) of Muncaster Castle, Cumbria, assumed the name Pennington in 1925 in accordance with the will of Lord Muncaster.

Description
Correspondence, telegrams, reports, contracts, financial papers, notices and minutes of meetings, returns, newspaper cuttings, maps and publications relating to sugar and rubber plantations in the Straits Settlements and Malaya. They document: the activities of the Penang Sugar Estates Co; Penang Rubber Estates Co; Straits Sugar Co; Straits Rubber Co; Rubana Rubber Estates Co; Bagan Serai Co; Batak Rabit Estate Ltd; Selaba Rubber Estates Ltd; Tali Ayer Rubber Estates Ltd; and Sabrang Rubber Estates Ltd. The bulk of the records is dated 1875–1925.

Correspondents include Sir John Ramsden, Sir John F. Ramsden, James Ray, Percy Taylor, E.L. Hamilton and William Duncan.

17-page list available for reference.

Entry 369   Reel M830

Name **PETERS, Edmund Henry (d.1905)**
Title Diary
Inclusive dates 1852–53
Quantity 1 reel of microfilm
Location of original Dr J.E.C. Peters, Isle of Wight, England

Note
Peters, a graduate in medicine from Edinburgh University, arrived in Melbourne in October 1852 with his brother John. They intended to take part

in the search for gold. Ill health forced his return to England in 1853. He finally settled at Ryde, Isle of Wight.

Description
Journal 25 October 1852–30 December 1853. The entries record Peters' arrival in Melbourne and travels around the diggings, cut short when bad health caused him to return to Melbourne. He stayed in lodgings in Melbourne until lack of funds forced him to live at Sandridge in a borrowed tent. The journal also describes Peters' return voyage to England via Cape Horn 4 September–30 December 1853. Although concentrating on the writer's state of health and details of medication, the journal also contains comments on the colony, the diggers, details of prices paid for various commodities, living conditions, and news from the diggings. The reel includes a copy of his gold licence dated 7 December 1852.

Entry 370   Reel M384

Name **PETINGALE, John George (1808–1870)**
Title Letters
Inclusive dates 1834–69
Quantity 1 reel of microfilm
Location of original Mr J. Petingale, London, England

Note
Settler in Australia and New Zealand. Petingale arrived in Sydney via Hobart Town in 1833 and worked as superintendent of a farm owned by Capt. John Coghill, 35 miles from Sydney. In 1847 he moved to New Zealand where he owned a farm outside Auckland. In 1845 and 1860 he revisited London.

Description
Original letters and handwritten transcripts and letters from John G. Petingale, mainly to his family in England. They are written from Sydney, Auckland and London and describe his voyage to Australia, first impressions of Hobart, Sydney and Auckland, his employment as a farmer in Australia and New Zealand, and the landscape and economic conditions of both countries.

Entry 371   Reel M972

Name **PETTET, James**
Title Diary
Inclusive dates 1882
Quantity 1 reel of microfilm
Location of original Mr N. West, Wiltshire, England

Note
Labourer and shearer. Pettet worked for the Murray Squatting Company and for the Kimberley Pastoral Company in Western Australia.

Description
Diary June–December 1882. Brief entries for 17–25 June 1882 record a voyage on the *Maudon* from Melbourne to Western Australia. More detailed entries for 30 July–17 October begin with a description of a voyage along the north-west coast of Western Australia from Cossack, near Roebourne, to the camp at Yeda [sic], near Derby, on the Fitzroy River. Pettet's companions on the voyage, all making the Yeda camp, included Daly, Buller, Harry Cuzens and Anthony Cornish, brother of Hamlet Cornish. Pettet was employed labouring and shearing for the Murray Squatting Co and for the Kimberley Pastoral Co. He comments on the vegetation, pastoral conditions, Aborigines, and the climate, recording shearing in temperatures of 104°. Daily activities at Yeda camp are described, together with a journey eastward from the camp and along the Fitzroy River. Among the entries for 9–18 December 1882 is a brief note recording the killing of Anthony Cornish by an Aborigine. Interspersed among the diary entries are jottings, including financial accounts, poems and Aboriginal vocabulary.

One-page list available for reference.

Entry 372   Reel M823

Name **PETWORTH HOUSE ARCHIVES**
Title Collections
Inclusive dates c.1749–1861
Quantity 1 reel of microfilm
Location of original Lord Egremont, West Sussex, England

Note
Sir George O'Brien Wyndham, 3rd Earl of Egremont (1751–1837), was a successful stockbreeder at Petworth and art patron. In addition to the Petworth estates, he owned property inherited by his father in the north and west of England. After his death

Petworth passed to his kinsman Col. George Wyndham (1789–1869), who was created Baron Leconfield on 14 April 1859.

Description
Correspondence, accounts, documents and maps relating to immigration to South Australia and Western Australia under the sponsorship of the Lord Egremont and Col. Wyndham through the Petworth Immigration Committee and the work of the Rev. T. Sockett.

1) Correspondence 1829–61, mainly of Rev. T. Sockett and Col. G. Wyndham, concerning: the administration of emigration schemes, including details of land companies in South Australia and Western Australia; letter 1830 from Thomas Henty about dispatch of cattle and horses to Swan River for the East Indies market; letters about wool sales, mining, land purchases and exploration. There is also mention of problems encountered, such as emigrants prematurely selling up, and Col. Wyndham's former Irish tenants alleging misrepresentation of Australian conditions. Much of the correspondence refers directly to individual migrants such as W.H. Yaldwyn and his sister-in-law Miss Bowles, Thomas Bannister of Western Australia, Dr Thomas Ryan as ship's surgeon on the *Portland Emigrant,* T.H. Ayliffe and family of Bovey Tracey, Devon, emigrants to South Australia, and Frederick Mitchell, Col. Wyndham's Australian agent.

2) Records concerning emigration expenditure by Rev. T. Sockett and Col. Wyndham 1838–43 including account-books listing expenses paid to assist 61 families to emigrate, or compensation approved in lieu 1838–43 and various bills and receipts for equipment, medicines and pre-fabricated huts.

3) Poster 1838 advertising free immigration for tenants and labourers on Col. Wyndham's Irish estates, and prospectus in letter form of the South Australian Co.

4) Maps, plans and drawings: Asia, India and East Indies 1773; Cook's discoveries late eighteenth century; land holdings of Col. Wyndham in the district of Adelaide 1839; special survey of the Hutt River, Western Australia, copied from sketch drawn by John McDouall Stuart 1842 showing holdings, including those of Col. Wyndham; and a photograph of the 1616 Leconwick World Map at Alnwick Castle.

12-page list available for reference.

Entry 373   Reels M3068–3072

Name **PHIPPS HORNBY FAMILY**
Title Papers
Inclusive dates 1847–1903
Quantity 5 reels of microfilm
Location of original National Maritime Museum, Romney Street, Greenwich, London SE10 9NF, England.

Note
Sir Phipps Hornby was Rear Admiral and Commander of Pacific Squadron 1847–50. His son Sir Geoffrey Phipps Hornby was Commander in Chief, Mediterranean Station 1877–80. Robert S. Phipps Hornby was Commander in Chief, North America and West Indies Station 1914–15. Windham M. Phipps Hornby, son of Robert, entered the Royal Navy in 1909.

Description
1) Papers 1847–51 of Sir Phipps Hornby concerning British and French interests in the Pacific. Correspondents include William Miller and George Pritchard.

2) Papers 1865–91 of Sir Geoffrey Phipps Hornby mainly relating to activities of HMS *Liverpool* on Australian Station in 1866–70.

3) Papers 1901–03 of Robert S. Phipps Hornby relating to service of HMS *Pylades* on the Australian Station.

4) Papers 1900–01 of Windham M. Phipps Hornby comprising journal kept by Corbet A.F. Radford on the *Woolloomooloo* on a voyage to Australia.

14-page list available for reference.

Entry 374   Reel M1579

Name **PICKERING FAMILY**
Title Papers
Inclusive dates 1850–64
Quantity 1 reel of microfilm
Location of original Mrs J. Pickerill, Stafford, England

Description
A small group of letters of John Pickering and other members of his family concerning their emigration to Australia and farming near Adelaide.

Two-page list available for reference.

Entry 375   Reels M2804–2805

Name **PITT RIVERS MUSEUM, Oxford**

Title Collections

Inclusive dates 1864–1949

Quantity 2 reels of microfilm

Location of original Pitt Rivers Museum, Oxford University, South Parks Road, Oxford OX1 3PP, England

Description
1) Papers 1893–1929 of anthropologist and curator Henry Balfour. They include diaries June–November 1914 of a visit to Sydney, Queensland, Bali, Java, Singapore and Malaya, and papers on Easter Island and Tasmanian archaeology. Correspondents include Kathleen S. Routledge, W. Scoresby Routledge, T.R. Johnson and C.M. Woodford.
2) Diaries April–October 1888 kept by James Blomfield on a journey to New Zealand, including accounts of visits to Tasmania, Ballarat, Melbourne, Sydney and Auckland.
3) Papers 1931–49 of Sir Francis Knowles, mainly comprising letters from A.S. Barnes concerning Aboriginal tools and weapons.
4) Catalogue 1864 of collection of Maori skeletal remains, implements and boats of H.G. Robley.

11-page list available for reference.

Entry 376   Reel M2503

Name **PLUNKETT, James Francis (1831–1917)**

Title Autobiography

Inclusive dates c.1917

Quantity 1 reel of microfilm

Location of original Oscott College, St Mary's College, Oscott, Sutton Coldfield, West Midlands B73 5AA, England

Note
Plunkett sailed to Australia on the *British Isles* and arrived in Port Phillip in 1853. After working on the goldfields, he opened a Catholic boarding school at Elsternwick called Oscott. He emigrated to New Zealand and opened a Catholic school for boys in Auckland in 1871. In 1875 he abandoned teaching and joined the *Southern Cross* as a reporter.

Description
Account of his early life and education, his journey to Australia, life on the Victorian goldfields and his later life in New Zealand.

Two-page list available for reference.

Entry 377   Reels M1718–1821

Name **PORT LINE LTD**

Title Records

Inclusive dates 1890–1968

Quantity 104 reels of microfilm

Location of original Liverpool University Archives, PO Box 147, Liverpool L69 3BX, England

Note
The Commonwealth and Dominion Line was registered in 1914. In 1916 it was taken over by the Cunard Steam-Ship Co and in 1936 the name was changed to the Port Line Ltd.

Description
The records comprise Board papers 1914–68, Registers and Transfers of Stocks and Shares 1914–70, correspondence and company administration 1890–59, correspondence of Directors, Manager and Secretary 1924–40, loss of ships files 1939–45, private letter-books, correspondence and indexes 1915–65, Charter Parties 1921–60, Accountant's Department files 1914–51, Publicity Department files 1893–1968, and miscellaneous files 1890–1967.

Subjects covered in the correspondence files include: ships' agents; visits by officials to Australia and New Zealand; Blue Star Line; Cunard White Star Line; outside competition and outward trade; chilled meat; meat companies; fruit guarantees; wool buyers; passengers; waterside workers; and statistics. Correspondents include J.R. Rooper, W. Donald, H.W. Corry, Sir James Corry, R.H. Senior and W.G. de Gruchy.

85-page list available for reference.

Entry 378   Reel M2117

Name **PORTSMOUTH CITY RECORDS OFFICE**

Title Collections

Inclusive dates 1787–1938

Quantity 1 reel of microfilm

Location of original Portsmouth City Records Office, 3 Museum Road, Portsmouth PO1 2LJ, England

Description
1) Calendars of prisoners tried at General Quarter Sessions 1842–54.
2) Papers 1896–1906 of Hewett and Anderson Families of Titchfield containing family news from New Zealand.

3) Papers 1931–38 relating to the First Fleet, including addresses given at memorial services for Capt. Arthur Phillip.

4) Letter 23 August 1863 from George Atkins of Melbourne to Harry J. Atkins of Fareham referring to unemployment in Victoria and growth of merchant navy.

5) Letters 1905–20 from relatives in Wellington, Dunedin and Waikuri to Norman and Katherine Stanley of Southsea.

6) Letters April–May 1787 of Newton Fowell to his father concerning imminent departure of HMS *Sirius*.

7) Letters 1848–50 of Francis Shields of Sydney to Charles Vignoles, mainly dealing with development of railways.

8) Papers 1878–1901 of Edney Family, including letters of James and Frank Edney in New Zealand.

Three-page list available for reference.

Entry 379   Reels M2263–2270, M2350–2391

Name **POST OFFICE ARCHIVES**

Title Records

Inclusive dates 1841–1939

Quantity 49 reels of microfilm

Location of original Post Office Archives, Freeling House, Mount Pleasant Complex, London EC1A 1BB, England

Description
M2263–2270:
Post 34. Selections from minutes 1828–1900 from the Secretary of the Post Office to the Postmaster-General dealing with overseas mail services, including legislation, contracts, rates, international agreements and shipping routes.

Post 44. Reports 1841–47 by Edward D. James and R. Richard Smith of postal services in New South Wales, Van Diemen's Land, South Australia, Western Australia and New Zealand. Each report summarises the history of postal services in the colony, as well as dealing with current staffing and administration, postal routes, revenue and expenditure, and number of letters sent and received.

M2350–2391:
Post 29. Records 1842–1939 comprising minutes, correspondence and other papers concerning the packet boat service and overseas mail services generally, including mail services to Australia and New Zealand.

Lists available for reference.

Entry 380   Reel M1688

Name **POWELL, Wilfred (1853–1942)**

Title Papers

Inclusive dates 1871–1940

Quantity 1 reel of microfilm

Location of original University of Cambridge, West Road, Cambridge CB3 9DR, England

Papers formerly held by the Royal Commonwealth Society, London.

Note
Traveller, British consular official and author of *Wanderings in a Wild Country* (1883).

Description
Papers mainly relating to Powell's work as Deputy Commissioner for the Western Pacific at Samoa 1885–87. They include: official documents, letters and reports on his travels in the Pacific and New Guinea and on the administration and politics of Samoa; manuscripts and cuttings on Samoa; the Pacific labour trade; the annexation of New Guinea; accounts of the Samoan hurricane of 1889; and photographs of Samoa. Correspondents include J.B. Thurston.

Four-page list available for reference.

Entry 381   Reels M387–388, M1661–1666

Name **PUBLIC RECORD OFFICE OF NORTHERN IRELAND**

Title Collections

Inclusive dates 1798–1958

Quantity 8 reels of microfilm

Location of original Public Record Office of Northern Ireland, 66 Balmoral Avenue, Belfast BT9 6NY, Northern Ireland

Description
M387–388:
1) Correspondence 1851–58 of James Getty with his family in Ballymoney, County Antrim, and friends in Kilmore and Beechworth.

2) Papers 1934–58 of George Lutton of Cranfield, County Down, on family history, including letters of W. MacDiarmid of Sydney.

3) Copies of letters 1852–55 of the political convict John Mitchel, written from Bothwell, Van Diemen's Land, referring to conditions in the colony and Irish affairs.

4) Letters 1862–78 from Frank R. Robb of Tooma, New South Wales, and Alexander Robb to their family in County Down.

5) Letters 1890–1907 from William C. Quinn of Broken Hill and Kalgoorlie and Patrick Quinn of Auckland to their family in Belfast.

6) Journal December 1865–March 1866 of Elizabeth Anketell on a voyage from Plymouth on the *Queen of Australia*, including her first impressions of Melbourne.

7) Letters 1845–51 of Thomas Vogan of Goulburn and Melbourne to his brother in County Armagh.

8) Incomplete diary June–September 1849 of the political convict John Martin on the voyage to Australia on the *Mount Stewart Elphinstone*.

9) Correspondence 1877–86 of the Barton Family of Sydney including a letter-diary 1884 describing a voyage to Australia.

10) Journal July–October 1861 of Charles Elliot kept on a voyage from Liverpool to Melbourne on the *Prince of the Seas*.

11) Papers 1823–94 of John Milliken including letters 1884–87 from his brother James in New South Wales.

12) Deeds, official documents, financial papers and newspaper cuttings 1837–43 of William Verner of Parramatta.

Three-page list available for reference.

Reels M1661–1666:
1) Letter 1823 of Sir Thomas Brisbane referring to sheep farming and agriculture in New South Wales and his astronomical observations.

2) Letters 1853–55 of James Farrell to George Dunbar referring to trade with Victoria.

3) Diary 1839–43 of a marine on HMS *Terror* on the voyage to the Antarctic.

4) Letters 1859–80 of Sampson and Charles Lawrence at Castlemaine, Victoria, describing work on goldfields, droughts and bushfires.

5) Letters 1842–43 of William McDonald describing landscape, climate, flora and fauna of Van Diemen's Land, including Port Arthur.

6) Papers 1874–83 of Frederick Blackwood, 1st Earl Dufferin, Governor-General of Canada and India, including letters of Sir George Bowen in Melbourne and J. Henniker Heaton in Sydney.

7) Diary 1858, probably of William Bates, on voyage from Glasgow to Melbourne on the *Minnehaha*.

8) Diaries 1929–30 of Lady Craigavon kept on a tour of Australia and New Zealand. They include cuttings, invitations, programs, photographs and letters from governors and politicians.

9) Papers 1852–72 of Maguire Family, including letters of Hugh Maguire, J.J. Maguire and J. Ranken in Melbourne.

10) Papers 1881–1934 of Crawford Family, including diary of Frederick Crawford on a visit to Australia in 1892 and letters and reminiscences of Alexander Crawford describing his life in Victoria and Western Australia.

11) Papers 1849–62 of John Martin concerning transportation of the Young Irelanders, including letters of Kevin and Eva O'Doherty, William Smith O'Brien and P. Smyth.

12) Letters 1845–66 of Thomas Woore to Rev. Henry Scott discussing economic, political and church affairs in New South Wales.

13) Diary 1879–80 of Charles C. Greenfield, a sailor on the *Andares*, on a voyage from London to New Zealand and the return voyage on the *Hankow*.

14) Papers 1798–1819 of the politician Lord Castlereagh relating to the 1798 United Irishmen Rebellion, the transportation of political prisoners, military and naval affairs, trade in the East Indies, and the appointment of Lachlan Macquarie as Governor of New South Wales.

15) Papers 1809–12 of ensign Alexander Huey, including a diary kept on a voyage from England to Sydney and New Zealand, a letter of John Lewin and sketches of Sydney.

16) Letters 1891–1907 of James Twigg describing his voyage to Western Australia, farming, goldmining at Coolgardie, wages and prices, and the effects of Federation on the colony.

17) Correspondence 1853–59 of James Getty of Melbourne concerning trade in Victoria and family matters.

18) Papers 1829–49 of Capt. F.C. Irwin including a letter of Capt. J. Stirling referring to Irwin's book on Western Australia.

19) Notebooks and drawings 1825–26 of Richard Beechey relating to the Pacific voyage of HMS *Blossom*.

20) Letters 1860–82 of Oliver McSparron, Jane McSparron and other members of the family in Australia and New Zealand.

24-page list available for reference.

Name **RAPER, George (c.1768–1797)**

Title Papers

Inclusive dates 1787–1824

Quantity 1 reel of microfilm

Location of original Vice-Admiral Sir George Raper, Somerset, England

Note
George Raper joined HMS *Sirius* as an able seaman and in 1787, while on a voyage to Botany Bay, he was promoted to midshipman. He remained in New South Wales and Norfolk Island until 1792.

Description
An abbreviated logbook 1787–94 and maps, plans and coastal profiles of Botany Bay, Port Jackson and Norfolk Island.

Three-page list available for reference.

Name **READE, Thomas Mellard (1831–1909)**

Title Letters

Inclusive dates 1883–1906

Quantity 1 reel of microfilm

Location of original Harold Cohen Library, University of Liverpool, Ashton Street, Liverpool L69 3DA, England

Note
Geologist, architect and civil engineer at Liverpool. Reade began serious work in geology about 1867. In addition to two books, he wrote nearly 200 papers and addresses dealing with glacial and post-glacial geology, the mineral structure and changes of sedimentary rocks and questions of geomorphology.

Description
16 letters written to T.M. Reade by J. Anderson and others concerning laying of the cable from Java to Australia for the Eastern Telegraph Co Ltd, from H.B. Guppy concerning the geology of New Zealand and the Solomon Islands, and from J.M. Maclaren concerning submarine ridges in the Pacific and his geological work in New Zealand.

Name **RHODES HOUSE LIBRARY**

Title Collections

Inclusive dates 1800–87

Quantity 4 reels of microfilm

Location of original Rhodes House Library, South Parks Road, Oxford OX1 3RG, England

Description
1) Papers 1834–37 of Sir Thomas F. Buxton concerning abolition of slavery. Subjects include inquiries concerning effect of British settlement on natives in New Zealand, protection of native rights, and removal of Tasmanian Aborigines to Flinders Island.

2) Papers 1855–57 of Henry Labouchere, Secretary of State for Colonies, relating to church affairs in Australia and New Zealand.

3) Papers 1826–36 of Sir Richard Bourke, including letters of Judge W. Burton.

4) Autobiography of A.J. Cutlack, describing his life in Queensland and New South Wales 1870–1875.

5) Diary 1852–53 of Ebenezer Hunt kept on a voyage from Plymouth to Melbourne on the *Lady Eveline* and describing his experiences at the Forest Creek goldfields.

6) Diary 1853–54 of Alfred Joy on a voyage from Gravesend to Melbourne on the *Thomas Harrison*.

7) Letter-book 1850–55 of J.R. Phillips concerning Aborigines in Albany.

8) Reminiscences 1852–72 of G.D. O'Byrne of his voyages to Australia on *Tory Lady Eveline* 1852 and *Golden Era* 1856 and experiences as a gold miner in Victoria.

9) Australian mortgages, conveyances and deeds, including documents 1854–60 concerning George Leslie and 1872–81 concerning the Tasmanian Main Line Railway Co.

10) Letters 1849–63 of David Burn to Serle referring to accounts of Burn's work as editor of *Maori Messenger* and *New Zealander*, Capt. Edward Stanley; Sir George Grey; Maori War; and New Zealand Constitution.

11) Papers 1867–87 of Rev. R.H. Codrington, including diaries of visits to Mota, Solomon Islands, New Hebrides and Queensland, letters to members of his family, and letters from natives of Melanesia.

12) Letters 1878–87 from Vernon Walker to his mother describing visits to Fiji, New Caledonia and New Hebrides.

Ten-page list available for reference.

Entry 385 Reel M437

Name **RICOU, J.P.**

Title Diary

Inclusive dates 6 April–3 July 1872

Quantity Part of 1 reel of microfilm

Location of original Mr F.P. Ricou, London, England

Access conditions Permission from the owner is required to reproduce any part of the diary.

Note
J.P. Ricou was a passenger on board the *Indus* on a voyage from London to Brisbane in 1872.

Description
Diary kept by J.P. Ricou on the voyage of the *Indus* from London to Brisbane 6 April–3 July 1872 containing daily reports of weather conditions, descriptions of other passengers, sighting of land and arrival at Moreton Bay.

Entry 386 Reels M2619–2625

Name **RIVERS, William Halse Rivers (1864–1922)**

Title Papers

Inclusive dates 1898–1954

Quantity 7 reels of microfilm

Location of original Cambridge University Library, West Road, Cambridge CB3 9DR, England

Note
Doctor and anthropologist. Rivers took part in the Cambridge Anthropological Expedition to Torres Straits in 1898 and went on expeditions to Melanesia in 1908 and 1914. Author of *History of Melanesian Society* (1914).

Description
Papers include correspondence, notes, notebooks, typescripts, photographs and cuttings concerning social anthropology of the Torres Strait, New Hebrides, Tonga, Samoa, Hawaii, Fiji and Solomon Islands. Subjects include: notes on Ambrym; social organisation; marriage and childbirth; kinship; Mekeo system; totemism; medicine and funeral customs.

Correspondents include Frederick Bowie, R.H. Codrington, A.R. Radcliffe-Brown, Sidney Ray and Beveley Humes.

17-page list available for reference.

Entry 387 Reel M400

Name **ROBARTS, Edward (b. c.1771)**

Title Journal

Inclusive dates 1824

Quantity 1 reel of microfilm

Location of original National Library of Scotland, George IV Bridge, Edinburgh EH1 1EW, Scotland

Note
Information about Robarts is elusive. He appears to have been a skilful seaman and navigator, as well as being a well-educated, highly literate man.

Description
Narrative (171 p.) written in 1824, describing events in the life of Robarts between 1797 and 1824. In 1797 he left England aboard the *Euphrates,* a whaling vessel, which sailed via Rio de Janeiro, Cape Horn and along the coast of Chile as far as St Mary's Isle. There, near the Spanish settlement at Conception Bay, the hunt for sperm whale met with success. Robarts writes of encounters with other whalers at the Galapagos Islands, and describes turtle and terrapin caught there and eaten by the crew. In December 1798 the *Euphrates* sailed to the Marquesas Islands, where Robarts abandoned ship on learning that mutiny was intended. He lived on the Marquesas for eight years and the narrative contains very detailed descriptions of the islands' inhabitants, their social and religious customs, and the topography and natural history of the region. A Marquesan vocabulary is located near the end of the narrative. Robarts refers to finding the possessions of a missionary from the *Duff*, possibly William Pascoe Crook.

In February 1806 Robarts left the Marquesas aboard the English ship *Lucy* (Capt. Ferguson) taking his Marquesan wife and child with him. The narrative describes their stay on Tahiti, where Robarts met the missionaries Yuill, Eyre, Henry and Elder. Robarts describes in detail conditions in Tahiti, where he stayed for almost a year, and notes visits by ships seeking sandalwood. The Robarts Family left Tahiti aboard the *General Wellesley,* which visited the Bay of Islands, New Zealand, where timber was taken aboard for spars. The writer relates incidents connected with the Maori timber-getters who were working under the runaway convict from Port Jackson, George Bruce, and gives his impressions of the country and its inhabitants.

In 1808 Robarts reached Penang where he worked first for a Mr Thompson, then for Thomas Raffles, but by 1810 he was overseer at the Botanical Gardens in Calcutta. In 1815 he journeyed to Port Jackson but after an interview with Governor Macquarie decided to return to Calcutta where he was still living in 1824. The narrative gives very detailed accounts of all the places visited by Robarts and impressions of people he met.

Entry 388   Reel M856

Name **ROBERTS, James**
Title Letters
Inclusive dates 1850–52
Quantity 1 reel of microfilm
Location of original Miss M. Roberts, Wiltshire, England

Description
Five letters from James Roberts to his family from Adelaide, Port Lincoln and Sydney describing the voyage from England, work conditions, 'the savage aborigines' and the landscape of Australia.

One-page list available for reference.

Entry 389   Reel M844

Name **ROBINSON, Thomas (b.1850)**
Title Papers
Inclusive dates 1844–89
Quantity 1 reel of microfilm
Location of original Mr T.W. Townsend, Lincolnshire, England

Note
Emigrant to Western Australia in 1889. His marriage certificate of 1873 states that he was a wheelwright and was married in Lincolnshire.

Description
1) Letters 25 October–13 December 1889 from Thomas Robinson to his wife describing his voyage to Western Australia on the *Cuyco* and his first few days in Australia. He arrived at Albany on 1 December and describes his lodgings, houses and labour conditions. After calling at Vasse he arrived at Bunbury where he comments on the townspeople and the layout of the town. His final letter is from the property of a Mr Buckby at Dardanup Park.
2) Family documents including a family tree of 'The Townsends of Buckminster, Leicestershire'; a copy of the marriage certificate of John Townsend and Jane Machin 24 March 1844; a copy of the birth certificate of Ann, daughter of John and Jane Townsend, born 29 July 1847; and the marriage certificate of Thomas Robinson and Ann Townsend 21 June 1873.

One-page list available for reference.

Entry 390   Reels M1959–1960

Name **ROSCOE FAMILY**
Title Papers
Inclusive dates 1899–1961
Quantity 2 reels of microfilm
Location of original Buckinghamshire Record Office, County Hall, Aylesbury HP20 1UA, England

Note
Edward S. Roscoe (1849–1932) was Registrar of the Admiralty 1904–32 and an author. He married Katherine Gawne. Their daughter Theodora Roscoe (1897–1962) was a lecturer at the Harefield Park Australian Military Hospital 1917–18 and a writer. She married her cousin Capt. E.C. Roscoe.

Description
1) Letters 1927–28 from H. Greenfield to Edward S. Roscoe concerning living conditions in New Zealand and Rabaul.
2) Letters 1899–1924 of John M. Gawne to his sister Katherine Roscoe containing accounts of army life in Singapore, South Africa and the Philippines.
3) Letters 1934 of Theodora Roscoe to her mother describing South Australia and Northern Territory.
4) Papers 1916–52 of Theodora and Edward C. Roscoe relating to Sir Thomas White; Harefield Park Hospital; conscription in Australia; Capt. E. Roscoe's expedition to Northern Territory 1934; Hermannsburg Mission; Tasmanian Aborigines; and Road Transport Unit. Correspondents include W.M. Drummond, F. Albrecht and Jeannie Gunn.

Eight-page list available for reference.

Entry 391   Reels M2780–2793

Name **ROTH, George Kingsley (1903–1960)**
Title Papers
Inclusive dates 1872–1959
Quantity 14 reels of microfilm
Location of original Cambridge University Library, West Road, Cambridge CB3 9DR, England

Note
Anthropologist and administrator. Secretary for Fijian Affairs 1954–57; Honorary Keeper of Fijian Collection at Cambridge University Museum of Anthropology and Ethnology 1958–60.

Description
Correspondence 1872–1959, notes, photographs, off–prints, book reviews relating to society and culture, including language, administration, totemism, ceremonies, housing, kava ceremonies, music and art. Correspondents include A.B. Brewstar, Lorimer Fison, Edward W. Gifford, Harry Wright, J.B. Thurston and Robert Swanston.

28-page list available for reference.

Entry 392　　　　　　Reels M2566–2569

Name **ROYAL ARMY MEDICAL CORPS**
Title Collections
Inclusive dates 1863–1978
Quantity 4 reels of microfilm
Location of original Contemporary Medical Archives Centre, Wellcome Institute for the History of Medicine, 183 Euston Road, London NW1 2BE, England
Special Conditions Microfilm must be purchased from the Wellcome Institute.

Description
1) Papers 1915–17 of Lieut. Col. M. Dunning relating to campaigns in Dardanelles and Middle East.
2) Notes 1943–45 of Brigadier L.R.S. Macfarlane concerning treatment of amoebic dysentery among prisoners of war in Thailand.
3) Papers 1940–44 of Major General Sir Percy Tomlinson, referring to Australian and New Zealand casualties, medical units and hospitals in Middle East and Western Desert.
4) Papers 1941–54 of Brigadier Julian Taylor relating to his service as consulting surgeon, Malaya Command, and at the Prisoners-of-War Camp in Changi.
5) Papers July–September 1915 of Lieut. Col. G.J.S. Archer relating to the 40th Field Ambulance at Gallipoli.
6) Reports 1942–45 relating to the Japanese occupation of Malaya and Singapore.
7) Diaries 1914–15 of Private A. Horrocks kept while serving in Egypt, referring to problems with Australian troops.
8) Medical reports 1943–45 concerning Changi POW Camp.
9) Papers concerning radioactive contamination of the crew of fishing boat *Fukuryu Maru* after hydrogen bomb testing at Bikini Atoll in 1954.
10) Reminiscences of Irish soldier Private Arthur Morgan and Australian soldier Corporal Cockfield while serving at Gallipoli in 1915.

11) Diaries 1901–46 of Lieut. Col. John G. Bell with entries relating to his service at Gallipoli, Singapore and Malaya.
12) Papers 1923–48 of WO Edward F. Doughty relating to his service in Far East and imprisonment at Changi.
13) Account by Sgt Major John A. Cox of service with RAMC in 1939–45, including visits to Singapore, Sydney, Melbourne and Auckland.

22-page list available for reference.

Entry 393　　　　　　Reels M1704–1712

Name **ROYAL ASTRONOMICAL SOCIETY**
Title Records
Inclusive dates 1819–1940
Quantity 9 reels of microfilm
Location of original Royal Astronomical Society, Burlington House, Piccadilly, London W1V 0NL, England

Description
1) RAS papers, comprising Secretary's letter-book 1822–24, original papers submitted to the Society 1820–1900, and correspondence of Joint Permanent Eclipse Committee 1898–1912. Subjects include: Pacific exploring expedition; observations made by Sir Thomas Brisbane at Parramatta 1822–25; report on Melbourne Observatory for 1878; expedition to Sumatra 1901 to observe total eclipse; and observation of 1908, 1910 and 1911 eclipses in Australia and Pacific.
2) Papers 1829–30 of Francis Baily concerning publication of observations of Charles Rumker at Parramatta in 1822–23.
3) Correspondence 1843–61 of John Lee on observations of P.P. King at Port Stephens, cost of building new observatory at Parramatta and publication of Charles Rumker's *Catalogue of Southern Hemisphere*.
4) Papers 1868–93 of Arthur C. Ranyard concerning the observations of the total solar eclipses of 1868, 1872 and 1882.
5) Correspondence 1914–27 of John H. Reynolds concerning erection of reflecting telescope at Canberra. Correspondents include W.G. Duffield and W.F. Gale.
6) Letter 1846 from George Airy to Richard Sheepshanks concerning the Parramatta Observatory.
7) Report of New Zealand Survey Department of total eclipse of the sun in New Zealand on 9 September 1885.

8) Letters 1833–1940 received by the Secretary or Assistant Secretary of the Society. Subjects include: election of Fellows; observations of comets in the Southern Hemisphere; catalogue of the Southern Stars; astronomical publications for Australian and New Zealand libraries; Parramatta observations of J. Dunlop; and work of Australian observatories.

Correspondents include R.L.J. Ellery, J. Tebutt, H.C. Russell, Sir Charles Todd, E. Dunkin, W.J. MacDonnell, R. Innes, W.F. Gale, Pietro Baracchi, J.T. Stevenson, W.E. Cooke, C.E. Adam and G.F. Dodwell.

44-page list available for reference.

Entry 394   Reels M730–788

Name **ROYAL BOTANIC GARDENS, Kew**
Title Records
Inclusive dates 1793–1928
Quantity 59 reels of microfilm
Location of original Royal Botanic Gardens, Kew, Richmond, Surrey 7W9 3AB, England

Note
The Kew Gardens botanical collection was commenced in the late seventeenth century by Lord Capel, while the arboretum dates from 1759, from which time George III greatly encouraged expansion of the collections. The first director of the Gardens was William Aiton, whose son succeeded him in the post in 1793. From 1841 to 1865 the director was Sir William Hooker, whose own herbarium and extensive library were added to the Kew Gardens' collections. In turn he was succeeded by his son Sir Joseph Hooker, who held the position until 1885. Collecting expeditions were encouraged by all the directors, as was the distribution of plants to those parts of the world where they could economically be grown.

Description
1) Kew Collectors Series: correspondence and lists 1800–59; specimens collected by John Amstrong, George Barclay, George Caley, Allan Cunningham, William Grant Milne and Berthold C. Seemann. Correspondents include Sir Joseph Banks, William T. Aiton and James Bowie.

2) Official correspondence:

(a) Letters 1825–65 addressed to Sir William Hooker, Director, from both professional and amateur botanists. Correspondents include William Archer, James Backhouse, Sir Henry Barkly, Henry S. Chapman, Allan Cunningham, Richard Cunningham, Sir William Denison, James Drummond, Ronald C. Gunn, Phillip Parker King, Ludwig Leichhardt, Sir Ferdinand von Mueller, Berthold C. Seeman and James Stirling.

(b) Letters 1865–1928 addressed to the Director and other members of staff, relating to each of the Australian States, the Pacific and Southeast Asia. Correspondents include William Farrer, John J. Shillinglaw, Sir Julius von Haast, Sir William MacGregor, Sir John Thurston and Sir George Bowen.

3) Miscellaneous manuscripts: correspondence, diaries, journals, lists, maps, descriptive notes, sketches, by James Backhouse, Sir Joseph Banks, George Bentham, Isaac H. Burkill, HMS *Challenger*, Frederick W. Christian, Charles B. Clarke, Rev. William Colenso, H.F. Comber, Allan Cunningham, Charles Darwin, John F. Duthie, A.D.E. Elmer, Henry O. Forbes, William Forsyth, Henry B. Guppy, Clara Hemsley, William B. Hemsley, John S. Henslow, Arthur W. Hill, Sir Joseph Hooker, J. Hutton, William Kerr, Aylmer B. Lambert, L.V. Garland-Lester, John Lindley, John MacGillivray, Albert C. Maingay, Franz J.F. Meyen, Friedrich A. Wilhelm, William Mitten, Sir Ferdinand von Mueller, William Munro, William Paterson, W.W. Perry, J. Richardson, Henry N. Ridley, J. Smith, O. Stapf, F.C. Stern, William Swainson, William T. Thiselton-Dyer, L. Wigg. Also inwards and outwards books 1793–1895 containing lists of collections of plants and seeds collected for and dispatched from Kew Gardens, and plant lists of collections assembled.

4) Miscellaneous papers: reports, maps, dispatches, correspondence, parliamentary papers and newspaper cuttings dealing with economic botany. They include references to New South Wales 1846–1928, Victoria 1862–1916, Queensland 1857–1928, South Australia 1849–1927, Western Australia 1848–1928, Tasmania 1843–1928, New Zealand 1843–1921, New Guinea 1850–1928 and Fiji 1860–1919.

Detailed lists totalling 200 pages available for reference.

Entry 395   Reels M1690–1697, M1698–1703

Name **ROYAL COMMONWEALTH SOCIETY**

Title Collections

Inclusive dates 1822–1963

Quantity 14 reels of microfilm

Location of original Cambridge University Library, West Road, Cambridge CB3 9DR, England

Note
The Colonial Society was founded in 1868 and assumed the title Royal Colonial Institute in 1870. The name was changed to the Royal Empire Society in 1928 and the Royal Commonwealth Society in 1958.

Collections formerly held by the Royal Commonwealth Society, London.

Description
M1690–1697: Manuscript collections
1) Records 1929–38 of Margaret Best of Public Schools Empire Tours.
2) Manuscript 1870 'Colonies in their Commercial Relation to the Mother Country' by Charles W. Eddy.
3) Notes 1847–48 of Henry Grey, 3rd Earl Grey, on transportation of convicts to the colonies and Australian bishops.
4) Letters 1912–17 of E.J. Harding, Secretary of Royal Commission on Natural Resources, Trade and Legislation of Dominions, to his family. They describe visits of the Royal Commission to Australia and New Zealand and refer to meetings with politicians and visits to galleries, libraries, and the site of Canberra.
5) Albums of cuttings 1910–14 of Thomas Sedgwick relating to Imperial migration.
6) Papers 1929–44 of Sir Campbell Stuart. Subjects include amalgamation of cable and wireless companies and Imperial Communications Advisory Committee.
7) Scrapbooks 1882–1921 of Sir William Allardyce concerning his career in Colonial Service in Fiji and as Governor in Tasmania.
8) Papers 1822–89 of Peter and George B. Murdoch referring to convict system in Van Diemen's Land, proposed railway extensions to Wagga, Orange and Tamworth, and Emu Plains Establishment.
9) Reports 1833–35 of James Backhouse and George W. Walker of visits to penal settlements at Port Arthur and Norfolk Island, and Aboriginal settlement at Flinders Island.
10) Documents concerning voyages of convict transport *Barrossa* 1839, *Margaret* 1842 and *Lord Petre* 1843.

11) Letter-book 1846–54 of Major General Henry Despard concerning service of 99th Regiment in Australia.
12) Minute-book 1855–62 of General Association for the Australian Colonies.
13) Monumental inscriptions in New South Wales and Victoria 1913–22.
14) Typescript 'John Gardiner Pioneer Overlander' by Leslie J. Wilmoth (1936).
15) Diary 1838–51 of Samuel W. Viveash describing the voyage from Portsmouth to Swan River in 1838, farming and Viveash's medical practice at Yangedine, near York.
16) Copies of diaries 1840–41 of Archdeacon John R. Wollaston referring to church affairs in Western Australia 1829–41 and his voyage from London to Perth 1840–41 on the *Henry*.
17) Typescript copies of letters 1838–42 written by Mary Thomas to her brother George Harris describing: voyage to South Australia; Aborigines; the execution of Aboriginal murderers; J. Hindmarsh; G. Gawler; and H. Fisher.
18) Papers 1921–26 of Sir Matthew Nathan relating to his governorship of Queensland. They refer to Imperial Press Conference 1925, discussion between E.G. Theodore and H.V. Ashley on possible competition for design of Queensland University, visit by N.A.R. Pollock to Gulf country 1922, and cotton growing in Queensland.
19) Reports 1885 on Etheridge, Gladstone and Hodgkinson goldfields in Queensland.
20) Papers 1862–84 of H. Ling Roth concerning North Queensland exploration, Queensland sugar industry and South Sea labour trade.
21) Papers 1823–1914 of Crichton Family mainly relating to farming in New South Wales.
22) Journal May–November 1818 of John Oxley's second expedition into the New South Wales interior.
23) Letters 1862–1919 of Thornhill Family written in New Zealand to Henrietta Thornhill in London. They refer to discovery of coal, Maori War, construction of railways, and recruitment in World War I.
24) Letters 1849 from Edward Gibbon Wakefield to George F. Young referring to government opposition to New Zealand Co and opposition of Lord Grey to Colonial Reformers.
25) Log 1828–29 of *Alfred* on whaling voyage from Sydney to Solomon Islands, Santa Cruz Islands.
26) Report 1892 by Admiral Edward H.M. Davis on Gilbert and Ellice Islands.

15-page list available for reference.

M1698–1703: Records
1) Council minutes 1868–1929. Subjects include: annexation of Fiji and New Guinea; French aggression in Pacific; Pacific steamship service; Australian expedition to Antarctic; purchase of Australian drawings of William Westall; Australian Federation; work of Lorimer Fison on Australian ethnology; double taxation; conference on emigration; tours of Sir Rider Haggard 1916 and J.R. Boosé 1922.
2) Letter-books 1868–88. Subjects include: pearl fisheries in northwest Australia; Australian wine; annexation of Fiji; New Guinea deputation; French activities in Pacific; German annexation of New Guinea; Australian Antarctic Expedition; and Australian Federation.
3) New Guinea papers 1875–85 including minute-book of Gambia and New Guinea Deputation Committee (1883).
4) Emigration papers 1910–35 including correspondence, letter-book, committee minute-book and reports.
5) Papers 1915–16 on Post-War Settlement Mission of Sir Rider Haggard. They include letters of Rider Haggard and A.R. Corbett describing their visits to Australian and New Zealand.
6) Papers 1914–22 of Travelling Commissioner James R. Boosé relating to his Australian and New Zealand tours.
7) Minor correspondence 1883–93.
8) Autograph collection 1876–1915.
9) Library talks 1958–65.
10) Walter Frewen Lord Prize essays, including essays by R.E. Latham, J.W. Davidson, W.D. Borrie and A.G. Serle.

23-page list available for reference.

Entry 396   Reels M2015–2020

Name **ROYAL INSTITUTION OF GREAT BRITAIN**
Title Collections
Inclusive dates 1837–1970
Quantity 6 reels of microfilm
Location of original Royal Institution of Great Britain, 21 Albemarle Street, London W1X 4BS, England

Note
The Royal Institution of Great Britain was founded in 1799 to promote knowledge of science and technology. Under the leadership of Humphrey Davy and Michael Faraday, it soon established a tradition of popular public lectures and scientific research carried out in its own laboratories.

Description
1) Albums 1840–69 of Rev. John Barlow including letters of Sir John Franklin and King Kamehameha.
2) Papers 1838–70 of Michael Faraday including analysis of water forwarded from Australia by T.L. Mitchell and lecture on preservation of plants.
3) Correspondence 1851–92 of John Tyndall referring to: purchase of scientific instruments for South Australian Institute; visit to Sydney of HMS *Rattlesnake*; observations of Aborigines; and race relations in New Zealand. Correspondents include Sir John Herschel, J. Tidmarsh and G.B. Airy.
3) Papers 1882–1969 of Sir William Bragg. They refer to: Bragg's work at Adelaide University; controversy about experiments on velocity of roentgen ray; radium research; Bragg's return to England; his 1915 Nobel Prize; and include drafts of autobiography and notebooks 1904–08. Correspondents include O. Hann, J.A. Pollock, Sir Ernest Rutherford, Natalie Allen, T.R. Lyle, Horace Lamb, F. Soddy and W. Sutherland.
4) Papers 1883–1970 of Sir Lawrence Bragg. They refer to his early life in Adelaide; his appointment as Professor of Physics at Cambridge University; relations with Australian scientists; academic appointments; and his lecture tour of Australia and New Zealand in 1960. Correspondents include Sir Mark Oliphant, Lord Florey, Jean Kidman, Sir William Dargie and Sir Ernest Marsden.
5) Discourse 1960–61 on 'The Southern Milky Way' by B.J. Bok.

28-page list available for reference.

Entry 397   Reels M945–946

Name **ROYAL IRISH ACADEMY**
Title Collections
Inclusive dates 1828–c.1877
Quantity 2 reels of microfilm
Location of original Royal Irish Academy, 19 Dawson Street, Dublin 2, Ireland

Note
Richard Robert Madden (1798–1886), surgeon, writer, colonial official, active in anti-slavery movement. From 1847 to 1850 he was Colonial

Secretary of Western Australia, where he took a special interest in Aborigines. Thomas Francis Meagher (1823–67), Irish nationalist, was one of a group sentenced in 1848 to transportation to Van Diemen's Land for seditious activity. Other members of the group included John Mitchel and William Smith O'Brien. Meagher escaped from Tasmania in 1852.

Description
Madden Papers:
1) Papers relating to colonial administration in Western Australia 1828–49. The papers are divided into four groups:

    a) Papers including: establishment of the Swan River colony and the affairs of the settlement to 1847; allocation of land; list of passengers on the *Parmelia*; reports on progress of the colony; and copies of the *Western Australian Almanack*1842 and 1844.

    b) Papers relating to Madden's term as Colonial Secretary in Western Australia 1847–49. Includes material on: administration; land prices; convicts; sheep farming; the work of the Jesuits; and documents on Madden's resignation.

    c) Correspondence 1846–49 mainly between Madden and Rev. John Brady on: the Roman Catholic mission in Western Australia; education of Catholic children; official attitude towards the Ladies of Mercy; letters concerning land at Victoria Plains; and other church matters.

    d) Papers relating to: Aboriginal affairs 1832–49 including: legal status of Aborigines; flogging as a form of punishment; the work of the Wesleyan Mission; and reports by Madden on improvement of conditions and education of Aborigines.

2) Newspaper cuttings, notes and unpublished essays written by Madden 1848–55; correspondence by Madden; literary, historical, political and travel notes, including references to Antarctic exploration.

Meagher Papers:
1) Notes (82 p.) for the autobiography of Thomas F. Meagher, containing details of his early life and education, political beliefs, the formation of the Irish Confederation, and his arrest with O'Brien and Mitchel on a charge of sedition.

2) Extract of a letter from Meagher to William German 28 October 1851 about a boat built in Hobart for communication between his farm and cottage; letter from Meagher to Charles Gavan Duffy about his escape from Tasmania in 1852; note about a presentation by the people of Victoria to W.S. O'Brien 1855.

Three-page list available for reference.

Entry 398   Reels M2636–2637

Name **ROYAL MARINES MUSEUM**
Title Records
Inclusive dates 1786–1962
Quantity 2 reels of microfilm
Location of original Royal Marines Museum, Royal Marines, Eastney, Southsea, Hants PO4 0PX, England

Description
1) Diary 1841–45 kept by Lieut. Gerard Montague on HMS *Dublin* visiting Oahu and Tahiti.

2) Diary 1945–46 of Major Alfred C. Hood on a voyage to Australia on the *Stirling Castle* with returning Australian and New Zealand troops.

3) Diary 1799–1802 of John Robyns on *La Virginie* in East Indies referring to captured Dutch ship, description of Island of Ambon, expedition against Ternate, and meeting with the French expedition under N. Baudin.

4) Diary January–October 1951 of Michael Browne kept as Intelligence Corporal of 42 Commando in Malaya.

5) Letters 1869–71 of F.H. Poore written from HMS *Galatea* giving impressions of New Zealand and Tahiti.

6) Diary 1913 of A.E. Crosby kept on HMS *New Zealand* on its world cruise.

7) Copies of letters 1786–87 from Major General Arthur Collins to the Admiralty referring to formation and departure of Botany Bay detachment of Marines.

8) Copies of letters 1786–92 from the Admiralty to Plymouth Division. Subjects include: formation of a detachment of Marines to accompany ships to Botany Bay; desertion of Lieut. James Morrison; and court martial of Capt. James Meredith at Port Jackson.

9) Sketches 1884–89 of Col. Cyril Field drawn while serving with HMS *Nelson* on Australian Station.

Nine-page list available for reference.

Entry 399　　　　Reels M1927–1940

Name **ROYAL SOCIETY**

Title Records and Collections

Inclusive date 1699–1932

Quantity 14 reels of microfilm

Location of original The Royal Society Library,
6 Carlton House Terrace, London SW1Y 5AG,
England

Note
The Royal Society, one of the major scientific
societies in the world, was founded in 1660.

Description
M1927–1937:
Records 1699–1937 of the Royal Society
comprising council and committee minutes,
correspondence, letter-books, manuscripts, referee
reports and other archives.

Among the many subjects dealt with in the records
are: the 1769 transit of Venus; the voyages of Capt.
James Cook; the Cook Medal; Australian and New
Zealand fauna; meteorological, magnetic and
astronomical observations; the Great Melbourne
Telescope; elections of Fellows; publications; solar
eclipse expeditions; the 1883 Krakatoa eruption; the
Funafuti coral reef expeditions; Antarctic exploration;
award of medals; and scientific conferences.

Correspondents include Capt. James Cook, Sir
Joseph Banks, Sir Everard Home, Capt. M. Flinders,
Sir Thomas Brisbane, C. Rumker, W.B. Clarke,
G. Neumayer, R.L.J. Ellery, Sir George Verdon, Sir
James Hector, Sir Julius von Haast, A. Liversidge, Sir
Ferdinand von Mueller, A.C. Haddon, Sir Edgeworth
David, Sir William Bragg, Sir Orme Masson, Lord
Rutherford, Sir Douglas Mawson and L. Cockayne.

85-page list available for reference.

M1938–1940: Personal Collections
1) Letters 1774–1820 received by Sir Charles
   Blagden referring to: illness of Omai; crossing of
   Blue Mountains; cession of Bencoolen to Dutch;
   Capt. N. Baudin; Daniel Solander; and William
   Bligh. Correspondents are Sir Joseph Banks,
   C.M. Pole and Lord Mulgrave.

2) Correspondence 1822–70 of Sir John
   F.W. Herschel. Subjects include: astronomical
   observations of Sir Thomas Brisbane and
   C. Rumker; Melbourne telescope; Parramatta
   Observatory; Tasmanian Aborigines;
   preservation and identification of Aboriginal
   dialects; colonial legislation; Hobart
   Observatory; and Antarctic expedition of Capt.
   J.C. Ross. Correspondents include G.B. Airy,
   F. Baily, Capt. F. Beaufort, Capt. R. FitzRoy,

H. Lloyd, Sir Edward Sabine, W.H. Smyth,
Sir John Franklin and Sir Redmond Barry.

3) Letters 1905–21 sent to Sir Joseph Larmor
   referring to New Zealand magnetic survey, and
   publication of papers by Australian and New
   Zealand scientists.

4) Correspondence 1832–59 of Sir John
   W. Lubbock relating to 1840–44 Antarctic
   Expedition and establishment of fixed magnetic
   observatories. Correspondents include Lord
   Northampton and Sir Edward Sabine.

5) Photocopies of correspondence 1890–1936 of
   Lord Rutherford. Subjects include: Rutherford's
   research; award of 1908 Nobel Prize; academic
   appointments; visits to New Zealand;
   publications; and World War I. Correspondents
   include A. Bickerton, Sir William Bragg, T.H.
   Laby, E. Marsden, J. Marsden and J.A. Pollock.

6) Correspondence 1825–73 of Sir Edward Sabine
   mainly concerning: magnetic and meteorological
   observations at Java and Australia; Melbourne
   Observatory; expedition of Capt. J.C. Ross; and
   the purchase of the Great Melbourne Telescope.
   Correspondents include C. Buys-Ballot,
   R.L.J. Ellery, Sir John Herschel, J.H. Kay,
   G. Neumayer, W.P. Wilson and C. Elliot.

30-page list available for reference.

Entry 400　　　　Reel M1828

Name **ROYAL SOCIETY OF ARTS**

Title Records

Inclusive dates 1788–1885

Quantity 1 reel of microfilm

Location of original Royal Society of Arts, 8 John
Adam Street, Adelphi, London WC2N 6EZ, England

Note
The Royal Society of Arts was founded in 1754 to
promote improvements in agriculture, manufacturing,
trade and the sciences. After 1850 it was chiefly
concerned with organising lectures and publishing
papers.

Description
1) Transactions 1788–1845 including report on
   Tahitian bread-fruit, wine and wool imported
   from New South Wales, and New Zealand flax.

2) Committee minute-books 1793–1885 referring to
   wool, brandy and wine imported from New South
   Wales, flax from New Zealand, bark cloth from
   Sandwich Islands, and tinned meat from Australia.

13-page list available for reference.

Entry 401   Reel M2400

Name **RUTHERFORD, Sir Ernest, 1st Baron (1871–1937)**

Title Papers

Inclusive dates 1904–39

Quantity 1 reel of microfilm

Location of original Cambridge University Library, West Road, Cambridge CB3 9DR, England

Note
Born in New Zealand. Professor of Physics, McGill University, Montreal 1898–1907; Professor and Director of Physical Laboratories, University of Manchester 1907–19; Cavendish Professor of Experimental Physics at Cambridge 1919–37. Awarded Nobel Prize for chemistry in 1908.

Description
Correspondence, notes, laboratory notebooks, a notebook kept on his Australian tour in 1925, newspaper cuttings and photographs. Subjects include: scientific research in New Zealand; visits to Australia and New Zealand; Rutherford's biography; academic appointments; family news; and research and teaching.

Correspondents include Sir William Bragg, T.H. Laby, P.W. Burbidge, J. Cox, J.A. Erskine, E. Marsden, J.A. Pollock and members of the Rutherford Family in New Zealand.

11-page list available for reference.

Entry 402   Reels M1181–1182

Name **ST JOSEPH'S FOREIGN MISSIONARY SOCIETY**

Title Records

Inclusive dates 1882–1972

Quantity 2 reels of microfilm

Location of original St Joseph's College, Lawrence Street, Mill Hill, London NW7 4JX, England

Note
The missionary seminary St Joseph's College at Mill Hill was founded in 1866 by Bishop Herbert Vaughan. In 1886 it established a Maori Mission within the Diocese of Auckland which has continued to the present day.

Description
1) Correspondence 1882–1905 of Cardinal H. Vaughan, Father F. Henry and other Mill Hill priests with Bishop J. Luck, J.R. Madan, J. Becker, J.W. Smiers and other missionaries in New Zealand.

2) Reports 1896–1902 of Maori Mission.

3) Diary 1912–13 of Father F. Henry on journey to United States, New Zealand, Australia and Uganda.

4) List of superiors and members of Maori Mission 1886–1972

5) *The Story of Mill Hill in New Zealand 1886–1966* (1966) and other histories of the Maori Mission.

Three-page list available for reference.

Entry 403   Reel M875

Name **SAMUEL, Sir Saul (1820–1900)**

Title Correspondence

Inclusive dates 1837–1900

Quantity 1 reel of microfilm

Location of original Sir Jon Samuel, Surrey, England

Note
Politician and merchant. In 1837 Samuel formed a mercantile firm at Bathurst, New South Wales, and later managed a number of pastoral companies in that area. In 1854 he entered politics, representing the counties of Roxburgh and Wellington in the Legislative Council. From 1859 to 1872 he was a Member of the Legislative Assembly, then returned to the Legislative Council, and sat until 1880. He held a number of ministerial appointments during this time, including Treasurer and Postmaster-General. In 1880 he was appointed Agent-General for New South Wales in London, a position he held until 1897.

Description
The correspondence has been arranged chronologically, with letters from Charles Cowper, Lord Belmore, Sir Henry Parkes and the Samuel Family separated into distinct groups. Most of the correspondence with Charles Cowper is dated 1870 and relates to Samuel's resignation from the Executive Council. The letters from Lord Belmore are dated 1868–85, with many written 1868–72, when he was Governor of New South Wales. The largest group contains letters from a number of correspondents dealing with personal matters and official business such as appointments, securing loans and relations with the Colonial Office.

There are also letters from Sir Henry Parkes 1872–90, and letters to and from members of Samuel's family.

17-page list available for reference.

Entry 404   Reel M1583

Name **SAMWELL, David (1751–1798)**

Title Journal

Inclusive dates 1776–79

Quantity 1 reel of microfilm

Location of original British Library, Great Russell Street, London WC1B 3DG, England

Note
Naval surgeon and poet. Served on Royal Navy ships 1776–96 including surgeon's mate on HMS *Resolution* 1776–78 and surgeon on HMS *Adventure* 1778–80. Active in Welsh cultural organisations.

Description
Journal 1776–79 kept while serving on HMS *Resolution* and *Adventure* on the third Pacific voyage of Capt. James Cook. It includes an account of the death of Cook.

Entry 405   Reel M386

Name **SANFORD FAMILY**

Title Correspondence

Inclusive dates 1851–55, 1883

Quantity 1 reel of microfilm and 41 pages of photocopies

Location of original Lord Methuen, Wiltshire, England

Note
William Ayshford Sanford (1812–1902) was Colonial Secretary of Western Australia 1851–55. He had a lifelong interest in natural history, archaeology and architecture. His brother Henry Ayshford Sanford (b.1822), a captain in the 43rd Regiment, was placed in charge of building a town and the making of 30 miles of road near Toodyay, West Australia, in 1852. In 1853 he took up land at Port Gregory, had a share in neighbouring lead mines and in 1854–55 was engaged in whaling. He also held the offices of Magistrate and Sub-Collector of Customs in Western Australia.

Description
1) Correspondence 1851–54 between W.A. Sanford and H.A. Sanford and with their family in England. Some of the letters describe conditions in Fremantle.

2) Letters 1851–55, 1883 received by W.A. Sanford as Colonial Secretary and after his return to England. They deal with: education; the churches; customs; immigration; convicts; and Aborigines. Correspondents include

Governor Charles Fitzgerald, Rev. James Brown, W. Cowan, M.W. Clifton, Dr W. Harvey, Edmund Y. Henderson and John W. Sillifant.

3) Accounts, both personal and official, 1852–55 including household bills, rent and freight on goods imported.

Photocopies:
Letter 8 March 1851 from Ellen Layton, Secretary of the Colonial Committee of the British Ladies Female Emigrant Society; two private letters to W.A. Sanford from Mr Rochester 29 May 1852, and Jane Tiphett 19 July 1854; nine letters 1851–54, almost all to W.A. Sanford and one by him to his brother. Other correspondents include Thomas Brown, Rev. W.B. Brown, M.W. Clifton, W. Harris and H. Campfield.

Nine-page list available for reference.

Entry 406   Reels M681–686

Name **SCHOOL OF ORIENTAL AND AFRICAN STUDIES**

Title Collections

Inclusive dates 1769–1960

Quantity 6 reels of microfilm

Location of original School of Oriental and African Studies, Thornhaugh Street, Russell Square, London WC1H 0XG, England

Note
William Marsden (1754–1836) was a collector of Oriental coins and manuscripts and published a number of books on the Far East. Sidney Herbert Ray (1888–1939) was an authority on Oceanic languages. In 1898–99 he visited the Torres Strait Islands, New Guinea and Borneo with the Cambridge Anthropological Expedition.

Description
M686: Marsden collection
1) Vocabularies of the languages of Tonga and New Caledonia, compiled by officers of the French frigates *L'Esperance* and *La Recherche,* with some documents concerning the crews of the ships 1793.

2) Volume of Malay and Sumatran manuscripts of the eighteenth century.

3) D.C. Solander, 'Vocabulary of the Language of Tahiti'.

4) Vocabularies compiled by Sir Joseph Banks during Cook's first voyage 1768–71. They relate to the languages of Tahiti, Prince's Island, Sulu, Samarang, New Holland, New Zealand, Savu, Madagascar, Malabar and Peru.

5) Notebooks of William Dawes concerning languages spoken in the Sydney area c.1790.

M681–685: Ray Papers

1) Manuscript notes used for his published works and many notes and manuscripts collected by Ray. They contain vocabularies and notes of languages in Polynesia, Melanesia, Micronesia and dialects of New Guinea. There are also letters 1891–93 from R.H. Rickard, O. Michelsen, L. Fison, W. Gunn and R.H. Mathews. The vocabularies were compiled by Ray, W.G. Ivens, A.E. Hunt, E.B. Savage, J.H.L. Waterhouse, Charles M. Woodford, Copeland King, Herbert W. Williams, C. Oswald Lelean, William A. Heighway, J.R. Metcalfe, W. Mersh Strong, Arthur Capell, R.C. Nicholson, Rev. R.H. Rickard, J.M. Steward, Fred R. Isom, Henry Welchman, A.C. Tinoni, C.W. Howard, S.G. Caulton, G. Bogese, E. Bourne, R.L. Turner, O. Charles Shaw, J. Percy Money, G.O. Manning, A.B. Milner, William Gray, Oscar Michelsen, H.N. Drummond, J.W. Blencowe, Arthur Maurice Hocart, H.B.T. Somerville, S.C. Weigall, Rev. S.R. Rooney, Allan H. Cropp, Frederick William Christian, H.E.B. Case, Rev. R.H. Codrington, Alexander Morton, A. Brittain, Thomas Levuhi and William Halse Rivers. There are also notes on the vocabulary and epigraphy of the Easter Island tablet compiled by Ray and sections from the catalogue of Ray's printed books and manuscripts.

2) Other manuscripts include: an index to A. Dalrymple's collection of maps and list of the contents of his memoirs; official documents 1808 of Henry Dundas, 1st Viscount Melville; two vocabularies by W.G. Ivens of the Torres Strait Islands and the New Hebrides; C.G. Seligman and G. Pim, 'Vocabulary of the Language of the Ottai tribe, Queensland'.

17-page list available for reference.

Entry 407   Reels M2468–2475

Name **SCOTT, Walter Jervoise (1835–1890)**

Title Papers

Inclusive dates 1866–98

Quantity 8 reels of microfilm

Location of original Sir James Scott, Hants, England

Note
Emigrated to Queensland with his brother George Arthur Scott (1833–95) in 1863. They invested

in the Valley of Lagoons Station in the Burdekin district. In 1864 Walter became a managing partner and remained there until his death.

Description
Letterbooks, photograph albums, correspondence and financial papers relating to the Valley of Lagoons. Correspondents include Walter, Arthur and Charles Scott, James Winter Scott, R.G.W. Herbert, Sir George Bowen, R.H. Gamlen, Archibald E. Scott, W. Kilgour, Villiers Brown, R.J. Atkinson, William Wood and W.A. Love.

Three-page list available for reference.

Entry 408   Reels M584, M985–986

Name **SCOTTISH RECORD OFFICE**

Title Collections

Inclusive dates 1760–1925

Quantity 3 reels of microfilm

Location of original Scottish Record Office, HM General Register House, Princes Street, Edinburgh EH1 3YY, Scotland

Description
M584:

1) Ailsa muniments: two letters from John Hutchison, HMS *Captivity* 1811, and Governor Lachlan Macquarie 1812, concerning John Hutchison, then employed by Simeon Lord.

2) Breadalbane muniments: three letters 1834–45 including one from Walter R. Davidson of Sydney asking for a position in the Survey Department, New South Wales, and one from W.E. Cormack of Auckland criticising the Treaty of Waitangi.

3) Campbell of Jura deposit: copies of letters about the Sydney business affairs of William Cadell, mainly from James Campbell 1839–41; letters 1848–61 from A.C. McDougall of Port Phillip and Dunolly, Victoria, and John Rutherford 1859, of Gardiner's Creek near Melbourne, containing descriptions of the colony, goldfields and bushrangers, as well as family matters.

4) Clerk of Penicuik muniments: letter from James Clerk, HMS *Queen Charlotte* 1793 about fighting the French; one of the new crew Peter Heywood being a *Bounty* mutineer; documents about Antarctic expeditions and the Van Diemen's Land Observatory, including the recommendation of Sir George Murray as director 1843; letters about a claim for compensation by Robert M. Neill of Albany

1842–43, including sketches of Albany and of Aborigines; papers containing statistics of imports and prices of wheat imported into New South Wales and Van Diemen's Land 1841–43; British vessels in the East Indies 1845; comments on the French in Tahiti; letters 1844–57 concerning the business affairs of Sir George Clerk, his sons Henry and George, and Alexander Clerk of Auckland, with Australian negotiations handled by W.M. Bell and Co of Melbourne.

5) Cuninghame of Thorntoun muniments: correspondence from William Macredie of Melbourne 1839; from George E.B. Wrey of Sydney and New Zealand 1877–82; and from Christiana Cuninghame and Sarah Wrey 1847–54, all describing life in the colonies.

6) Dalhousie muniments: letters 1846–47 about the mutiny of troops at Porirua, New Zealand; printed matter and memoranda on military and political affairs in Australia and New Zealand 1852–56; 15-page letter from Lauderdale Maule, Sydney Barracks 1830 to Lord Ramsay, giving his views on social and political conditions in the colony.

7) Macpherson of Cluny muniments: letters and papers 1855–66 concerning Col. Donald Macpherson of the 39th Regiment and his estate, including letters on the case *Berry v Stirling* from William and Allan Macpherson to James Norton and Alexander Berry.

8) Murray of Lintrose muniments: documents concerning land in Western Australia originally granted in 1837 to William B. Habgood, with indentures between Robert M. Habgood and John Fairbairn 1857, and the former and John G. Murray 1870; papers regarding land dealings of Murray and his family 1870–81, and Murray and Stirling Families of Western Australia 1839–52.

9) Riddell papers concerning Campbell D. Riddell, member of the New South Wales Executive Council 1848–54, including financial papers.

10) Robertson of Kindeace muniments: abstracts of accounts for Major Robertson's company of the 96th Regiment, Auckland and Launceston 1841–44.

11) Seaforth muniments: six printed leaflets and forms 1831–33 on aid to emigrants and conditions in Australia and North America; letter from George Mackenzie of Chester 1836, about emigration of a shepherd named Tweedie.

M985–986:
1) Melville Castle muniments: selected letters and papers 1783–1860 of Henry Dundas, 1st Viscount Melville, and Robert Dundas, 2nd Viscount Melville, on colonial and foreign affairs, including military and naval matters and East India Co concerns. There are letters on: surveys of the Australian and New Zealand coasts 1826–27; the system of hiring transport ships 1800; supplying timber from New South Wales 1804; and requests seeking naval and other appointments 1783–1829. A large number of documents deal with the East Indies and East India Co affairs, including the expedition against Java in 1811.

2) Seafield muniments: letters and papers 1760–65 of Capt. Charles C. Grant of HMS *Lenox* and HMS *Seahorse* containing material on the Philippines, the East India Co, and naval affairs, including the observation of the transit of Venus in 1761. Six letters 1794–1802 from John Grant, who was transported to New South Wales in 1794 and assigned on arrival to John Macarthur. The letters describe conditions aboard the convict ship and at Rio de Janeiro, and the political situation in New South Wales.

3) Account 1871–72 of a voyage by Alexander Strathern from Glasgow to Melbourne and back to Liverpool aboard the *Loch Tay*.

4) Letter 7 July 1896 to John Rodger on the death of his brother Andrew at Timaru, New Zealand.

5) Elphinstone muniments: journal 1884–85 of travels in Australia, New Zealand and the Pacific, and reprint from the *Brechin Advertiser* April 1925 by W. R. Burns entitled 'Australian Exploration, The Honourable David Carnegie'.

6) Buchanan of Leny collection: memorandum c.1820 on New Zealand, its climate and people.

7) Murray of Murraythwaite papers: letters 1853–54 from Henry W. Murray of Wellington, New South Wales, about sheep-farming, commenting on the low state of morals in the colony.

8) Fraser Stodart and Ballingall Papers: letters 1920–23 and financial papers of Beatrice M. Bell of Australia.

9) Bruce and Kerr papers: letter 5 August 1819 of Governor Lachlan Macquarie stating his desire to return home.

28-page list available for reference.

Entry 409 Reels M1914–1917

Name **SCRATCHLEY, Sir Peter (1835–1885)**

Title Papers

Inclusive dates 1836–1938

Quantity 4 reels of microfilm

Location of original Mrs M.L. Scratchley, Kent, England

Note
Commissioned in Royal Engineers 1850, served in Crimea 1855–56, India 1857–59 and Victoria 1860–65. Returned to Australia in 1877 to assist Sir William Jervois in advising colonies on defence. Became Commissioner of Defences of Australia and New Zealand in 1879. Appointed first Special Commissioner for New Guinea in 1884.

Description
1) Journals 1855–85. Subjects include: Indian Mutiny; impressions of Melbourne and other Victorian towns; Melbourne defences; Victorian politics; reports on Australian defences; and social events. Also includes accounts by his secretary of Scratchley's illness and death.

2) Official papers, correspondence and notes 1854–85. Subjects include Scratchley's reports on defences of Australia and New Zealand, notes on field fortifications, letters on his work in Tasmania, and correspondence with Sir William Jervois.

3) Notes on New Guinea.

4) Paper and cuttings on New Guinea and death of Scratchley 1885–1901. Correspondents include G.S. Fort, Lord Carrington, Lady Loch, Bishop J. Moorhouse, W.G. Lawes, H.O. Forbes and P.A. Scratchley.

5) Lists of New Guinea artefacts collected by Scratchley.

Five-page list available for reference.

Entry 410 Reels M590, M1093–1100

Name **SELWYN, George Augustus, Bishop (1809–1878)**

Title Papers

Inclusive dates 1831–1952

Quantity 9 reels of microfilm

Location of original Selwyn College, Grange Road, Cambridge CB3 9DQ, England

Note
First Anglican Bishop of New Zealand 1841–68. He travelled widely throughout his vast diocese and also in Melanesia to promote Christianity. He also took a leading part in debate on the major constitutional and political issues in New Zealand. He returned to England in 1868 and was appointed Bishop of Lichfield.

Description
M590:
1) Diary January 1843–March 1844 noting daily routine and details of journeys undertaken with sketches of some of the localities visited. This diary and the following notes contain unofficial censuses of many New Zealand districts in 1844 and 1851; they list the Pakeha and Maori residents by name, showing in many cases ages, family, length of residence, number of deaths in the area. Notes include itineraries for journeys during which Selwyn performed baptisms and marriages in outlying areas, lists of church members and Maori converts, and jottings on finance.

2) Letters written by Selwyn 1843–57 including lengthy letters to his family describing various voyages throughout the Melanesian island groups. Some letters contain sketches and maps and all record Selwyn's impressions of the natives, traders, treatment of the islanders by Europeans, prospects for mission work and education.

3) Letters 1842–64 written by the Bishop's wife, Sarah Selwyn, mainly to the Rev. Edward Coleridge and his wife at Eton. The letters document domestic and family activities, together with local and church affairs, and give her impressions of New Zealand and its inhabitants. She recorded her husband's activities and referred to Sir George Grey and the Maori Wars.

4) Miscellaneous material including a photograph of Selwyn, sketch and plan of the first *Southern Cross* mission ship, copies of official dispatches 1864–69, several referring to Selwyn's assistance during the Maori Wars, and

23 addresses presented to Selwyn 1868 on his departure from New Zealand.

5) Letters 1861–69 written by Bishop J.C. Patteson, one a personal letter to Lady Martin 1861, one dated 1868 dealing with traffic in native labour, and a typescript copy of a personal letter to Bishop C.J. Abraham 1869.

6) Papers relating to the death of Patteson and the punitive visit to the islands by HMS *Rosario* (Capt. A.H. Markham) 1871–72. They include correspondence between Selwyn and Markham and the printed Parliamentary Paper on the voyage of the *Rosario*.

7) Three addresses presented to Sir William Martin, first Chief Justice of New Zealand, on his departure in 1874.

M1093–1100:

1) Correspondence 1831–72 of Selwyn, Sarah Selwyn, Rev. E. Coleridge and Rev. William Cotton, domestic chaplain to Selwyn. Principal correspondents are George and Sarah Selwyn, Bishop Charles Abraham, Caroline Abraham, Bishop W.G. Broughton, Archbishop W. Howley, William Cotton, D. Coates, Henry Venn, Sir William and Lady Martin and T.B. Hutton. The letters contain material on many aspects of religious and domestic life in New Zealand. Personal and family matters are recorded, together with descriptions of journeys within the diocese, and to and from England. Ecclesiastical and missionary affairs, including financial details, are dealt with at length. Other subjects discussed are: education and religion in Australia, New Zealand and Melanesia; the goldrushes; relations between Maori people and government officials; settlers and missionaries; and attitudes towards other missionaries, particularly the Wesleyans. The mapping of New Zealand is referred to briefly. The Maori Wars and land dealings are the subject of much of the correspondence.

2) Letter-book 1840–60 containing letters from D. Coates, Henry Venn, Archdeacon H. Williams, Sir George Grey and others. Subjects include: relations with the New Zealand Co; grants of land by Maoris to missions; the Maori Wars; German missionaries in the Chatham Islands; relations between Selwyn and the Church Missionary Society; and the history of the Society.

3) Sermons by Selwyn.

4) Typescript copy of recollections of Sarah Selwyn 1892 (220 p.)

5) Plans and sketches of St John's College, Auckland; photographs of Selwyn, and of New Zealand churches; map of Waimate; sketch of the first *Southern Cross* and of the *Tomatin* leaving Plymouth 1841.

6) Letters patent appointing Selwyn Bishop of New Zealand and Bishop of Lichfield; pamphlets relating to St John's College, Auckland; printed addresses presented to Selwyn; newspaper cuttings.

7) Later papers include correspondence concerning Selwynesque churches in New Zealand, correspondence of Bishop J.R. Selwyn, and papers concerning Selwyn College and other memorials to Selwyn.

39-page list available for reference.

Entry 411   Reels M1543–1547

Name **SEYMOUR, Sir George, Admiral (1787–1870)**

Title Papers

Inclusive dates 1834–62

Quantity 5 reels of microfilm

Location of original Warwick County Record Office, Priory Park, Cape Road, Warwick CV34 4JS, England

Note
Naval officer. Commander-in-Chief of the Pacific Station 1844–48. His nephew Sir Frederick Beauchamp Seymour (1821–1895) commanded HMS *Pelorus* on the Australian Station 1857–63 and the Naval Brigade in New Zealand 1860–61.

Description
Journals, diaries, order books, memoranda, letter-books and family correspondence mainly referring to naval and political events in the Pacific 1844–48, in particular Anglo-French relations in Tahiti and the Sandwich Islands and the possible annexation of the Sandwich Islands by the United States. Correspondents include Sir George and Lady Seymour, Francis Seymour, Lord Haddington, General W. Miller and Queen Pomare.

There are also several letters 1859–60 of Frederick Seymour describing life on the Australian Station, politics in Victoria, and the war against the Maoris.

Six-page list available for reference.

Entry 412   Reel M1198

Name **SHAKESPEAR, A.T., Brigadier (1884–1964)**
Title Papers
Inclusive dates 1934–42
Quantity 1 reel of microfilm
Location of original Mrs N. Davies, Hants, England

Note
Officer of the Royal Engineers, serving as Assistant
Adjutant and Quarter-Master General in Malaya
1934–37.

Description
Album 1934–36 containing newspaper cuttings,
invitations and photographs of Singapore,
Malaya and Ceylon, a small group of letters and
a notebook. There is also a diary kept by Mrs A.T.
Shakespeare 1934–35 describing the voyage from
England and the first three months in Singapore.

A short contents list is located at the beginning of
the reel.

Entry 413   Reels M2722–2726

Name **SHEFFIELD CITY ARCHIVES**
Title Collections
Inclusive dates 1772–1975
Quantity 5 reels of microfilm
Location of original Sheffield City Archives,
52 Shoreham Street, Sheffield S1 4SP, England

Description
1) Letter 1866 of E.H. Allies to Michael J. Ellison
   referring to an attack by Aborigines, and
   purchase of Brovunia sheep station in Gayndah,
   Queensland.
2) Papers 1849–58 of Capt. Charles Barker
   referring to the Spanish attacks on Sulu and
   impressions of Singapore and Honolulu.
3) Correspondence 1895–1920 to Edward
   Carpenter concerning his books *Intermediate
   Sex* and *Towards Democracy*, his poetry and
   other works. Correspondents include Winifred
   Moore, Robert Dashwood, Grace E. Wills and
   Eleanor Barton.
4) Correspondence 1840–1946 of Elmhirst Family
   referring to life in Australia, the effects of
   drought, and Sydney politics. Correspondents
   include Laura Elmhirst Hughes and Philip Potts.
5) Letters 1860–63 of Charles Fowler of Sydney to
   his father referring to family news and economic
   conditions.

6) Letters 1857–65 of Elizabeth Whitton referring
   to the work of her husband, John Whitton,
   as a parliamentarian and his appointment as
   consulting engineer for all trades in New South
   Wales.
7) Foreign day-book of steelmakers John Vessey
   and Sons Ltd 1938–58. The firms listed include
   George H. Martin, Iron and Steel Co of New
   Zealand Ltd, and F.C. Matthew & Sons Ltd.
8) Records 1969–72 of Sheffield Chamber
   of Commerce relating to trade missions to
   Australia and the Far East.
9) Papers 1835–44 of Ellin Family referring to
   trade and investment opportunities in Australia
   and family news. Correspondents include
   Hannah and Benjamin Law of Hobart, and
   Thomas Ellin.
10) Order books 1907–29 of the steel company
    Edgar Allen & Co Ltd, including orders from
    Broken Hill South Silver Mining Co, John
    Chambers & Son Co Ltd, and North Broken Hill
    Mining Co.
11) Letters 1817–26 of George Bennett in Tahiti
    to Joseph, Elizabeth and Catherine Read
    concerning preaching and teaching the South
    Seas Islanders, native customs and costume
    and preparation for the coronation of Pomare III.
12) Records 1849–80 of cutlery manufacturer
    Needham, Veal and Tyzack. The Australian
    firms with which it traded included W. Bennett,
    Edward Duchett, Farrhurst & Co, and Mene
    & Edwards.
13) Business diary 1905 of L.J. Coombe kept during
    a visit to Australia and New Zealand.
14) Correspondence 1821–40 of James
    Montgomery including account of George
    Bennett's visit to Australia, New Zealand and
    the Pacific, and missionary work in the Pacific.
15) Records 1897–1939 of Sheffield Smelting Co
    Ltd referring to New Zealand Consolidated
    Dental Co Ltd, Grundy Bothers, Sydney Mint,
    Bank of New Zealand and Bank of New South
    Wales. Correspondents are Talbot, Oliver and
    John Wilson.
16) Letters of Thomas A. Browne (Rolf Boldrewood)
    to Edward Montagu-Stuart-Wortley-Mackenzie,
    1st Earl of Wharncliffe, referring to friends
    in Australia, Australian politics, cricket,
    bushrangers and political issues in Victoria,
    including universal suffrage.
17) Papers 1772–1834 of Wentworth Family
    including a letter 1772 from Joseph Banks
    to Edmund Burke, notes on Norfolk Island
    1791–92, and correspondence concerning
    D'Arcy Wentworth in New South Wales and
    Norfolk Island.

Correspondents include Lord Fitzwilliam, D'Arcy Wentworth, W.C. Wentworth, P.G. King and John Hunter.

18) Papers 1880–1900 of composer Joseph Gillott including scores and programs.

19) Papers 1973–75 of Labour politician John Mendelson referring to British campaign for the release of political prisoners in Indonesia.

33-page list available for reference.

Entry 414   Reel M398

Name **SHERBROOKE, Robert Lowe, 1st Viscount (1811–1892)**

Title Correspondence

Inclusive dates 1819–96

Quantity 1 reel of microfilm

Location of original Mrs R.T. Sneyd, Avon, England

Note
Robert Lowe, 1st Viscount Sherbrooke (created 1880), politician, lawyer, writer. From 1842 to 1850 Lowe lived with his first wife Georgiana in Sydney, where he practised as a lawyer. He was a nominated member of the New South Wales Legislative Council 1843–44 and an elected member from 1846 until he returned to England. Liberal MP 1852–80; Chancellor of the Exchequer 1868–73; Home Secretary 1873–74.

Description
1) 20 letters 1840–49 written mainly by Georgiana Lowe to her sister-in-law Agnes Lowe and a relative, Mrs Sherbrooke. The letters describe life in Sydney, conditions in the colony in general, and political developments.

2) Miscellanea including notes on debates at Oxford 1831, in which Lowe participated; newspaper cuttings including material on Australia and items of biographical interest; letter 28 July 1896 from Joseph Chamberlain containing reminiscences of Sherbrooke.

Three-page list available for reference.

Entry 415   Reels M2021–2024

Name **SHROPSHIRE RECORD OFFICE**

Title Collections

Inclusive dates 1786–1913

Quantity 4 reels of microfilm

Location of original Shropshire Record Office, Shirehall, Abbey Foregate, Shrewsbury SY2 6ND, England

Description
1) Calendars 1786–1845 of prisoners, Shrewsbury Gaol, listing convicts tried at both Assizes and Quarter Sessions.

2) Papers 1839–1904 of Humphrey, Jonathon and Edward Sandford referring to survey of Adelaide and leases of properties.

3) Correspondence 1877–78 concerning emigration of Lewis Kay to Queensland.

4) Papers 1874–77 of Lord Hill dealing with mining lease at Ravenswood, Queensland.

5) Log and letter-book 1863–65 of Rear-Admiral Robert Jenkins, kept while serving in New Zealand. Includes an account of the attack on Gate Pah, Tauranga, by 68th Regiment and Naval Brigade.

Six-page list available for reference.

Entry 416   Reel M834

Name **SIDDELLS, George**

Title Log

Inclusive dates 1855–56

Quantity 1 reel of microfilm

Location of original Rev. W.F. Browning, Oxfordshire, England

Note
Mate on the first *Southern Cross* under Capt. George Sustine. The ship was bought from subscriptions raised in England by Bishop G.A. Selwyn for the Melanesian Mission. In 1855 it made its first voyage to New Zealand and sailed to Melanesia the next year. After four voyages the *Southern Cross* was wrecked north of Auckland in 1860.

Description
Log of the first *Southern Cross* 6 January 1855–24 May 1856, London–Southampton–New Zealand–Norfolk Island. It mainly records weather conditions, bearings and the activities of the crew.

Name **SLADEN, Douglas (1857–1947)**

Title Papers

Inclusive dates 1886–1921

Quantity 2 reels of microfilm

Location of original Central Library, Little Green, Richmond-upon-Thames, Surrey TW9 1QL, England

Note
Sladen emigrated to Victoria in 1879. Professor of Modern History, University of Sydney 1882–84. Returned to England in 1884 and wrote over 50 books, including a number of publications on Adam Lindsay Gordon.

Description
1) Personal and general correspondence 1886–1920 referring to *A Century of Australian Song* (1888, 1891); *Australian Ballads and Rhymes; For the Term of his Natural Life; Adam Lindsay Gordon*; Sir John Monash; and Sladen's reminiscences of life in Australia. Correspondents include Sir John Henniker Heaton, A.P. Martin, C. Mackellar and J. Howlett Ross.

2) Literary and business correspondence 1905–20 concerning Sladen's editorial work on: *Australian Poets 1788–1888* (1888); *Adam Lindsay Gordon and his Friends in England and Australia* (1912); *Poems of Adam Lindsay Gordon* (1912) and *The Autobiography of Sir John Monash.*

3) Literary agency 1912–21 relating to Sladen's interest in Australian literature and his writings, including: *The Finger of Mr Blee*; *Peter Blundell*; *The Cities of Zenobia and Saladin*; *Poems of Adam Lindsay Gordon* (1912) and W.M. Hughes' *The Industrial Battlefield*. Main correspondent is F. Butterworth.

4) Books and literary projects 1911–16 comprising correspondence and reviews of *Adam Lindsay Gordon and his Friends in England and Australia* (1912) and *From Boundary-Rider to Prime Minister* (1916). Correspondents include Edith Humphris, Sir John McColl, K. Murdoch, H.M. Hyndman and W.M. Hughes.

19-page list available for reference.

Name **SMITH, Cicely Fox**

Title Papers

Inclusive dates 1852–1936

Quantity 3 reels of microfilm

Location of original National Maritime Museum, Romney Road, Greenwich, London SE10 9NF, England

Note
Author of books on sailing ships.

Description
1) Logs and remark books kept on the *Blackwall* 1851–52 and *Prince of Wales* by H.R. James, *Rodney* 1887–90 and *Hesperus* 1890–95 by F.W. Corner, and *City of Adelaide* 1891–1901 by various members of the crew.

2) Autobiography of G. Sorrell containing details of voyages 1860–80 including journeys on the River Murray.

3) Autobiography of Capt. T. Young describing voyages to Australia on the *City of Agra* 1865–93.

4) Correspondence 1925–36.

5) Notes and cutting concerning the loss of HMS *Pandora* 1791 and the wreck of HMS *Porpoise* 1803.

Five-page list available for reference.

Name **SMITH, John**

Title Diary

Inclusive dates 1838

Quantity 1 reel of microfilm

Location of original National Library of Australia, Canberra ACT 2600

Description
Diary kept by John Smith, surgeon on the convict ship *Clyde,* on a voyage from Dublin to Sydney, via the Cape of Good Hope, April–September 1838.

Name **SMYTH, Arthur Bowes (1750–1790)**

Title Journal

Inclusive dates 1787–89

Quantity 1 reel of microfilm

Location of original British Library, Great Russell Street, London WC1B 3DG, England

Note

Surgeon on board the *Lady Penrhyn,* one of the smaller transports of the First Fleet. He was known on board as Arthur Bowes, although this journal is lettered 'Smythe's Journal'.

Description

Copy of a journal kept by Arthur Bowes Smyth, the first entry dated 20 March 1787 and the final entry dated 13 August 1789. This copy was possibly written some years after the voyage, and does not appear to be in Smyth's hand. It differs from both the original journal held in the National Library of Australia and the copy held by the Mitchell Library, Sydney. It contains several illustrations, not included in the original journal, omits some details found in the original, but includes additional observations apparently made in retrospect. The journal describes the voyage of the First Fleet via Rio de Janeiro and Cape Town, Smyth's stay in Australia and his return voyage via Tahiti and China. Entries include navigational and weather observations and accounts of shipboard routine. Details are given of treatment of the women convicts during the voyage and events in the first three months of the new colony, including comments on the behaviour of convicts and marines, very detailed descriptions of the Aborigines and early encounters with them. Smyth left Port Jackson in May 1788, but in the short time he spent in New South Wales he recorded observations on the fauna and flora of the mainland, Lord Howe and Norfolk Islands, with special emphasis on the bird life. The journal contains detailed lists of the ship's company, officers stationed in New South Wales, and female convicts aboard the *Lady Penrhyn* together with a list of children on board.

Name **SOCIETY FOR PROMOTING CHRISTIAN KNOWLEDGE**

Title Records

Inclusive dates 1786–1966

Quantity 21 reels of microfilm

Location of original SPCK, Holy Trinity Church, Marylebone Road, London NW1 4DU, England

Note

Founded in 1699, the Society funded Anglican schools, libraries and the publication of books and tracts, and took a strong interest in overseas churches and missions.

Description

1) Annual reports 1815–1952 referring to supply of books to convict hulks, Bishop W. Broughton, work of Society in Australia, New Zealand and Pacific, assistance to emigrants, translations into Maori and Pacific languages, and church building.

2) General Board minute-books 1786–1838. Subjects include meetings with Sir Joseph Banks, Rev. Samuel Marden, Rev. Richard Johnson, supply of books and grants for churches in Australia.

3) Standing Committee minute-books 1826–1929 referring to letters from bishops in Australia, New Zealand and the Pacific.

4) Minutes of Committee re correspondence with District and Diocesan Committees 1821–24 referring to distributions of books and tracts for use by schools and convicts in New South Wales.

5) Foreign Translation Committee minute-books 1841–1917 referring to printing of prayer books in Maori and Hawaiian languages.

6) Emigration Committee minute-books 1882–1966. Subjects include appointment of port and voyage chaplains and expansion of migration to Australia after 1945.

7) Ladies Emigration Committee minute-books 1897–1921.

8) Overseas Grant Books 1840–1961 referring to grants for endowment of bishoprics and clergy, creation of churches and schools, supply of goods, scholarships and assistance for emigration.

9) Secretary's letterbox 1843–60. Subjects include dispatch of books and tracts, grants to churches and schools, supply of books to emigrants, and financial matters.

10) Pitcairn Island papers 1853–59 including minute-book 1852–58 of Committee for

Managing the Pitcairn Island Fund, letter-book 1853–59 of Pitcairn Island Fund Committee, and Pitcairn Island Register 1790–1959. Correspondents include Rev. T.B. Murray, Rev. G.H. Nobbs, Bishop G.A. Selwyn, J. Adams, Sir Charles Lucas and Sir Everard im Thurm.

52-page list available for reference.

Entry 422   Reels M693–707

Name **SOCIETY OF FRIENDS**

Title Records

Inclusive dates 1785–1934

Quantity 15 reels of microfilm

Location of original Society of Friends Library, Friends House, Euston Road, London NW1 2BJ, England

Note
The first meeting of the Society of Friends in Australia was held on 12 February 1832 when James Backhouse and G.W. Walker met soon after arriving in Hobart. The Hobart Town monthly meeting was established on 12 September 1833 and the first meeting on the mainland was held in Sydney on 4 January 1835. Among the Society's achievements were the Hobart Savings Bank, the Boys' Reformatory founded by Backhouse and Walker and, at a later stage, the Friends School, Hobart, which was founded in 1887. Communication with the parent Quaker body in England was formerly through the Continental Committee of the Meeting for Sufferings and after 1903 with the Australia (afterwards Australasian, then Australia and New Zealand) Committee.

Description
Minutes, some original records and annual reports scattered throughout the official correspondence, miscellaneous and private papers held in the Friends House Library. Some journals and correspondence are primarily of religious interest, others such as those of Daniel Wheeler, James Backhouse, William Benson, Ann F. Jackson and E. Maria Bishop contain detailed descriptions of people and places. The collection has been divided and filmed in the following groups:

1) Selections from minutes of London Yearly Meeting 1834–1916, London Meeting for Sufferings 1828–1916, Continental Committee 1817–1905, and Australasian Committee 1903–19. Most of the minutes are indexed.

2) Entries 1840–72 from *Testimonies Concerning Ministers Deceased* for Daniel Wheeler, John

Bell, Robert Lindsey, James Backhouse and Thomas Pierce.

3) Australasian material in the Casual Correspondence volume of the Epistles of the London Yearly Meeting, comprising official correspondence 1785–1881, mainly epistles, sent to and from the London Meeting and members of the Society in Van Diemen's Land, South Australia and Sydney.

4) Portfolio series of miscellaneous volumes including records of the Continental Committee, some official correspondence of James Backhouse and Daniel Wheeler, reports and minutes.

5) Manuscript Boxes. Small collections of correspondence, official and personal, accounts of visits, copies of minutes of meetings, newspaper cuttings, lists of members and printed pamphlets 1835–1934 including material about the Hobart Friends School, conscription and the Wellington Friends Hostel. Also includes correspondence, minutes and cuttings of Charles J. Holdsworth.

6) Items 1831–1922 relating to Australasia from manuscript boxes (lettered), including letters of George Washington Walker, list of Friends 1854, letters of Lucy F. Morland, and notes on the history of Friends in Australia and New Zealand.

7) Letters, papers and extracts from the journals 1832–46 of Daniel Wheeler covering his travels in the South Seas.

8) Letterbooks, journal letter transcripts and an account book 1831–68 of James Backhouse (1794–1869) of Van Diemen's Land.

9) Selections from the journals 1852–61 of Robert Lindsey and his wife Sarah describing two visits to Australia and New Zealand.

10) Extracts from the journals 1866–68 of William Benson including sketches of buildings, zoological specimens and maps.

11) Selections from the autobiography of Alfred Wright referring to his visits to Australia in 1874–75 and 1890–92.

12) Extracts from diaries 1880–82 of Isaac Sharp describing his travels in Australia and New Zealand.

13) Collection of autographs of C.S. Gibson including 'Plants named after Friends'.

14) Correspondence 1887–90 of Howard Hodgkin relating to economic conditions in Ireland and emigration to Australia.

51-page list available for reference.

Entry 423   Reels M2540–2554

Name **SOLANDER, Daniel (1736–1782)**

Title Papers

Inclusive dates 1769–[c.1810]

Quantity 15 reels of microfilm

Location of original Botany and Zoology Libraries, British Museum (Natural History), Cromwell Road, South Kensington, London SW7 5BD, England

Note
Naturalist. Solander joined the scientific staff of the *Endeavour* in 1768. After returning to England he became Sir Joseph Banks' secretary and librarian and was later appointed Keeper of Natural History at the British Museum.

Description
The papers comprise descriptions and lists of plants, fishes, birds and other fauna collected by Banks. There are also lists of species collected on Cook's other voyages.

19-page list available for reference.

Entry 424   Reels M2504–2511

Name **SOMERS FAMILY**

Title Papers

Inclusive dates 1876–1937

Quantity 8 reels of microfilm

Location of original Mr James Hervey-Bathurst, Ledbury, Herefordshire, England

Note
Members of the Somers Family included Anna Eckford Somers Cocks and Arthur Somers Cocks, 6th Baron Somers. Lord Somers was Governor of Victoria 1926–31.

Description
1) Papers 1876–90 of Anna E. Somers Cocks referring to family in Australia.
2) Papers 1926–31 of Lord Somers, including letters, photographs, cashbooks, brochures and programs. They refer to appointment of governors, migration to Australia, effects of police strike and political affairs.

   Correspondents include Lord and Lady Somers, Dame Nellie Melba, Sir Isaac Isaacs and Sir Robert Gibson.
3) Papers 1926–27 of Lady Somers, including letters from her daughter and a scrapbook.

Eight-page list available for reference.

Entry 425   Reels M1949–1950

Name **SOMERSET RECORD OFFICE**

Title Records

Inclusive dates 1806–1953

Quantity 2 reels of microfilm

Location of original Somerset Record Office, Obridge Road, Taunton TA2 7PU, England

Description
1) Register of prisoners at Shepton Mallet Gaol 1842–72 containing many references to transportation.
2) Papers 1806–1906 of Acland Hood Family including correspondence of Sir Alexander Acland Hood concerning estate of Samuel Tucker of Tallangatta, Victoria, and naval papers concerning the possibility of French squadron and American frigates attacking Sydney in 1813.
3) Papers 1829–46 of W. Fawcett relating to properties in Van Diemen's Land and Western Australia.
4) Scrapbook 1896–97 of Thomas Cole, secretary of Incorporated Association of Gas Engineers, recording a visit to Australia and New Zealand.
5) Papers 1876–78 of Capel Family concerning estate of John Capel of Murray River, Victoria.
6) Diaries 1862–63 of John L. Hatswell describing voyage from Gravesend to Auckland and first impressions of New Zealand.
7) Journals 1880–81 of Capt. M. Medlycott on voyage of HMS *Turquoise* in the Pacific Ocean.
8) Papers 1831–56 of Sandford Family, including letters of Henry and John Sandford referring to settlement at Port Gregory and relations with Aborigines in Western Australia.
9) Diaries and notes 1952–53 of Mrs E. Cook describing voyage on SS *Strathaird* from Tilbury to Australia and referring to her stay in Sydney, Australian Aborigines and travels in outback.

Seven-page list available for reference.

Entry 426   Reels M2579–2580

Name **SOMERSETSHIRE REGIMENT, 2ND (40th REGIMENT)**

Title Records

Inclusive dates 1832–1988

Quantity 2 reels of microfilm

Location of original Regimental Headquarters, Queen's Lancashire Regiment, Peninsula Barracks, Warrington, Cheshire WA2 7BR, England.

Note
The Regiment served in Australia 1852–60 including the Eureka Uprising in 1854, and in New Zealand 1860.

Description
1) Records 1823–66 giving a synoptic history of the Regiment, its movements, action, casualties and personnel.
2) Regimental order books 1824–65. Subjects include movement of troops in Australia and guard detail for executions at Sydney Gaol.
3) Guard reports 1854 comprising reports of Emigration Barrack Guard, Gaol Guard and Treasury Guard.
4) New Zealand records 1860–69 referring to conflicts and interviews with Maoris.
5) Correspondence files 1967–88 referring to service in Australia and action at Eureka Stockade.

Four-page list available for reference.

Entry 427   Reels M1921–1922

Name **SOUTH SEA COMPANY**

Title Records

Inclusive dates 1784–1856

Quantity 2 reels of microfilm

Location of original British Library, Great Russell Street, London WC1B 3DG, England

Note
Formed in 1711, the company was granted a monopoly of British trade with South America and the Pacific Islands. Its commercial activities ended in 1750, but it retained its exclusive privileges in the Pacific until 1807.

Description
1) Minutes of Court of Directors 1784–1802 referring to applications for licences to proceed to the southern whale fishery.

2) Register of Instruments 1735–1856 recording licences granted to ships to sail and fish within the limits of the jurisdiction of the company.

Two-page list available for reference.

Entry 428   Reel M815

Name **SOUTH STAFFORDSHIRE REGIMENT (80th REGIMENT)**

Title Records

Inclusive dates 1793–1905

Quantity 1 reel of microfilm

Location of original South Staffordshire Regiment, Whittington Barracks, Lichfield, Staffordshire WS12 9PY, England

Note
The 80th Regiment of Foot was formed in 1793 at the beginning of the wars with France. Between 1835 and 1837 soldiers of the Regiment acted as guards on convict ships to New South Wales and in 1837 the Regiment's headquarters were set up at Windsor, near Sydney. As well as being in charge of convict road gangs, detachments also furnished escorts on the Bathurst and Parramatta roads. In 1840 a detachment was sent to New Zealand for four years where, as well as performing military duties, it erected the stone barracks at Auckland. On 12 August 1844 the Regiment left Sydney for Calcutta. During 1872 it spent some time at Singapore and Hong Kong.

Description
1) Digest, vol. 1 (1793–1897); vol. 2 (1793–1899). The digest was initially written about 1881 and maintained until 1889. It records service of the Regiment giving details of stations at which employed, dates of arrival and departure from these stations, and military operations. It also mentions officer movements and comments on the effect of convict guard duty on the discipline of the Corps.
2) Roll 1804–81. 'Nominal and Descriptive Roll of the 80th Regiment' with entries for name, date of enlistment, age at enlisting, height, trade or occupation, place of birth and remarks such as transferred, discharged, or death. Arranged by date of enlistment.
3) Record of Stations 1793–1905 listing dates of embarkation and disembarkation.
4) Letter 'Purchase of Ensigncy in 98th Foot by Mr Stafford W. Vardon 31/5/59'. Directed to General Monteith of the Indian Army from the Horse Guards.

Entry 429   Reels M2066–2076

Name **SOUTHAMPTON CITY RECORD OFFICE**

Title Collections

Inclusive dates 1804–1950

Quantity 11 reels of microfilm

Location of original Southampton City Record Office, Civic Centre, Southampton SO14 7LY, England

Description

1) Records 1834 of St Mary's Church relating to the sending of young women to New South Wales.

2) Papers 1874–1905 of William V. Jackson relating to his investments and properties in New Zealand.

3) Quarter Session records 1804–29 referring to convicts Joseph Wilkinson on hulk *Laurel*, Henry Butler, William White, Robert Burbridge on the hulk *York*, Richard Ridar, George Ball, Frederick Head and John Peckham.

4) Registrar of Shipping and Seamen records 1866–1913 comprising crew lists of vessels of Shaw, Savill & Albion, P&O Co and other shipping lines. Some logbooks of ships visiting Australia and New Zealand are also included.

Nine-page list available for reference.

Entry 430   Reel M1538

Name **SOUTHWELL, Daniel (c.1764–1797)**

Title Papers

Inclusive dates 1783–93

Quantity 1 reel of microfilm

Location of original British Library, Great Russell Street, London WC1B 3DG, England

Note

Midshipman on HMS *Sirius* 1787, appointed mate on the voyage to New South Wales. He visited the Cape of Good Hope 1788–89 and was placed in charge of the lookout station at South Head, Port Jackson, 1790. Left Sydney on the *Waaksamheyd* in March 1791.

Description

Letters and diaries describing: the voyage to Botany Bay; encounters with Aborigines; cultivation of crops; shortage of provisions; voyage to the Cape of Good Hope; discovery of Lord Howe Island; wreck of HMS *Sirius* at Norfolk Island; and Southwell's return to England in 1791.

Two-page list available for reference.

Entry 431   Reels M2422–2425

Name **SPENCER, Sir Walter Baldwin (1860–1929)**

Title Papers

Inclusive dates 1880–1928

Quantity 4 reels of microfilm

Location of original Pitt Rivers Museum, University of Oxford, Parks Road, Oxford OX1 3PP, England

Note

Biologist and ethnographer. Professor of Biology at Melbourne University 1887–1919. His published works included *Native Tribes of Central Australia* (1899), *Northern Tribes of Central Australia* (1904) and *The Arunta* (1927).

Description

Correspondence, notebooks, diaries and papers relating to the Horn expedition to central Australia in 1894; Spencer's anthropological interests, research and writings on the Australian Aborigines. There are also many references to Melbourne and Oxford Universities. Most of the letters are dated 1884–1903.

Major correspondents are A.W. Howitt, L. Fison, A.C. Haddon, E.B. Tylor, G.C. Bourne, Sir E. Ray Lankester, G.B. Howes, F.J. Gillen, H. Goulty, A. Lang, P. Cahill, H. Balfour, Sir James Frazer and W.A. Horn.

89-page list available for reference.

Entry 432   Reel M829

Name **STAFFORDSHIRE RECORD OFFICE**

Title Collections

Inclusive dates 1765–1931

Quantity 1 reel of microfilm

Location of original Staffordshire Record Office, Eastgate Street, Stafford ST16 2LZ, England

Description

1) Daniel Bate (Calverley) documents: cost estimates 1880 for machinery for New Zealand Government in Auckland.

2) Papers 1865–95 of Lord Hatherton concerning: his shares in the Queensland Land Co and the Queensland Co Ltd; letters 1894–95 from Algernon Littleton, in Tasmania, to his parents; letters 1867 relating to Lieut. Col. Hassard, 57th Regiment, killed in New Zealand.

3) Bill (Farley) collection: papers 1880–1913 concerning Aberfeldie Station, New Zealand, owned by Charles Bill; map 1880 of Australia and New Zealand with the Fiji Islands.

4) Papers 1790–1892 of the Duke of Sutherland including: an investment register 1861–92 for Australia and New Zealand; four printed works, with maps on Borneo 1878; letters 1886–90 to Lady Alexandra Leveson-Gower from Lady Stafford and Lady Broome in Australia; and copy of commission of Governor Arthur Phillip 1790.

5) Documents 1875–88 concerning the will of Joseph K. Barnett.

6) Manby and Steward, solicitors of Wolverhampton: papers 1908–09 concerning the estate of George Pauton of Sydney; personal papers and documents 1890–1909 of the Woodward Family referring to Frank Woodward of Canterbury, New Zealand.

7) Papers 1829–37 of Dyott Family including: report 1830 on exploration of the Swan River; reports 1836–37 by William Palmer on the female factory in Parramatta and the principal Felons Gaol in Sydney; report 1829 in the *Tasmanian and Austral-Asiatic Review* on the court martial of Lieut. Carew; 'Panoramic View of King George's Sound, part of the Colony of Swan River' engraved by Robert Havell from a drawing of Lieut. Robert Dale of the 63rd Regiment 1834.

8) Papers 1882–1900 of Whitehouse Family of Sedgely including letters of Charles Whitehouse in New South Wales, and photograph of the Post Office in Adelaide.

9) Sutherland papers: letter 1790 of Lord Thurlow to Lord Stafford about fishing rights in the South Seas, and the reasons for France entering into war with England; letter 1906 to Lord Stafford on sale of South Seas artefacts in the Leverian Museum.

10) Papers 1765–1800 of William, 2nd Earl of Dartmouth, concerning: trade in the East Indies and the North West Passage, including a letter 1776 from Sir Harry Trelawney on the neglect of not having baptised the Indian Omiah (of Otaheite); letter 1852 from R. Dawson of Sydney referring to a water supply scheme for Sydney; and the effects of gold discovery on life in Australia.

11) Records 1928–39 of St Mary's Parish, Stafford, concerning missionary boats for New Zealand and Borneo.

19-page list available for reference.

Entry 433 Reel M2064

Name **STANBROOK ABBEY**

Title Records

Inclusive dates 1847–90

Quantity 1 reel of microfilm

Location of original Stanbrook Abbey, Callow End, Worcester WR2 4TD, England

Note
Benedictine monastery originally established at Cambrai, France, in 1623. The Stanbrook estate was acquired in 1835. Sisters from Stanbrook Abbey established the first Benedictine convent in Australia at Parramatta in 1849.

Description
1) Letters 1847–55 of Bishop J.B. Polding referring to donations for an Australian seminary and books, vestments for the Australian mission, and plans to establish a Benedictine convent in New South Wales.

2) Letters 1848–74 of Dame Magdalen le Clerc referring to: establishment of convent at Parramatta named 'Subiaco'; the Benedictine monastery in Sydney; services and festivals; recruitment of novices; destruction of St Mary's Cathedral (1869); Bishop J.B. Polding; Dr H.G. Gregory; and Bishop C.H. Davis.

3) Letters 1861–62 of Dame Scholastica Gregson concerning Abbot H.G. Gregory.

4) Letters 1874–87 of Bishop W.B. Ullathorne to Kate Merewether.

5) Account of voyage of Princethorpe nuns to Australia in 1856.

Five-page list available for reference.

Entry 434 Reel M1904

Name **STANHOPE FAMILY**

Title Papers

Inclusive dates 1700–1900

Quantity 1 reel of microfilm

Location of original Kent Archives Office, County Hall, Maidstone ME14 1XQ, England

Note
Philip Stanhope (1805–1875), 5th Earl Stanhope, was a Conservative politician and the biographer of William Pitt. His son Edward Stanhope (1840–93) was Secretary of State for Colonies 1886–87 and Secretary of State for War 1887–92.

Description

1) Papers 1840–43 of Philip Stanhope, Lord Mahon, referring to: motion of William Molesworth for abolition of transportation; land sales in South Australia; draft motion deploring increase in number of convicts on hulks; and convict discipline in Australia.

2) Letters 1863–65 of Philip Stanhope while serving on HMS *Sutlej* on Pacific Station.

3) Papers 1886–91 of Edward S. Stanhope. Subjects include: Australian divorce bills; admission of foreign troops and warships to colonies; New Guinea; Borneo; Adelaide International Exhibition 1887; Melbourne Centennial Exhibition 1888; defences of King George's Sound and Thursday Island; Samoa; Sir Henry Parkes; and Australian Federation. Correspondents include Lord Knutsford, Lord Salisbury, W.H. Smith, Lord Carrington, Lord Kintore, Sir Frederick Weld and Major Gen. J.B. Edwards.

4) Manuscript chart of coast of New Guinea 1700.

5) Letters 1791–1803 of William Pitt referring to Dutch East Indies, panopticon proposal of Jeremy Bentham, and conditions at Port Jackson.

Five-page list available for reference.

Entry 435   Reel M463

Name **STANLEY FAMILY**

Title Papers

Inclusive dates 1832–50

Quantity 1 reel of microfilm

Location of original Cheshire Record Office, Duke Street, Chester CH1 1RL, England

Note

Capt. Owen Stanley (1811–50), naval officer and marine surveyor, was the eldest son of Edward Stanley, later Bishop of Norwich. In 1838 he sailed to Port Essington in northern Australia and in 1840 assisted in the foundation of Auckland and surveyed the harbour. In 1847 he returned to Australia in command of HMS *Rattlesnake,* and for three years was engaged in survey work along the southern coast of New Guinea. His brother Charles Edward Stanley (1819–49), a captain in the Royal Engineers, was private secretary to Sir William Denison when the latter was Lieut.-Governor of Tasmania.

Description

1) Miscellaneous typescript notes on Capt. Owen Stanley collected by Adelaide Lubbock for her book *Owen Stanley*, including a biographical sketch and chronology of his life, and a photograph of his grave at Sydney. There are notes on his voyages 1837–1850, references collected from various published sources and a copy of the Stanley Family tree.

2) Correspondence of the Stanley Family 1837–50 containing some original letters, some handwritten copies and typescript copies of all letters. A major part of the correspondence consists of letters between Owen Stanley and his father, Bishop Edward Stanley. There are also letters from Owen Stanley to other members of the Stanley Family. Also included are two letters from Owen Stanley to Dr J. Thomson 1846, three letters from Dr Thomson to his wife 1849–50, and letters from Owen Stanley to C.J. Tyers 1847–49. With the correspondence for 1849 is a manuscript copy of Owen Stanley's account of the fifth cruise of HMS *Rattlesnake* 3 June–2 October 1849, and a continuation of this account addressed to his sister Mary, 16 October 1849–January 1850. There are also typescript extracts from Thomas Huxley's diary of the fifth voyage of the *Rattlesnake* 1849–50. It includes several references to Stanley interspersed with comments by Adelaide Lubbock.

3) Correspondence of Charles Stanley 1832–49 with his family, especially his sister Catherine Stanley. They relate chiefly to his voyage to Tasmania on the *Windermere* and to his life in Tasmania. With this correspondence are miscellaneous sketches, maps and plans done by Stanley, some of which relate to his voyage to Tasmania.

Six-page list available for reference.

Entry 436   Reel M2014

Name **STAPYLTON, Granville (1800–1840)**

Title Journals

Inclusive dates 1836–38

Quantity 1 reel of microfilm

Location of original Mr H.P. Chetwynd-Stapylton, Chichester, West Sussex PO19 1XL, England

Note

Assistant surveyor in New South Wales in 1828. Second-in-command to Sir Thomas Mitchell's expedition to Australia Felix in 1836. In 1838 he was surveyor under Robert Hoddle in Port Phillip.

Description
1) Journals 1836 kept by Stapylton while on surveying expeditions under Sir Thomas Mitchell referring to encounters and relations with Aborigines, survey of Lachlan and Murrumbidgee Rivers, journey to Australia Felix, Grampian Mountains, Glenelg River, Stapylton's relations with Mitchell and other members of party.
2) Diary April 1838 of journey in Goulburn River district.

Three-page list available for reference.

Entry 437   Reel M855

Name **STEPHENSON, Heathfield Harman (1833–1896)**
Title Papers
Inclusive dates 1861–90
Quantity 1 reel of microfilm
Location of original Mr H.S. Healy, London, England

Note
Captain of the first English cricket team to visit Australia in 1861. Seven of the team, including Stephenson, were Surrey players. They arrived in Melbourne on 24 December 1861 on the *Great Britain* and played matches in Victoria, New South Wales and Tasmania, losing only two out of 15 matches. Stephenson was considered an able captain and was one of the finest players of his time, performing as batsman, bowler or wicketkeeper.

Description
1) Memorandum of agreement September 1861 regarding the 1861–62 cricket tour of Australia.
2) Photograph December 1861 of the English team in Melbourne.
3) Addresses by the Queenscliff, Melbourne and Castlemaine Cricket Clubs to the visiting team.
4) Printed items: *The Cabinet: A Repository of Facts, Figures and Fancies Relating to the Voyage of the "Great Britain" SS from Liverpool to Melbourne, with the Eleven of All England, and other Distinguished Passengers* (1862); J.C. Brodie, *The Victorian Cricketers Guide* (1861); *England v Australia at the Wicket: A Complete Record of all Cricket Matches played between English and Australian Elevens* (1887); H.H.Montgomery, *Old Cricket and Cricketers* (1890).

Two-page list available for reference.

Entry 438   Reel M467

Name **STOBART, Henry, Rev. (d.1896)**
Title Papers
Inclusive dates 1846, 1852–56, 1896
Quantity 1 reel of microfilm
Location of original Miss M.G. Newman, Sussex, England

Note
Anglican priest. Ordained deacon in 1849 and then spent five years travelling overseas as the tutor and companion of Lord Henry Scott (second son of the Duke of Buccleuch), visiting Egypt, India, Australia and New Zealand. In 1865 he was appointed by the Duke of Buccleuch to the living of Warkton in Northamptonshire, which he held until 1881.

Description
1) Letters from Stobart to his mother, Mrs Thomas Chilton, 15 August 1846, October 1852–April 1856, on board the ships *Resolute, Early Bird, Singapore, Bengal, Calcutta, Indus* and *Lotus* and from Sydney, Brisbane, Wollongong, Ceylon, India, the Nile, Cairo, Jerusalem, Paris and Cannes. Many are written in diary form and they are chiefly descriptive. In most cases the original manuscript letters are accompanied by typescript copies.
2) Journal of Stobart commenced on board the ship *Resolute* November 1852–7 July 1853. It describes the voyage to Australia and travels in New South Wales and Queensland with notes on the prices of commodities, land and livestock.
3) Sketches, including views of Armidale Church, Nobby's Head, Newcastle, and a station residence.
4) Newspaper clippings on the death of Stobart, January 1896.
5) Portrait of Stobart.

Three-page list available for reference.

Entry 439   Reels M3051–3054

Name **STOKES, John Lort, Admiral (1812–1885)**

Title Papers

Inclusive dates 1837–72

Quantity 4 reels of microfilm

Location of original National Maritime Museum, Romney Road, Greenwich, London SE10 9NF, England

Note
Naval officer. Served on HMS *Beagle* surveying South American and Australian coasts 1825–43. In 1846–51 he carried out New Zealand surveys while commanding HMS *Acheron*.

Description
Logs, letter-books, correspondence and other papers concerning voyages of HMS *Beagle*, HMS *Acheron* and HMS *Havannah*. They refer to surveys of Northern Australia, Western Australia, Tasmania and New Zealand. Correspondents include E.J. Eyre, P.P. King and J.S. Roe.

17-page list available for reference.

Entry 440   Reel M2539

Name **STONEHAVEN, Lady Ethel (1875–1974)**

Title Albums and scrapbooks

Inclusive dates 1889–98, 1923–41

Quantity 1 reel of microfilm

Location of original Mrs E. Goschen, Somerset, and Mr N.J. Chance, Oxfordshire, England

Note
Lady Ethel and Lady Hilda were the daughters of Algernon Keith Falconer, 9th Earl of Kintore. They first came to Australia in 1889, when Lord Kintore was Governor of South Australia. Lady Ethel married the Conservative politician John Baird, 1st Viscount Stonehaven, who was Governor-General of Australia 1925–30.

Description
1) Scrapbooks 1923–46 of Lady Stonehaven. The cuttings record visits to Canberra, Central Australia and New Guinea. Some of the volumes contain menus, photographs, watercolour sketches and letters.
2) Photograph albums 1889–98 and 1927–30 of Lady Hilda Keith-Falconer. Includes photographs of Government Houses in Adelaide, Hobart and Singapore, scenes in Adelaide Hills, Thursday Island, New Zealand and Malaya.

Five-page list available for reference.

Entry 441   Reels M2983–2994

Name **STRATHCLYDE REGIONAL ARCHIVES**

Title Collections

Inclusive dates 1821–1935

Quantity 12 reels of microfilm

Location of original Strathclyde Regional Archives, Mitchell Library, North Street, Glasgow G3 7DN, Scotland

Description
1) Papers 1889–1900 of Ebenezer McAlister relating to his estates in Glasgow and Singapore.
2) Agreement 1821 between Sir Thomas Brisbane and Hugh Crawford concerning Brisbane's debts.
3) Papers 1821–28 of Robert and Thomas Crawford in Sydney and Hill End referring to voyage on *Royal George*, relations with Sir Thomas Brisbane, wool sales, farming, bushrangers and financial matters.
4) Papers 1849–90 concerning estate of Andrew Bald of Nelson, New Zealand.
5) Minutebooks 1871–91 of New Zealand and Australian Land Co.
6) Papers 1841–1921 of Maxwell Family of Nether Pollock including letters of Sir Ronald Munro-Ferguson in Melbourne and Aymer Maxwell in Java and Johore.
7) Correspondence 1838–77 of Stirling Family of Keir and Cawder referring to activities of John Stirling in New South Wales and Sir James Brooke in Sarawak.
8) Papers 1862–1935 of Isabella Gore-Booth, Susan Smith and other members of Smith Family including letters of Harry Parker, George Parker and others in New Zealand.
9) Papers 1864–1916 of Anderson Family including letters of Anna Anderson Mackie in Singapore, Manila and Batavia and Caleb Anderson in Castlemaine and Melbourne.
10) Papers 1876–97 of George Houstoun including letters of Sir Arthur Gordon, Lord Glasgow and G.H. Reid.
11) Letters 1859–85 of Robert Henry of Brisbane and Bundaberg to his family.
12) Journal 1864 of Miss S.A. Bray on voyage from Plymouth to Adelaide on *City of Adelaide*.
13) Diaries and papers 1893–1901 of Charles Cochrane-Baillie, 2nd Baron Lamington, Governor of Queensland.

46-page list available for reference.

Entry 442   Reels M2775–2779

Name **STRATHCLYDE UNIVERSITY. Archive Department**

Title Collections

Inclusive dates 1856–1980

Quantity 5 reels of microfilm

Location of original Archive Department, Strathclyde University, McCance Building, 16 Richmond Street, Glasgow G1 1XQ, Scotland

Description

1) Records 1971–80 of the '96 Group relating to the painter John A. Gillfillan (1793–1864) who settled in New Zealand and Australia. Correspondents include Flora Spurdle, W.R. Long, Douglas Pike and N.B. Nairn.

2) Papers 1972–78 of Louis McGougan including reports on higher education in Indonesia.

3) Papers 1892–1932 of Sir Patrick Geddes referring to agriculture in Australia, the depression in New Zealand, Scottish migrants in New Zealand, teachers' training in New South Wales, and A.C. Haddon's plans for field work in Torres Strait and New Guinea.

4) Diary 1856 kept at Ballarat gold diggings and on voyage back to England on the *James Baines*, together with correspondence and notes 1971–75.

5) Papers 1948–59 of town planner Sir George Pepler. Subjects include: Australian Planning Institute; Town Planning Institute in New Zealand; amalgamation of planning institutions in Australia; visit of James Fraser to Australia; and rebuilding of villages in North Borneo.

21-page list available for reference.

Entry 443   Reel M992

Name **STRZELECKI, Sir Paul Edmund de (1797–1873)**

Title Maps

Inclusive dates 1839–43

Quantity 50 black-and-white photographic prints, 50 colour transparencies and 50 colour photographic prints

Location of original Institute of Geological Sciences, Exhibition Road, South Kensington, London SW7 2DE, England

Note
Polish-born scientist and explorer. Arrived in Sydney in 1839 and spent the years until 1843 in exploration in New South Wales and Tasmania. His principal interest was geology and after his return to England in 1843 he published *Physical Description of New South Wales and Van Diemen's Land* (1845).

Description
Photographically reduced copies of a geological map and sections of Tasmania, eastern New South Wales and Victoria, referred to on pages 54-55 of *Physical Description of New South Wales and Van Diemen's Land*. The original map was 25 feet long and five feet wide, and neither it nor the sections were reproduced in Strzelecki's *Physical Description*. The map and sections published in the book contain less detail than the versions held in the Institute of Geological Sciences.

Entry 444   Reel M403

Name **STURT, Charles, Capt. (1795–1869)**

Title Papers

Inclusive dates 1844–48

Quantity 1 reel of microfilm

Location of original The Hon. Mrs Mary Anna Marten, Dorset, England

Note
Soldier and explorer. Charted the Murray River 1829–30. In August 1844 Sturt left Adelaide in search of an inland sea in central Australia. He returned in January 1845 without reaching the centre or finding an inland sea. He resumed his work as Registrar-General and Colonial Treasurer in Adelaide. In 1853 he returned to England.

Description
1) Letter of instructions from Governor George Grey including a minute on Sturt's proposal to cross Australia from south to north, a schedule of men and animals proposed for the expedition, and a list of provisions required.

2) Journal, 11 August 1845–12 January 1846, apparently kept during the expedition, with extra drafts of some passages.

3) Return of provisions and letter to Sturt, 29 January 1846, from Louis Piesse, the expedition's storekeeper, reporting on proceedings at the camp at Rala-rala and the journey from that place to Adelaide.

4) 'Vocabulary of the Dialect Spoken by the Murray River Tribes in South Australia, May 1844' and 'Specimens of the Language of the Natives of the Upper Darling'.

5) Seven letters from the Colonial Secretary, A.M. Mundy, to Sturt July 1845–May 1847 concerning the 1844–46 expedition.

6) Drafts of notes by Sturt on the royalties from mines in South Australia and on the general revenue of the colony; and a draft of part of Sturt's *Notice of the Province of South Australia* published with his *Narrative* (London, 1849).

7) Four drawings of landscapes and two charts.

8) Letter February 1847 from Louis Piesse to Sturt, letter February 1848 about Sturt Family matters.

Six-page list available for reference.

Entry 445   Reel M404

Name **STURT, Evelyn Pitfield Shirley (1816–1885)**

Title Papers

Inclusive dates 1852–1960

Quantity 1 reel of microfilm

Location of original The Hon. Mrs Mary Anna Marten, Dorset, England

Note
Brother of the explorer Charles Sturt. Arrived in New South Wales in 1836 and was for many years a grazier in South Australia, until his appointment as a police magistrate in Melbourne in 1849. Superintendent of the Melbourne Police 1850–53, but in 1854 he resumed magisterial duties, presiding over the city bench of magistrates until 1878.

Description
1) Address presented to Sturt, signed by Justices of the Peace in Melbourne (n.d.).

2) Address presented to Sturt, signed by fellow Melbourne magistrates 1858.

3) Commission 14 October 1863 appointing Sturt to Major in the Victorian Volunteer Force.

4) Letters patent 4 September 1855 appointing Sturt as Resident Magistrate at Melbourne.

5) Extract of marriage entry 14 February 1852 of Sturt and Mary Frances Grylls.

6) Typescript chart showing the relationship between Evelyn and Charles Sturt.

Entry 446   Reel M982

Name **SUFFOLK RECORD OFFICE, Bury St Edmunds Branch**

Title Collections

Inclusive dates 1771–1936

Quantity 1 reel of microfilm

Location of original Suffolk Record Office, 77 Raingate Street, Bury St Edmunds, Suffolk IP33 2AR, England

Description
1) Records 1828–51 of Barningham and Mildenhall Parishes referring to emigration to Australia.

2) Commonplace book of Sir Thomas Cullum referring to cannibalism in the South Seas in 1821.

3) Papers 1875–87 concerning legacies to members of Abraham Family.

4) Account of Lieut. R. Shannon of visit to Pitcairn Island in 1815.

5) Property deeds 1931–36 of Maxwell Maxwell-Gumbleton, former Bishop of Ballarat.

6) Papers 1839–82 of George Johnson of Wellington, New Zealand.

7) Letters 1771–1813 received by Sir Thomas Cullum from naturalists and zoologists and others including Sir Joseph Banks, Charles Miller, James Burney, Daines Barrington and Thomas Pennant, mainly relating to natural history of East Indies.

16-page list available for reference.

Entry 447   Reels M941–943

Name **SUFFOLK RECORD OFFICE, Ipswich Branch**

Title Collections

Inclusive dates 1740–1954

Quantity 3 reels of microfilm

Location of original Suffolk Record Office, Ipswich Branch, Gatacre Road, Ipswich IP1 2LQ, England

Description
1) Ipswich Borough Records: documents and correspondence 1789 concerning the transportation of Susana Hunt to New South Wales on the *Lady Juliana;* photograph, Council's address to Queen Kafiolani of Hawaii 1887.

2) Parish records 1793–1930: correspondence, orders, circulars, notices, printed forms,

prospectus and other documents mainly concerning emigration but also referring to transportation of convicts, deeds of gifts, a lecture 1878 on 'The Martyrs of the South Sea Islands' by Rev. H.T. Dudley and the attempted assassination of the Duke of Edinburgh in Australia in 1868. There is also a log 1825–27 of the *Merope* on a voyage to the East Indies and the Sandwich Islands, list and accounts of the crew, and sketches of China and Formosa by G. Parkyns.

3) Rous Family archives, including: a diary 1924 of George Rous, 3rd Earl of Stradbroke, Governor of Victoria 1921–26; a printed paper 1833 on cultivation of flax; a printed notice stating the aims of the Society for Reform of Colonial Government; letter 1845 regarding the appointment of Thomas Welch as Judge at Port Phillip; documents 1836–74 concerning emigration; documents 1846–50 concerning the convict James Lowe.

4) Rope collection: three letters 1842 from Charles S. Webber, aboard the *Sir Charles Napier,* and after arrival in Hobart.

5) Loraine Family archives, including cutting and letters 1851–52 from Hugh Hamilton, Assistant Gold Commissioner at Ophir, near Bathurst, New South Wales; letter 1860 from James Hamilton of Christchurch, New Zealand; diary, financial documents and letters 1876–78 regarding journey to Australia of William C. Loraine; correspondence, cuttings and pamphlet 1901–12 of Sir Lambton Loraine regarding the Australian flag and his proposal for an Imperial Navy.

6) Albermarle manuscripts: logbook and journal 1740–44 of Lord Anson's voyage round the world, kept by Augustus Keppel on HMS *Centurion.*

7) Journal 1870–74 of Commander F.P. Doughty on voyage of HMS *Magpie,* including notes on his voyages in the Pacific and to China, and on his family history.

8) Greenup Family papers 1834–66 concerning the marriage, emigration to Australia and death in 1866 of Richard Greenup of Parramatta, including a letter 1841 from W. Marsh describing Sydney.

9) Lingwood Family papers: correspondence, articles, photographs and copies of letters 1804–1954 concerning Margaret Catchpole. Also notices 1910 and 1922 of performances of the play *Margaret Catchpole* by Walter Frith, and a typescript copy (246 p.) of 'Homespun Heroine: Portrait of Margaret Catchpole' by Harold R. Lingwood (c.1947).

10) Letter 1915 from Lieut. Col. William Donnan referring to the mutiny in Singapore.

14-page list available for reference.

Entry 448   Reel M2502

Name **SUFFOLK RECORD OFFICE, Lowestoft Branch**

Title Collections

Inclusive date 1855–1958

Quantity 1 reel of microfilm

Location of original Lowestoft Branch, Suffolk Record Office, Central Library, Clapham Road, Lowestoft, Suffolk NR32 1DR, England

Description
1) Correspondence 1956–58 of Gordon Auchterlonie describing an *umukai* (feast) and life in Aitutaki, New Zealand.

2) Correspondence 1855–77 of Suggate Family referring to visits to Grafton and Sydney and family news.

3) Photographs 1949–53 of hopper barges, cabin cruiser and other boats ordered by the Maritime Services Board of New South Wales from the boat builder Brooke Marine Ltd.

Five-page list available for reference.

Entry 449   Reel M973

Name **SUFFOLK REGIMENT ASSOCIATION**

Title Collections

Inclusive dates c.1972–74

Quantity 1 reel of microfilm

Location of original Suffolk Regiment Association, The Keep, Gibraltar Barracks, Bury St Edmunds, Suffolk IP33 3RN, England

Note
The 12th or Suffolk Regiment, under the command of Col. H. Meade Hamilton, was stationed in New Zealand 1860–66. During this time the Regiment fought in the Maori Wars.

Description
Typescript papers relating to medals awarded for service in New Zealand during the period 1845–66. Many of the papers were compiled from WO100/18, held at the Public Record Office, London.

Parts 1 and 2 of the papers contain the roll of servicemen of the 1st Battalion, 12th Regiment, presented with medals on 30 March 1870. The roll shows for each recipient name, rank, at the time the medal was earned, dates of action, and a note on subsequent service, discharge or death. Interspersed are typescript notes compiled from *The History of the 12th (the Suffolk Regiment)* and Gilbert Mair's *The Story of Gate Pa* (1937). The notes include material about the cemetery near Tauranga, New Zealand, where many of the Regiment's dead were buried.

Part 3 contains a list of claims of non-effective officers, NCOs and men of the 1st Battalion, 12th Regiment, showing name, rank, dates of action, and subsequent service. Many are shown as having died in New Zealand, or as having been discharged during the period of the Wars, presumably remaining as settlers.

Part 4, entitled 'The New Zealand War Medal 1845–1866' gives details of army and navy personnel awarded medals for action in the Maori Wars, lists ships serving in New Zealand waters 1845–66 and regiments serving in New Zealand in the same period, and concludes with a chronological list of some recipients of medals. Part 4 also includes corrigenda to lists in Parts 1–3.

One-page list available for reference.

Entry 450   Reels M708–712

Name **SURGEONS' JOURNALS**

Title Journals

Inclusive dates 1848–80

Quantity 5 reels of microfilm

Location of original Public Record Office, Ruskin Avenue, Kew, Richmond-upon-Thames, Surrey TW9 4DU, England

Note
At the time of filming these journals were held in the Royal Naval Hospital, Haslar, Portsmouth, England. They are now located in the Public Record Office in Kew.

Description
Journals kept by surgeons on ships of the China, Australia and Pacific Stations, and also 26 journals kept by surgeons on convict ships sailing to Australia 1848–64. The journals contain details of illnesses and lists of patients, as well as movements of the ship and brief descriptions of places visited.

1) Journals of the following Royal Navy surgeons: R.R. Siccama (HMS *Modeste* 1876), Anthony Gorham (HMS *Ringdove* 1873, 1876), George M. Cuffe (HMS *Growler* 1877), Edward T. Lloyd (HMS *Fly* 1875), John Buckley (HMS *Rinaldo* 1870–72), Robert Nelson (HMS *Juno* 1876–77), William Patrick (HMS *Niger* 1856–60), Gilbert L. King (HMS *Sphinx* 1861–62), Thomas Coghlan (HMS *Sphinx* 1863), A.B. Messer (HMS *Perseus* 1867, HMS *Pearl* 1874–75, HMS *Curacoa* 1863–64), Thomas L. Bickford (HMS *Charydbis* 1874–76), John T. Caddy (HMS *Pylades* 1858–59), Godfrey Goodman (HMS *Dido* 1875, HMS *Basilisk* 1872), Peter Comrie (HMS *Basilisk* 1874), Robert Edward (HMS *Pelorus* 1861), W. Fasken (HMS *Fawn* 1862), Walter Reid (HMS *Wolverene* 1876, 1879), George Mair (HMS *Danae* 1880), Henry Slade (HMS *Miranda* 1862, 1864), D. Hilston (HMS *Harrier* 1862–63), Alexander Rattray (HMS *Salamander* 1865, 1867), Charles Forbes (HMS *Topaze* 1863), William Hoggan (HMS *Repulse* 1875), John C. Messer (HMS *Charybdis* 1869), W.H. Adam (HMS *Megara* 1871).

2) Journals of the following surgeons on convict ships: Charles A. Anderson (*Lord Dalhousie* 1852), Samuel Donnelly (*Adelaide* 1855), John W. Elliott *(Castle Eden* 1855–56), Charles Smith (*Duchess of Northumberland* 1852–53), T.H. Keown (*Hyderabad* 1850), Robert William (*Horatio* 1852), Robert W. Clarke (*John William Dare* 1851–52), Joseph Cladwell (*Lady Kennaway* 1850–51), Samuel Donnelly (*Lady Montague* 1852), John W. Bowler (*Phoebe Dunbar* 1853), Daniel Ritchie (*Ramillies* 1854), Harvey Morris (*Robert Small* 1853), George D. MacLaren (*Scindian* 1855), Joseph Caldwell (*Sea Park* 1853–54), John Stewart (*Sibella* 1853), Thomas Crawford (*Martin Luther* 1852), Alexander Kilroy (*Mermaid* 1850–51), Robert Stevenson (*Mermaid* 1856), David Thomas (*Midlothian* 1852–53), John Gibson (*Minden* 1851), John Kidd (*Nile* 1850), D. Geddes (*Oriental Queen* 1852–53), William Smith (*Merchantman* 1862–64), James Booth (*London* 1850–51), John Moody (*Lord Auckland* 1848–49), John Davidson (*Lord Auckland* 1852–53), I.G. Williams (*Maria Soames* 1850), Frederick LeGrand (*Marion* 1851–52).

14-page list available for reference.

Entry 451   Reel M1840

Name **SURREY RECORD OFFICE.**
Guildford Branch

Title Collections

Inclusive dates 1854–1941

Quantity 1 reel of microfilm

Location of original Guilford Muniment Room,
Surrey Record Office, Castle Arch, Guildford
GU1 3SX, England

Description
1) Papers 1888–1905 of Sir William Hillier Onslow,
   4th Earl of Onslow, Governor of New Zealand
   1889–92. Subjects include: Maoris; Federation
   of Australia; Chinese crisis in New South Wales;
   defences of New Zealand and Australia; and
   New Zealand birds. Correspondents include
   Queen Victoria, Lord Knutsford, Richard Seddon
   and J. Chamberlain. Also papers of his son
   Sir Richard Onslow including an account of
   a visit to Australia and New Zealand 1889–90.

2) Letters 1922–41 of Arthur and Fred Gammon
   of Kaikohe, New Zealand, to Harold Gammon
   referring to conditions of soldiers' settlement
   farm and impact of the Great Depression.

3) Papers 1854–65 of Martin Ware comprising
   letters from former boys of Ragged Schools
   and Shoeblack Society referring to Australian
   churches, life at the Ovens River diggings,
   Maori War, work on railways in Queensland,
   and Aborigines. Also journal of Martin S. Ware
   kept on journey to North America, Fiji, Australia
   and New Zealand 1911–12.

Eight-page list available for reference.

Entry 452   Reels M1834–1839

Name **SURREY RECORD OFFICE.**
Kingston-upon-Thames Branch

Title Collections

Inclusive dates 1812–1934

Quantity 6 reels of microfilm

Location of original Surrey Record Office, County
Hall, Penrhyn Road, Kingston-upon-Thames
KT1 2DN, England

Description
1) Calendar of prisoners 1848–53 for Surrey
   Quarter Sessions at Newington Gaol.

2) Papers 1812–55 of the politician Henry Goulburn
   and his brother Lieut. Col. Frederick Goulburn,
   Colonial Secretary in New South Wales 1820–24.

A large group of papers relate to properties and
investments of Frederick Goulburn in the colony
and include letters of M.D. Meares, J. Norton,
W. Burton and H.G. Douglass. Other papers
comprise letters of Sir Robert Peel, Lord Stanley,
W.E. Gladstone and others to Henry Goulburn
referring to convict transportation, Australian
exploration, New Zealand Co and colonial
appointments. Also a manuscript map by John
Oxley and a plan 1817 by J. Meehan of the
Government Farm at Toongabee.

3) Records 1843–1915 of Royal Philanthropic
   Society School at Redhill, including annual
   reports, emigration letter-book and ledgers with
   copies of letters from boys who emigrated to
   Australia 1856–72.

4) Papers 1886–1934 of Thomas C. Farrer, 2nd
   Baron Farrer, comprising letters of W. Shand
   in Queensland and E.J. Eddy in Sydney. The
   letters from Eddy mostly deal with railways and
   economic conditions. The letters from Shand
   refer to: his first impressions of Queensland;
   the Australian accent; Queensland elections;
   exclusion of Chinese from Queensland;
   Sir Anthony Musgrave; attitudes to Aborigines;
   Australian politics; 1891 shearers strike;
   activities of the Australian Labor Party; and
   his work as a judge in Townsville.

14-page list available for reference.

Entry 453   Reel M445

Name **SWANSTON, Charles, Capt. (1790–1850)**

Title Papers

Inclusive dates 1891–93, 1960

Quantity 1 reel of microfilm

Location of original Mrs N. Swanston,
Herefordshire, and Major General C.D. Moorhead,
Kent, England

Note
Banker. Joined the East India Company's army
in 1805. He obtained a commission as captain
and served in the Deccan. In 1829 he settled in
Tasmania and two years later became managing
director of the Derwent Bank, a position he held
until its liquidation in 1849. Swanston also traded
extensively with India and Mauritius and was
a founder of the Port Phillip Association.

Description
1) Two printed pamphlets: *Statement of the
   Services of Capt. Charles Swanston*, 33 p.
   (1891) and *Rough Diary of a Journey from*

Scutari to Baghdad 1814 by Lieut. C. Swanston, 16 p. (1893).

2) Typescript essay 'The Swanston Family 1789–1960' by Major Gen. C.D. Moorhead (August 1960), containing the Swanston Family tree, a short biography of Charles Swanston and a history of the family of Charles Swanston's son-in-law, Edward Willis, of Koolomurt Station, Victoria.

3) Two photographs of Charles Swanston.

Entry 454   Reel M1558

Name **TASMAN, Abel (1603–1659)**
Title Journal
Inclusive dates 1642–43
Quantity 1 reel of microfilm
Location of original British Library, Great Russell Street, London WC1B 3DG, England

Note
Dutch navigator, discovered Tasmania and New Zealand 1642–43 and charted the north coast of Australia 1644.

Description
An 18th century copy, together with an English translation made for Sir Joseph Banks, of the journal of Tasman on the voyage of the *Heemskerck* 1642–43.

Entry 455   Reel M2611

Name **TATE GALLERY LIBRARY ARCHIVE**
Title Collections
Inclusive dates 1914–56
Quantity 1 reel of microfilm
Location of original Tate Gallery Archive, Millbank, London SW1 3RG, England

Description
1) Letters 1953–56 of Grace English regarding the loan of a colour drawing by Ethel Walker for the exhibition *British Watercolours 1914–53*.

2) Scrapbook c.1928–31 containing letters, telegram and postcards from the artist Frances Hodgkins to Arthur Howell and L. Harmston.

3) Records 1951–65 of Artists International Association referring to exhibits by Rachel Roxburgh, Phyllis Waterhouse and James Cant.

4) Correspondence 1947–56 of Mrs Margaret Nash referring to the loan of Paul Nash's work for an exhibition *British Watercolours 1914–53*

to tour Australia and New Zealand and the purchase of Nash's paintings by the Felton Bequest Trust for the National Gallery of Victoria.

5) Letters 1938–44? of Henry Lamb to Arnold Palmer concerning his paintings.

6) Correspondence and autograph notes 1936–42 of John Rothenstein concerning Charles Conder. Correspondents include William Moore and Sir Arthur Streeton.

Four-page list available for reference.

Entry 456   Reel M2514

Name **TAYLOR, Francis C.**
Title Journal
Inclusive dates February–June 1850
Quantity 1 reel of microfilm
Location of original National Maritime Museum, Romney Road, Greenwich, London SE10 9NF, England

Description
Journal kept by Francis Taylor on a journey on the *Stag* from London to Adelaide, including descriptions of other emigrants, reading of Australian books and impressions of Adelaide.

One-page list available for reference.

Entry 457   Reel M679

Name **TEMPLE, William, Lieut. Col. (1833–1919)**
Title Papers
Inclusive dates 1861–1916
Quantity 1 reel of microfilm
Location of original Not known

Note
Assistant Surgeon in the Royal Artillery. Enlisted in the Army in 1858 and during his career served in New Zealand and India as well as in England. In 1862 he married Anne, daughter of Major Gen. J.R. Mould, in New Zealand. In 1864 Temple, together with Lieut. Arthur F. Pickard, was awarded the Victoria Cross for his actions at the battle of Ranjariri in the previous year.

Description
1) Three letters 1861–64 written by Temple in Rangariri and Auckland referring to the Maori Wars, conditions and prices in New Zealand, his purchase of land in Otahuhu township, and

giving a detailed account of the battle at Rangiriri in November 1863.

2) A plan of Rangiriri accompanied by a statement concerning the conduct of Lieut. Pickard in the battle.

3) Letter 1916 of W.F. Gordon of New Plymouth, New Zealand, to Temple concerning a gift to the Dominion Museum, Wellington, of photographs of people who served in the Maori Wars.

4) Seven photographs of soldiers, groups of Maoris, pitched tents (possibly at Ranjariri) and military equipment.

Entry 458   Reel M2090

Name **THOMAS, Robert (b.1836)**

Title Autobiography

Inclusive dates 1863–64

Quantity 1 reel of microfilm

Location of original National Library of Wales, Aberystwyth, Dyfed SY23 3BU, Wales

Note
Born in Llanfechain, Montgomeryshire, in 1836. Thomas came to Australia in 1852 and worked on the Victorian goldfields until 1854. He returned to London in 1862.

Description
An unpublished autobiography describing Thomas' early life in Llanfechain and other places in counties Montgomery and Salop, his voyage from Liverpool to Melbourne in 1852, his life on the goldfields and voyage back to London in 1862.

One-page list available for reference.

Entry 459   Reel M1133

Name **THOMSON, Robert (1829–1905)**

Title Letters

Inclusive dates 1851–54

Quantity 1 reel of microfilm

Location of original National Library of Scotland, George IV Bridge, Edinburgh EH1 1EW, Scotland

Special conditions Requests for copies of the microfilm to be referred to the owner through the National Library of Scotland.

Note
Robert Thomson emigrated to New Zealand on the *Simlah* in 1851 and settled at Owhiro, Otago.

In 1853 he moved to Sydney and went into business with Harry Heap. He became Secretary of the Australian Mutual Provident Society in 1854.

Description
Letters of Robert Thomson to his brother-in-law William Bottomley of Belfast. They describe the voyage from England, farming, church and social activities in New Zealand, his financial affairs, and insurance business in Sydney. There are also letters from Thomas Bottomley and John Heap in Sydney, and William Heap in England dealing with family and business matters.

Nine-page list available for reference.

Entry 460   Reel M1861

Name **THORNTON, Reginald (1887–1968)**

Title Papers

Inclusive dates 1926–29

Quantity 1 reel of microfilm

Location of original Mrs Peggy Poole, Merseyside, England

Note
London organiser of Big Brother Movement 1926–31. Visited Australia and Canada 1928.

Description
A diary of Thornton's tour of Australia and Canada 1928, correspondence and newspaper cuttings. The diary contains descriptions of voyage from London to Perth, impressions of Perth, Adelaide, Melbourne, Sydney and country districts in Australia, and discussions with officials, employers and officers of the Big Brother Movement. Most of the letters were written by Thornton to his wife Barbara in England.

Four-page list available for reference.

Name **THURSTON, Sir John Bates (1836–1897)**

Title Diaries and biographical papers

Inclusive dates c.1840–97

Quantity 1 reel of microfilm

Location of original National Library of Australia, Canberra ACT 2600

Note
Colonial official. Arrived in Australia in 1855 and farmed in New South Wales until 1860, when he became Collector to the Linnean Society, Sydney. In 1869 he became acting British Consul in Fiji and in 1872 Chief Secretary and Minister for Foreign Affairs in the Cakobau Government, which negotiated the cession of Fiji. Governor of Fiji and High Commissioner of the Western Pacific 1887–97.

Description
1) Biographical papers, including manuscript biographical notes and newspaper obituaries collected and compiled by various members of the Thurston Family.

2) Diary of a voyage from Sydney to England 1854–55 with descriptions of Australia and New Zealand, and a diary February–March 1863 of a trip to the Swan River, Western Australia, and Mauritius, with a short description of Perth. There is also an account of a 'Ramble on Rotumah' 1865, and various other notes on that island.

3) Commonplace book 1840s–1860s including remarks on primitive man, apparently written by Thurston, and a diary of his voyage from Rotuma to Fiji in 1865.

4) Diary and notebook 1874 concerning the cession of Fiji.

5) Diary 1894 with comments on law cases and referring to the murder of Bishop J.C. Patteson.

Name **THE TIMES**

Title Records

Inclusive dates 1852–1964

Quantity 2 reels of microfilm

Location of original Times Newspapers Ltd Record Office, News International Plc, 200 Gray's Inn Road, London WC1X 8EZ, England

Note
The Times newspaper was founded in London in 1785 by John Walter. Under the editorships of Thomas Barnes 1817–41 and John T. Delane 1841–77, it acquired its unique reputation as a national independent daily.

Description
1) Manager's letter-books 1852–1914. Subjects include: appointment of colonial judges; Australian railways; British–Australian communications; republican doctrines in Australia; Australian politics; attacks on British colonial policy; possible annexation of Fiji; annexation of Cook Island; visit of American Fleet to Australia and New Zealand in 1908; and White Australia policy. Main correspondents are M. Morris, J. MacDonald, C.M. Bell, F.H. Kitchin, A. Michie, A. Garran, F.W. Haddon and A. Jose.

2) Correspondence 1920–60 concerning the operation of its Australian office.

3) Correspondence and agreements 1912–56 of the Australia and Times News Service. Correspondents include K. Murdoch, H. Denison, H. Campbell Jones and L. Dumas.

4) Papers 1849–74 of John T. Delane, editor of *The Times*, referring to convict transportation, establishment of colony of Queensland and colonial politics. Correspondents include B. Howes, G. Elder and Sir James Fergusson.

5) Papers 1932–38 of H.A. McClure Smith of *Sydney Morning Herald* referring to British foreign policy.

19-page list available for reference.

Entry 463   Reel M2345

Name **TOWLE FAMILY**

Title Papers

Inclusive dates 1852–58

Quantity 1 reel of microfilm

Location of original Cmdr N. Towle, Southhampton, England

Note
Edward and Benjamin Towle sailed on SS *Great Britain* for the Australian goldfields in 1852. Benjamin Towle died in Australia in 1853 and Edward Towle returned to England.

Description
Diaries and correspondence. The diaries were kept by Edward Towle, describing the journey from Liverpool to Australia in 1852 and a visit to Java and Singapore in 1853. The letters of Edward and Benjamin Towle to their mother and sister contain news from the goldfields at Creswick and Ballarat.

Two-page list available for reference.

Entry 464   Reel M2837

Name **TRANSIT OF VENUS 1882**

Title Papers

Inclusive dates 1882–1987

Quantity 1 reel of microfilm

Location of original Rev. John Grover, Roxburghshire, Scotland

Note
The astronomers Charles Grover (1840–1921) and Sir Cuthbert Peek (1855–1901) visited Australia to observe the Transit of Venus in 1882.

Description
1) Papers c.1883–1911 of Charles Grover including notes on Australian life, a sketchbook and reminiscences of his visit to Australia in 1882. He referred to the observatories in Melbourne, Sydney and Brisbane, the journey to Jimbour in the Darling Downs, encounters with Aborigines, and the unsuccessful attempt to observe the Transit of Venus in December 1882. There are sketches of observatories, Jimbour and Thursday Island.

2) Notes of Sir Cuthbert Peek on journey to Australia in 1882 and observations of southern stars.

3) Photographs, postcard and cutting.

Two-page list available for reference.

Entry 465   Reel M854

Name **TRINITY COLLEGE LIBRARY, Dublin**

Title Collections

Inclusive dates 1636–1847

Quantity 1 reel of microfilm

Location of original Trinity College Library, University of Dublin, Dublin, Ireland

Description
1) Papers 1800–03 of Major Henry C. Sirr, Town Major and Head of Police in Dublin 1798–1826, including letters relating to Michael Dwyer and his party, information of Thomas Devoy relating to John Carroll, and petition of Mathias McElray on board the *Anne*.

2) Volume containing copies of courts martial proceedings in 1798 at Drogheda, Slane, Trim, Dublin and Loughlinstown, following the United Irishmen Rebellion. The papers include proceedings of courts martial of prisoners sentenced to transportation.

3) Papers collected by Dr R.R. Madden relating to the United Irishmen, including reports 1799–1800 of the trials of Michael Kehoe, Michael Quigly, James Scully, Michael Kelly and John Bryan, all sentenced to transportation.

4) 'Papeles de la Duncadion de la Santa Prouya: Relacion de los pleitos de Manila', Manila, 19 June 1636.

5) Conditional pardon 1847 of James Scully, sentenced to transportation for life, signed at Sydney by Governor Charles Fitzroy.

Three-page list available for reference.

Entry 466   Reel M1131

Name **TURNER, Alexander**

Title Diary

Inclusive dates 1883

Quantity 1 reel of microfilm

Location of original Scottish Record Office, HM General Register House, Edinburgh EH1 3YY, Scotland

Note
Passenger on the ship *Eastern Monarch* on a voyage from Glasgow to Townsville via the Cape of Good Hope and Tasmania July–October 1883.

Description
The diary covers the voyage from Scotland and the first week or so after the ship reached Townsville, when the emigrants were forced to stay at Magnetic Island on account of an epidemic.

Entry 467   Reel M2803

Name **TYLOR, Sir Edward Burnett (1832–1917)**

Title Papers

Inclusive dates 1882–1905

Quantity 1 reel of microfilm

Location of original Pitt Rivers Museum, Oxford University, South Parks Road, Oxford OX1 3PP, England

Note
Anthropologist and keeper of the University Museum, Oxford. Tylor's published works included *Primitive Culture* (1871) and *Anthropology: An Introduction (1881).*

Description
Correspondence and other papers relating to anthropological research in Australia and the Pacific, and Tylor's work at the University Museum, Oxford. Principal correspondents are Rev. Lorimer Fison, A.W. Howitt, Andrew Lang and Sir Baldwin Spencer.

18-page list available for reference.

Entry 468   Reels M1831–1833

Name **TYNE AND WEAR ARCHIVES DEPARTMENT**

Title Collections

Inclusive dates 1852–1929

Quantity 3 reels of microfilm

Location of original Tyne and Wear Archives Department, Blandford House, West Blandford Street, Newcastle upon Tyne NE1 4JA, England

Description
1) Correspondence 1878–81 of Stuart Rendel, a partner in the ordnance firm Sir W.G. Armstrong & Co, referring to purchase of guns and gunboats for New South Wales, South Australian, Victorian and Queensland Governments. Correspondents include Sir William Jervois, P. Scratchley and H. Sargood.
2) Letters 1881–84 of Elizabeth Spence Watson referring to the emigration of industrial girls to Queensland.
3) Records 1923–29 of Guardians of the Poor, Newcastle upon Tyne Union relating to emigration of paupers and children to Australia and Canada.
4) Papers 1908–26 of Charles H. Merz and William McLellan relating to the electrification of the railways in Melbourne, including estimates,

data files, calculations and a large number of photograph albums.
5) Papers 1882–85 of Swan Family relating to the activities of the Edison and Swan United Electric Light Co in Australia and New Zealand.
6) Letters 1852–53 of John Miller of Kyneton and Melbourne to his parents referring to his experiences as an emigrant, discovery of gold at Ovens River, prices and wages in Victoria, and his decision to leave the colony in 1853.

Seven-page list available for reference.

Entry 469   Reels M1201–1335, M1401–1516

Name **UNITED SOCIETY FOR THE PROPAGATION OF THE GOSPEL**

Title Records

Inclusive dates 1719–1952

Quantity 251 reels of microfilm

Location of original Rhodes House Library, South Parks Road, Oxford OX1 3RG, England

Special conditions The permission to copy any of these reels is needed from the copyright owner.

Note
The Society was founded in 1701 to promote the Christian religion in Britain's 'Foreign Plantations'. It provided financial support to Anglican clergy and missionaries in Australia from 1788, New Zealand 1840, Borneo 1848, Melanesia 1854, Straits Settlements 1861, Hawaii 1862 and Fiji 1880. Its activities in New Zealand and Australia largely ceased in 1880–82, although it continued to support dioceses in northern Queensland and Western Australia until 1939.

Description
Reels M1201–1335:
The records comprise minutes of the Standing Committee 1778–1819, 1900–35 and the Foreign Committee 1846–80, anniversary sermons, annual reports and journals of monthly meetings of the Society 1901–35, missionary reports 1852–1938, letters received from Australia, New Zealand, Melanesia and Southeast Asia 1821–1936, copies of letters of the Secretary, Assistant Secretary and Overseas Secretary 1842–1935, missionary rolls 1846–1910, candidates' papers 1821–57, testimonials, ledgers 1891–1936 and photograph albums, including photographs of Malaya, Singapore, Borneo and Melanesia.

Most of the letters were written to or by the Secretaries Ernest Hawkins, W.T. Bullock, H.W. Tucker and H.H. Montgomery. Other correspondents include Bishops W.G. Broughton, C. Perry, Frederick Barker, G.A. Selwyn, J.C. Patteson, W.G. Cowie, William Williams, J.R. Selwyn, Daniel Sandford, C.J. Abraham, F.T. McDougall, Rev. J.B. Wittenoom, Rev. J.R. Wollaston, Rev. W.B. Clark, Rev. W.J. Woodcock, Rev. W.H. Coombs, Rev. E. Coleridge and Sir James Brooke.

Reels M1401–1516:
The records include printed annual reports 1719–1872, minutes of the Standing Committee 1833–1901, journals of the monthly meetings of the Society 1783–1901, missionary returns, comprising annual reports of missionaries in Australia 1845–1900, Australian papers 1789–1859, and letters received from Australia 1857–1900.

Correspondents include Rev. Richard Johnson, Archdeacon T.H. Scott and Bishops W.G. Broughton, C. Perry, F.R. Nixon, Augustus Short, F. Barker, William Tyrell, Mesac Thomas, C.H. Bromby, E.W. Tufnell and Matthew Hale.

90-page list for M1201–1335 and two-page list for M1401–1516 available for reference.

Entry 470   Reels M867–868

Name **UNIVERSITY OF BIRMINGHAM**

Title Collections

Inclusive dates 1894–1962

Quantity 2 reels of microfilm

Location of original The Main Library, University of Birmingham, Edgbaston, Birmingham B15 2TT, England

Description
1) Papers of Joseph Chamberlain, Secretary of State for the Colonies 1895–1903:

a) Correspondence 1895–99 with Lord Salisbury including references to colonial shares in Suez and German influence in Samoa.

b) Imperial affairs: various correspondence 1895–99 relating to: the Pacific Cable Conference; Imperial Penny Postage; Agricultural Congress 1899; Anglo–French negotiations; Antarctic expedition; the Straits Settlements; tariffs; submarine cables; honours; and the appointment of governors.

c) Correspondence with Lord Salisbury 1900–02 referring to the appointment of governors, German interest in Samoa and Tonga, and Federation in Australia.

d) Colonial affairs: correspondence 1900–03 divided under the headings Australia, New Zealand, Fiji and Straits Settlements.

e) Miscellaneous letters relating to the Colonial Conference of 1902, Canterbury College, New Zealand and the Pacific Cable Conference.

f) Typed copies of correspondence with Queen Victoria and King Edward VII concerning vice-regal appointments, colonial troops and the Royal Visit to Australia of 1901.

g) Documents 1894–98 relating to colonial trade, shipping and tariffs.

h) Documents and correspondence 1901–14 concerning Imperial Conferences, colonial trade, tariff reform, colonial defence, South Africa, Empire unity and the Imperial Fund. Correspondents include Alfred Deakin and Sir Edmund Barton. Printed material includes eight pamphlets, newspaper cuttings and political cartoons concerning preferential tariffs and the United Empire Trade League.

2) Notes May 1925 by John Galsworthy of his recollections of New Zealand.

3) Correspondence and notes 1946–47, 1958–62 of Alan S.C. Ross for his book *Ginger: A Loan Word Study* (1952) and for a study on Pitcairniana.

Eight-page list available for reference.

Entry 471   Reels M2008–2009

Name **UPTON FAMILY**

Title Papers

Inclusive dates 1865–1930

Quantity 2 reels of microfilm

Location of original Mrs Francesca Upton, Shropshire, England

Note
Thomas Everard Upton emigrated to New Zealand in 1865 and worked for F. Napier Broome and Sir John Cracroft Wilson. In 1870 he married Eunice Adams and settled near Ashburton.

Description
1) Letter-diary 1865–66 of Thomas Everard Upton kept on the voyage to New Zealand.
2) Letters 1865–1906 of Thomas and Eunice Upton in New Zealand to the Upton Family in England, including family news, appointment as a gardener to F. Napier Broome, gold discoveries in New Zealand, railways, sheep breeding, and association with Broome, Lady Barker and Sir Cracroft Wilson.

3) Papers 1885–1900 of T.E. Tichborne Upton and Robert H.B. Upton referring to sporting events in Christchurch and death of Robert in Johannesburg.

4) Diary 1875–78 of Arthur Begbie describing his voyage on *Otago* to New Zealand, his work as a farmer and labourer in Otago and Canterbury, and his return to England.

Four-page list available for reference.

Entry 472   Reels M335–364, M585–589

Name **VAN DIEMEN'S LAND COMPANY**

Title Records

Inclusive dates 1824–1954

Quantity 35 reels of microfilm

Location of original Archives Office of Tasmania, State Library of Tasmania, 91 Murray Street, Hobart Tasmania 7000

Note
The Van Diemen's Land Co was formed in London in 1824 to develop land in the north-west of Tasmania by encouraging selected immigrants to farm the land, initially on a leasehold basis. In March 1826 the first group of company employees arrived in Hobart. Among them was their Colonial Agent Edward Curr and a party of surveyors. Large areas of land were explored, cleared and farmed, though not always profitably. In 1871 tin was discovered at Mt Bischoff and this resulted in the formation of subsidiary companies, such as the Emu Bay to Mt Bischoff Railway Co. The company was involved in exploration, agriculture and commerce 1825–1950s. The chief agents of the company to 1900 were Edward Curr, James Gibson, Charles Nichols and James W.N. Smith.

Description
M337–339, M340–343, M344, M585:
Minutes of Court of Directors in London 1824–1904 (reels M337–339); London Office outward letter-books 1825–1902 (M340–343); London Office outward letter-books 1839–78 comprising letters to correspondents in Ireland and Great Britain, including government departments (M344); minutes of annual general meetings of proprietors of the company 1826–1908 (M585).

M344–352, M360:
London Office inward letters 1833–1900 from correspondents in Australia, including the company's chief agents and J. & C.S. Henty and Co.

M353–358:
Copies of letters written to Australian correspondents from the company's offices in Tasmania 1826–48; Tasmanian letter-books 1848–59.

M359–360, M365:
Miscellaneous papers, including copies of instructions to Edward Curr and Stephen Adey 1825; papers concerning the establishment of a savings bank in Van Diemen's Land; two-page document by John Macarthur, *Statement of the Improvement and Progress of the Breed of Fine Woolled Sheep in New South Wales* (London, 1803); statistics of wool imported into Great Britain 1826–36; Colonial Office correspondence 1825–31 concerning the foundation of the company; Van Diemen's Land Company Acts, annual and other reports, and memoranda (M359–360, M365). Subjects covered include: Alexander Goldie's journey of exploration to the west coast of Tasmania 1826; the ship *Thomas Laurie* 1839; Roman Catholics 1849–54; Australian postal services 1854–56; discovery of gold; the town of Stanley, Tasmania; Emu Bay Butter Factory; and emigration.

M361–362, M589:
Emu Bay to Mount Bischoff Railway Co reports, documents, valuations, plans 1841–85.

M363, M586:
Invoice and accounts books of the Van Diemen's Land Co 1825–34 (M363), 1833, 1838–58, 1880–89 (M586), showing expenses involved in transporting merino sheep from Hamburg to Tasmania, listing equipment, furniture, supplies taken to Tasmania by the company's staff, and other transactions during these periods.

M366:
List of maps and plans of the company, housed in the State Archives of Tasmania; 23 sketches, paintings, maps, charts, including drawings by John H. Hutchison depicting Highfield and Hampshire Hills estates on the north-west coast of Tasmania, and maps of northern Tasmania, many by Henry Hellyer, 1824–31.

M589:
Conveyances 1851–1930 for company land in Tasmania, each group of documents being preceded by a nominal index; correspondence concerning the Emu Bay breakwater 1886–89, the Mt Bischoff Tin Mining Co, Mount Bischoff Tramway, and land at Circular Head, Tasmania, 1871–82.

Detailed lists appear on the reels.

Entry 473   Reel M1856

Name **VESSEY FAMILY**
Title Papers
Inclusive dates 1861–79
Quantity 1 reel of microfilm
Location of original Mrs Julie Cundy, Derby, England

Description
1) Letters 1861–68 of Rev. George Vessey of Melbourne to his family referring to opening of Baptist Chapel in Collins Street, church services, the distribution of tracts, and the 1865 constitutional crisis.
2) Diary 1869 of Leonard Vessey 1847–80 kept on voyage to Australia on the *Canaan*.
3) Letters 1869–79 of Leonard Vessey to his parents describing his voyage to Australia, impressions of Sydney, Hill End and Bathurst, roads in Blue Mountains, New South Wales politics, and his work as a surveyor in Southern Tablelands and South Coast of New South Wales.
4) Photographs of Leonard Vessey and surveyors at Hill End 1872.

Two-page list available for reference.

Entry 474   Reels M2587–2590

Name **VICKERS PLC**
Title Records
Inclusive dates 1916–64
Quantity 4 reels of microfilm
Location of original Cambridge University Library, West Road, Cambridge CB3 9DR, England

Note
The Sheffield steelmaking firm of Vickers, Sons & Co was incorporated in 1867. Under the chairmanship of Thomas E. Vickers (1833–1915) it became famous for engineering, armaments manufacture and shipbuilding. In more recent times its main activities have been armoured fighting vehicles, marine engineering, medical equipment, precision equipment for the aerospace industry and, since 1980, Rolls Royce and Bentley cars.

Description
Reports, correspondence, notes and other papers relating to the company's operations in Australia and New Zealand.

Includes papers on directors and agencies of subsidiary companies, papers on supply of aircraft, correspondence on flights of Sir Ross and Keith Smith, and reports by directors and executives of visits to Australia and New Zealand.
Correspondents include Sir Keith Smith, Sir Robert Knox, Sir Ronald Weeks and Lord Knollys.

11-page list available for reference.

Entry 475   Reel M402

Name **VYVYAN, J. Henry**
Title Correspondence
Inclusive dates 1857–68
Quantity 1 reel of microfilm
Location of original Cornwall County Record Office, County Hall, Truro, Cornwall TR1 3AY, England

Note
Vyvyan left England in 1853 and settled at Motueka, near Nelson, New Zealand. He bought a sheep property there but was forced to return to Cornwall in 1868 for economic reasons. He was the nephew of Sir Richard Rawlinson Vyvyan (1800–79), a Conservative parliamentarian.

Description
64 letters, including eight from J. Henry Vyvyan to his uncle Sir Richard Vyvyan, describing: conditions in New Zealand; land regulations; copper mining; the difficulties of his farming life; and the obstacles to his return to England. Most of the remaining letters are from J.H. Vyvyan's father, Rev. Vyell Vyvyan, and his uncle Sir Richard Vyvyan concerning family affairs, especially J. Henry Vyvyan's position in New Zealand.

Entry 476   Reels M2794–2795

Name **WAKEFIELD FAMILY**
Title Papers
Inclusive dates 1815–53
Quantity 2 reels of microfilm
Location of original British Library, Great Russell Street, London WC1B 3DG, England

Note
Arthur Wakefield (1799–1843) was the New Zealand Co agent at Nelson 1841–43. His brother, the colonial reformer Edward Gibbon Wakefield (1796–1862) emigrated to New Zealand in 1853 and was a Member of the House of Representatives 1853–55. William Hayward Wakefield (1803–1848) was Principal Agent for the New Zealand Co and supervised its settlements at Wellington, Nelson, Wanganui and Taranaki.

Description
Copies of letters 1815–53, transcribed by A.J. Allon, from Arthur, Edward and William Wakefield to their sister Catherine and other members of the family. Subjects include: the foundation of South Australia; the formation of the New Zealand Association in 1837; the publication of *The British Colonization of New Zealand*; arrival of William Wakefield and party in New Zealand in 1840; arrival of E.G. Wakefield in 1853; the murder of Arthur Wakefield by Maoris in 1843; the dispute with Lord Stanley; and the proposal in 1847 for a new colony in New Zealand.

Three-page list available for reference.

Entry 477   Reel M1887

Name **WAKEFIELD FAMILY**
Title Papers
Inclusive dates 1818–1962
Quantity 1 reel of microfilm
Location of original Mrs P. Mitchell, Devon, England

Note
Further papers of members of the Wakefield Family in New Zealand, including Edward Gibbon Wakefield, his brother Daniel Wakefield (1798–1858) and nephew Charles Marcus Wakefield (1838–1902).

Description
1) Scrapbook c.1837–74 of Charles Marcus Wakefield. Subjects include deaths of Edward Gibbon and Arthur Wakefield, activities of Wakefield in New Zealand, and Transit of Venus expedition in 1874.
2) Letters 1841–55 of E.G. Wakefield referring to relations between New Zealand Co and Maoris and land claims.
3) Letters and memoranda 1847–57 concerning resignation of Daniel Wakefield as Attorney-General and other matters.
4) Papers 1863–1907 of Charles M. Wakefield, including letters to his mother, referring to his work as a surveyor and his collection of New Zealand insects.
5) Copies of letters 1835–47 of E.G. Wakefield, Arthur Wakefield and William Wakefield, mostly written to their sister Catherine Torlesse, referring to New Zealand politics, progress of settlement at Nelson and family news.

Seven-page list available for reference.

Entry 478   Reels M407–409, M593, M718

Name **WARD, T.G.S., Capt.**
Title Letters
Inclusive dates 1821–66
Quantity 5 reels of microfilm
Location of original Capt. T.G.S. Ward, Berkshire, England

Note
Philatelist specialising in nineteenth-century Australian and New Zealand covers.

Description
Letters are grouped by State of origin, with any New Zealand letters following the Australian items. Within each State group the correspondence is divided, where necessary, into commercial, private and church letters.

M407–409:
1) New South Wales correspondents include Edwards & Hunter, Salting & Garrard, C.W. Roemer, H. Ferres, James Williamson, Thomas B. Allen, John McGarvie, Archibald Mosman, Felton Mathew, S. Raymond, J. Glanville, Sir Alfred Stephen, Henry Edwards, Jane Black, W.F. Scott, George G. Dickinson, Thomas Hall, William Buyers, Robert Ross, John Saunders, L. MacAlister, Mrs Betts, Joseph Davies, George Whitfield, William McKernan and Michael Moran.
2) Queensland material comprises a letter written by Spooner Coleman of North Brisbane in 1848 and a printed pamphlet on emigration to Queensland 1863.
3) South Australian correspondents include Acraman Main Lindsay and Co, F.G. Waterhouse, William Giles, W.G. Lambert, John Newman, James Ide, J.M. Skipper, E.A. Wright, John Hance and Thomas Q. Stow.
4) Tasmanian correspondents include Major George Deare, William Inkersole, Robert Pitcairn, R. Jacomb, Elizabeth Staples, Samuel Pratt Winter, C. Swanston, Charles McDonnell, W.H. Thomas, O. Gilles, Samuel Jackson, Edward T. Bell, Avison Terry, Aaron Allason, Henry D. Dowling and W. Goulston, and two surgeons reporting on the health of Peter Ewart.
5) Victorian correspondents include Mr Thatcher, David Young, Alex Anderson, Daniel McKenzie, Mary Walker, William Hull, R. Jacomb, J.W. Carlton, Charles H. Lyon, Robert Jobson, Frederick Miller, Richard Fletcher, Samuel Greenlees, Benjamin Hurst, R.T. Elliott, W. Westgarth and F.W. Campbell.

6) The Western Australian letters consist of one letter from John G. Bussell and seven from Fanny L. Bussell 1834–46, together with six letters written by members of the Carter Family of Gwambygine Farm.

7) The New Zealand correspondents are Alexander Kennedy, George Laurence, J.T. Tatum and Mr Rout.

M593:
100 commercial and private letters from Australia. Correspondents include Robert Campbell, Dr John Lhotsky, Robert Thomson & Co, Francis Halbed and Alex McKean.

M718:
Australian correspondents include William Fitzherbert, Robert Thomson & Co, Henry Mace, John Waugh, James Crichton, Robert Foster, Ann Gaywood, George S. Brodie, Henry Palmer, Rose Family, Adam W. Elmslie, and J. Sewell. The four New Zealand letters are from Fanny and James E. Fitzgerald of Lyttelton.

25-page list available for reference.

Entry 479   Reel M1197

Name **WARWICK COUNTY RECORD OFFICE**
Title Collections
Inclusive dates 1829–1939
Quantity 1 reel of microfilm
Location of original Warwick County Record Office, Priory Park, Cape Road, Warwick CV34 4JS, England

Description
1) Letter 1889 of Justice Sir Joseph Long Innes to F.A. Newdegate.
2) Papers 1852–1933 of Farr Family including letters of Edwin Bartlett of Ballarat and Annie Morley of Hastings, New Zealand.
3) Papers 1829–72 of Dormer Family including letters of Charles Dormer describing visits to Singapore, Labuan and Manila and letters and cuttings on the Tichborne Case.
4) Papers 1865–66 of Bree Family relating to John Gardner of Bendigo.
5) Diary 1882 of F. Bostock on voyage of *Torrens* from London to Adelaide and correspondence 1937–39 on genealogy of Bostock and Burgess families in Australia.

Eight-page list available for reference.

Entry 480   Reel M2065

Name **WATSON, David (1835–1901)**
Title Letters
Inclusive dates 1852–57
Quantity 1 reel of microfilm
Location of original Mrs Agatha Wood, Cambridge CB5 8SU, England

Note
Watson emigrated to Victoria in 1852, returning to Scotland in 1857. Established a major paper factory at Dundee.

Description
Typescript copies of letters 1852–57 of David Watson to various family members in Scotland. They were written from Leith, London, Plymouth, Melbourne, Forest Creek, Geelong and Sydney. Subjects include: his voyage to Australia; impressions of Melbourne, Sydney and Blue Mountains, Forest Creek and Ballarat diggings; economic conditions in Australia; Union Bank; churches in the colonies; and his travels in Western District of Victoria.

Two-page list available for reference.

Entry 481   Reel M680

Name **WATTS, John (1821–1902)**
Title Reminiscences
Inclusive dates 1901
Quantity 1 reel of microfilm
Location of original Mrs A.T. Peppercorn, Buckinghamshire, England

Note
Queensland farmer and politician. Arrived in South Australia in 1840 and returned to England in 1843. In 1846 he accepted the job of managing 'Budgelaing' station (now 'Felton') for Capt. Mallard and arrived in Brisbane in December 1847. He later became manager of 'Eton Vale' for Arthur Hodgson, and ultimately became one of its owners. In 1860 he was elected Member for Drayton and Toowoomba in the Legislative Assembly and was later member for Western Downs. Secretary for Land and Public Works 1866–67.

Description
Typescript volume entitled 'Personal Reminiscences, Being Recollections of Watts' Experiences in Australia from 1840 to 1867'. They describe in some detail farming activities, and

personalities of the Darling Downs. Includes sketches of scenes and photographs of himself, Arthur Hodgson, L.A. Steiger and Robert Ramsay. The later part of the volume includes descriptions of his work as Secretary for Public Works including matters relating to the construction of the Ipswich–Toowoomba railway.

Entry 482   Reel M1640

Name **WEBBER, Edmund (1817–1860)**

Title Papers

Inclusive dates 1841–42

Quantity 1 reel of microfilm

Location of original William Cookworthy Museum, Old Grammar School, 108 Fore Street, Kingsbridge, Devon, England

Note
Joined Royal Navy in 1830 and served on a number of ships. Emigrated to New South Wales on the *Favorite* in 1840. Sailed to New Zealand in 1841 and worked as clerk in Auckland. Returned to England in 1843 and resumed career in Navy.

Description
1) Memoirs written while working as clerk in Auckland in 1842. They describe his first 20 years (1817–37), including his service on the West African survey and the Mediterranean Station.
2) Journal 1841–42 kept by Webber on the voyage from Van Diemen's Land to New Zealand on the *Favorite* in 1841, referring to his life in Van Diemen's Land, meeting with members of the Antarctic expedition led by J.C. Ross, Hobart Observatory, arrival at the Bay of Islands, life at barracks, attempts to obtain a government post, Governor William Hobson, and relations with Maoris.

Three-page list available for reference.

Entry 483   Reel M1968

Name **WEDDERBURN, Sir David, 3rd Baronet (1835–1882)**

Title Diaries

Inclusive dates 1874–75, 1985

Quantity 1 reel of microfilm

Location of original Mr D.A. Percival, Essex, England

Copyright note Researchers wishing to publish or reproduce the diaries, or extracts from them, must obtain the permission of Mr D.A. Percival.

Note
Liberal MP 1868–82. Wedderburn travelled extensively, visiting Europe, North America, Asia, Australia, New Zealand and South Africa.

Description
1) Typescript 'Sir David Wedderburn, Baronet, MP 1835–1882: Life Sketch' (1985) by D.A. Percival.
2) Diaries 1874–75 (Vols 4 and 5) describe: the voyage from Italy to Australia; travels in Victoria, Tasmania, New South Wales, Queensland and New Zealand; social events; Bendigo goldfields; life on stations; opera; Melbourne Observatory; Sydney Mint; Sydney University; Sir Hercules Robinson; Henry Parkes; H. Russell; Louis Hope; encounters with Aborigines; inspection of copper mine at Copperfield; Sir William Macarthur; Sir George Grey; J.H. Hector; Anglo–Maori relations; Hokitika and western goldfields; observations of Transit of Venus; and voyage to Honolulu.

Three-page list available for reference.

See also MS8219.

Entry 484   Reel M728

Name **WELCHMAN, Henry, Rev. (c.1850–1908)**

Title Diaries

Inclusive dates 1892–95

Quantity 1 reel of microfilm

Location of original Rev. W.F Browning, Oxfordshire, England

Note
Missionary and doctor in the Melanesian Mission. Ordained a deacon in 1891 and in May 1892 arrived at Bogotu, the southern portion of Santa Isabel Island in the Solomon Islands. In 1893 he was ordained as a priest. From 1895 to 1903 he

was priest in charge of St Luke's College, Siota, in the Solomon Islands.

Description
Two journals, July 1892–November 1893 and December 1893–May 1895, giving a general day-to-day account of life in the Melanesian Islands, recording treatment of diseases and incidents in his life as missionary and teacher.

One-page list available for reference.

Entry 485   Reels M805–806

Name **WELCHMAN, Henry, Rev. (c.1850–1908)**
Title Papers
Inclusive dates 1887–1908
Quantity 2 reels of microfilm
Location of original Melanesian Mission, 15 Denewood Close, Watford, Hertfordshire, England

Note
Missionary and doctor in the Melanesian Mission. Ordained a deacon in 1891 and in May 1892 arrived at Bogotu, the southern portion of Santa Isabel Island in the Solomon Islands. In 1893 he was ordained as a priest. From 1895 to 1903 he was priest in charge of St Luke's College, Siota, in the Solomon Islands.

Description
Copies of correspondence 1887–89 and papers January 1889–July 1892 and June 1896–November 1908. Some of the correspondence was written from Norfolk Island, where Welchman stayed for more than a year and became interested in the Mota language.

Entry 486   Reels M2536–2538

Name **WELLCOME FOUNDATION**
Title Records
Inclusive dates 1882–1986
Quantity 3 reels of microfilm
Location of original Glaxo Wellcome, Greenford Road, Greenford, Middlesex UB6 0HE, England
Special conditions Microfilm must be purchased from the Wellcome Institute

Note
Burroughs Wellcome & Co, founded in 1880 by Silas Burroughs and Henry Solomon Wellcome, acted as agents for American medical companies.

In 1883 they started manufacturing their own products. Burroughs died in 1895 and Wellcome became the sole proprietor. He established various research laboratories. In 1925 they were consolidated into the Wellcome Foundation Ltd.

Description
Correspondence, notes, memoranda, financial papers, minutes of meetings, cuttings and notebooks relating to the company's activities in Australia and New Zealand. Subjects include: drug trials; value and problems of conducting drug trials in Australia and New Zealand; and sales and exports. Correspondents include J.D. Spink, S.M. Burroughs, E.W. Wrigley, A.B. Hector, Capt. R.F. Scott and Sir Ernest Shackleton.

18-page list available for reference.

Entry 487   Reels M2663–2668

Name **WELLCOME INSTITUTE FOR THE HISTORY OF MEDICINE, Library**
Title Western Manuscripts and Autograph Letters
Inclusive dates 1835–1925
Quantity 6 reels of microfilm
Location of original Library, Wellcome Institute for the History of Medicine, 183 Euston Road, London NW1 2BE, England
Special Conditions Copies of microfilm must be purchased from the Wellcome Institute.

Description:
1) Diaries 1869–70 of naval surgeon Fleetwood Buckle of a voyage around the world including impressions of Melbourne and Sydney.
2) Logs and notes 1910–13 of Dennis G. Lillie kept while marine zoologist on Scott's Antarctic expedition on the *Terra Nova*, referring to observations of whales.
3) Lectures on science 1842–55 delivered by Rev. John Lillie at the Mechanics Institutes at Hobart and Launceston.
4) Journals, diary and other papers 1839–43 kept by surgeon and naturalist Robert McCormick on J.C. Ross' Antarctic expedition on HMS *Erebus*. They refer to travels in Van Diemen's Land and visit to Maori settlement near the Bay of Islands.
5) Notes 1908–13 of Sir Raymond E. Priestley of flora and fauna observed on the Shackleton and Scott Antarctic expeditions.
6) Papers 1877–95 of George C. Wallich relating to deep sea exploration and *Challenger* expedition.

7) Papers 1907–22 of Sir Ambrose Stanton on research on beri-beri.

8) Letter 1804 from Sir Joseph Banks to J.B.J. Delambre requesting assistance in obtaining release of Capt. Matthew Flinders from Mauritius.

9) Diary 1861–62 of Harry Ramsdale on voyage to Moreton Bay and travels in Queensland.

10) Letters 1838–45 of Sir John and Lady Franklin in Van Diemen's Land.

11) Letters 1840–55 of John Gould concerning *Birds of Australia* and *Mammals of Australia*.

12) Miscellaneous letters of Henry Lee, Sir Richard Owen, Ray Moodie, W.B. Clarke, Allan Cunningham, Sir Joseph Hooker, J.J. de Labillardière, B.K. Malinowski, Queen Pomare and Alfred Wallace.

25-page list available for reference.

Entry 488   Reels M1888–1889

Name **WELLESLEY, Richard, 1st Marquess (1760–1842)**

Title Papers

Inclusive dates 1793–1805

Quantity 2 reels of microfilm

Location of original The British Library, Great Russell Street, London WC1B 3DG, England

Note
Tory MP 1784–97, Governor-General of India 1797–1805, Foreign Secretary 1809–12, Lord Lieutenant of Ireland 1821–28, 1833–34.

Description
Correspondence relating to: the spice trade; settlement in India of convicts from New South Wales; relations with Dutch East Indies; expedition against Batavia 1800–01; British defences at Malacca; and administration of Prince of Wales Island (Penang). There is also correspondence concerning the Residency of R.T. Farquhar at Moluccas and Prince of Wales Island, and a journal of Capt. W.C. Lennon with an account of Ambon and Banda 1795–96. Main correspondents are Lord Hobart, General D. Baird, R.C. Birch, C. Stokes, Sir Home Popham, Sir Edward Pellew, Admiral P. Rainier, Capt. R.T. Farquhar and Capt. W. Bathurst.

16-page list available for reference.

Entry 489   Reel M2054

Name **WEST DEVON AREA RECORD OFFICE**

Title Collections

Inclusive dates 1800–1936

Quantity 1 reel of microfilm

Location of original West Devon Area Record Office, Unit 3, Clare Place, Coxside, Plymouth PL4 0JW, England

Description
1) Papers 1800–26 of Mayor and Town Clerk of Plymouth concerning convicts and transportation.

2) Papers 1859–89 of Petherbridge Family relating to properties in Adelaide.

3) Papers 1923–36 concerning William Bligh, including research into his birthplace and education, and notes on genealogy.

4) Logbooks 1858–65 kept by Samuel W. Jordan on the *Prince of Wales* and the *Walmer Castle* on voyages to Melbourne.

5) Lecture 1952 by F.S. Blight on Capt. Tobias Furneaux.

6) Papers 1826–27 of Major Edmund Lockyer referring to his expedition to Swan River and King George's Sound.

Five-page list available for reference.

Entry 490   Reels M822, M1549–1550

Name **WEST SUSSEX RECORD OFFICE**

Title Collections

Inclusive dates 1813–1926

Quantity 3 reels of microfilm

Location of original West Sussex Record Office, West Street, Chichester, West Sussex PO19 1RN, England

Description
M822:
1) Papers of the Liberal politician and free trade campaigner Richard Cobden including three letters 1864–65 from Sir George Bowen in Brisbane, Henry H. Brown on the Maori wars, and Archibald Michie about the *Shenandoah*; letter 1926 from Stanley V. Larkin; two letters 1903 to Thomas Fisher Unwin (Cobden's son-in-law) from Senator E. Pulsford and Sir Josiah Symon; 'Papers Respecting Sir James Brooke's Policy and Position with Regard to Sarawak' (1863), with related dispatches; copy of a statement 1851 regarding a grant of land

in Sarawak by the Sultan of Brunei; pamphlet *'Sir Stamford Raffles and the Spice Islands'* (*Chambers Miscellany of Useful and Entertaining Tracts, no. 53*).

2) Cobden and Unwin papers: 18 letters 1881–92 to Emma and Margaret Cobden from the Richmond Family of Nelson, New Zealand; letters 1889–90 from Henry Norman, Singapore, to T.F. Unwin, one mentioning an expedition in Malaya; letter 1878 from J.W. Longmuir of Sydney about Cobden papers.

3) Cowdray archives: 14 documents 1867–75 relating to the estates of George James, 6th Earl of Egmont, and his relatives, members of the Perceval Family, in Canterbury, New Zealand and Melbourne.

4) Goodwood archives: papers of the politician Charles Lennox, 5th Duke of Richmond, including reports and printed pamphlets 1831–32 concerning: the promotion and funding of emigration to Australia and disposition of Crown lands; letters 1832 from the Colonial Office and Foreign Office relating to emigration, especially by women; document 1833 entitled 'The Duke of Richmond's mode for reducing the army in the colonies'; letter 1834 from I. Montgomery on the state of the Boys Establishment at Point Puer, Port Arthur, Van Diemen's Land; letter from T.J. Maslen to the Duke of Richmond proposing an expedition to survey the north-west coast of Australia in 1832, written on the back of an 1827 map of Australia drawn by Maslen.

5) Additional manuscripts: conveyance 1871 of Mary and Alfred Barker of Baldina Keringa, Burra Burra; two maps 1813, one depicting the world in two hemispheres, the other Asia, including the East Indies; letter 1860 from R.W. Nutt, Melbourne, to Richard Cobden including reference to the influence of his theories on economic thinking in Australia.

Eight-page list available for reference.

M1549–1550:
1) Papers 1837–57 of Charles Lennox, 5th Duke of Richmond, mainly dealing with the work of 1838 New Zealand Committee, voyage of his sister Lady Mary Fitzroy to Australia in 1846 and governorship of Sir Charles Fitzroy in New South Wales. Other correspondents include S. Bannister and Sir George Arthur.

2) Ledger 1815–19 of Walter S. Davidson referring to properties in New South Wales.

3) Papers 1841–46 of politician John Abel Smith including memorandum on future of Australian colonies.

4) Copies of papers 1836–84 of John B. Hack, an early settler in South Australia, including a typescript by L. Darton on the Hack Family and Henry Watson.

Eight-page list available for reference.

Entry 491 Reels M2857–2861

Name **WEST YORKSHIRE ARCHIVE SERVICE, Bradford**

Title Collections

Inclusive dates 1828–1973

Quantity 5 reels of microfilm

Location of original West Yorkshire Archive Service (Bradford), 15 Canal Road, Bradford, West Yorkshire BD1 4AT, England

Description
1) Transcripts of letters 1828–51 of John and Mary Glasson referring to discovery of gold in Bookanan, New South Wales, 1851.

2) Letters 1944–45 of William Moore, a naval officer serving in the Pacific, to his family referring to war news from Europe, end of war in Pacific, and visits to Canberra, Sydney and Nowra.

3) Papers 1929–57 of Hirsch Family relating to their wool and yarn exporting business.

4) Correspondence and papers 1954–57 relating to visits of Young Australia League boys and girls to Bradford.

5) Papers 1911–18 of Edward R. Hartley, including diary kept on a voyage on board the *Ionic* to New Zealand in 1911 and reports of his lectures on socialism.

6) Records 1919–73 of Illingworth Morris Plc, textile manufacturers, including ledger of wool shipped from Australia and correspondence with Australian banks.

7) Papers 1942–45 of Harry Eaddie relating to his imprisonment at POW Camp, Changi.

8) Papers 1939–45 relating to the Japanese POW Camps in Southeast Asia.

9) Papers 1882–1905 of William Cudworth, including journal kept on a voyage to Australia on the *Parramatta* 1882–83 and letter written from Sydney.

10) Journal 1891–92 of Ben Simpson kept on voyage from Hull to Melbourne.

11) Papers 1896–1924 of William P. Baildon including letters of Rev. J. Chalmers in New Guinea and Francis J. Bayldon in Sydney.

27-page list available for reference.

Entry 492   Reels M2772–2774

Name **WEST YORKSHIRE ARCHIVE SERVICE,
        Calderdale**

Title Collections

Inclusive dates 1838–1921

Quantity 3 reels of microfilm

Location of original West Yorkshire Archive Service
(Calderdale), Central Library, Northgate House,
Northgate, Halifax HX1 1UN, West Yorkshire,
England

Description
1) Papers 1838–82 of Frederick Walker, Son
   & Dickie, solicitors, relating to lease and
   conveyance of lands in Australia and New
   Zealand.

2) Legal documents 1838–52 relating to properties
   of John Rawson in Adelaide.

3) Typescript copies of letters 1852–96 of Grace
   and Thomas Hirst to family in England referring
   to Maori War and economic conditions of New
   Zealand.

4) Press cuttings relating to tour of England by the
   Australian cricket team 1899.

Five-page list available for reference.

Entry 493   Reels M2796–2797

Name **WEST YORKSHIRE ARCHIVE SERVICE,
        Kirklees**

Title Collections

Inclusive dates 1833–1962

Quantity 2 reels of microfilm

Location of original West Yorkshire Archive Service
(Kirklees), Central Library, Princess Alexandra Walk,
Huddersfield HD1 2SU, West Yorkshire, England

Description
1) Business records 1918–31 of woollen and
   worsted manufacturing firm Rowland Mitchell
   and Co Ltd referring to Australian and New
   Zealand orders, accounts and shipping.

2) Papers 1942–62 of Father Vivian Redlich
   relating to his work with the Bush Brotherhood
   at Rockhampton and its mission in New Guinea.

3) Papers 1839–91 of Matthew H.M. Dyson
   describing conditions in South Australia
   1838–46 and relating to his estate in Auckland
   1889–91.

4) Letters 1888–91 of George Lodge to Edgar
   Battye referring to: employment at Queensland
   Manufacturing Co in North Ipswich; Aborigines;

South Sea Islanders; Chinese and Germans in
Queensland; and his move to Parramatta.

Seven-page list available for reference.

Entry 494   Reels M2686–2696

Name **WEST YORKSHIRE ARCHIVE SERVICE,
        Wakefield**

Title Collections

Inclusive dates 1795–1965

Quantity 11 reels of microfilm

Location of original West Yorkshire Archive Service
(Wakefield), Newstead Road, Wakefield, West
Yorkshire WF1 2DE, England

Description
1) Minute-books 1797–1934 of the Elland Society,
   include references to Rev. Samuel Marsden.

2) Records 1948–59 of the woollen manufacturer
   Fred Armitage Lodge and Sons Ltd, pertaining
   to their business activities in Australia and New
   Zealand. Correspondents include Douglas
   P. Peacocke of Auckland and R.W. Davis of
   Melbourne.

3) Letters 1863–76 of David Tattersall of
   Daylesford, Victoria, to his family referring
   to departure of miners for New Zealand and
   Queensland goldfields, emigration agents,
   Victorian politics and family news.

4) Calendars 1823–49 of prisoners in the House
   of Correction at Wakefield.

5) Copies of letters 1866–73 of Betsy Jennison in
   New Zealand referring to conditions on
   Otakaramu cattle station.

11-page list available for reference.

Entry 495   Reel M2685

Name **WEST YORKSHIRE ARCHIVE SERVICE,
        Yorkshire Archaeological Society**

Title Collections

Inclusive dates 1790–1985

Quantity 1 reel of microfilm

Location of original West Yorkshire Archive Service,
Yorkshire Archaeological Society, 23 Clarendon
Road, Leeds LS2 9NZ, England

Description
1) Wills, probates and deeds 1790–1863 of Henry
   Alderson of Adelaide, Mary H. Chatterley of
   Melbourne, and Charles J.T. Troughton of
   London who died at sea near New South Wales.

2) Notes and family trees of George and Robert Hebden, who emigrated to Australia in 1839 and 1868, Marrison Family of South Yorkshire and Tasmania c.1960s, and Field Family in Australia by Anne Field of Sydney 1985.

3) Records of family of Joseph Buckton and Emma Buckton who emigrated from Leeds to New Zealand 1862.

Two-page list available for reference.

Entry 496   Reels M2413–2414

Name **WESTLAKE, Ernest (1855–1922)**

Title Papers

Inclusive dates 1893–1929

Quantity 2 reels of microfilm

Location of original Pitt Rivers Museum, Oxford University, South Parks Road, Oxford OX1 3PP, England

Note
Geologist. He became interested in the stone implements of Tasmanian Aborigines and visited Tasmania in 1908–10. Later he donated his collection of Tasmanian Aboriginal stone implements to the Pitt Rivers Museum.

Description
Correspondence and notebooks relating to Westlake's visit to Tasmania. They include: accounts of his journey to Tasmania on SS *Africa*; landings in Western Australia and Adelaide; his impressions of Tasmania; field work in Tasmania; notes on Trucanini and other Tasmanian Aborigines; his collection of stone implements; Professor Baldwin Spencer; and J.P. Moir.

Three-page list available for reference.

Entry 497   Reel M1651

Name **WESTMINSTER DIOCESAN ARCHIVES**

Title Records

Inclusive dates 1818–1930

Quantity 1 reel of microfilm

Location of original Westminster Diocesan Archives, Archbishop's House, 16a Abingdon Road, London W8 6AF, England

Note
The Roman Catholic dioceses in England ceased to exist during the Reformation. After 1688 England was divided into districts, each administered by a vicar-apostolic. In 1850 a restoration of the hierarchy took place and England was divided into the Archbishopric of Westminster and 12 suffragan sees.

Description
Papers of Bishop W. Poynter, Rev. R. Gradwell, Bishop J.Y. Bramston, Bishop T. Griffiths, Cardinal N.P.S. Wiseman, Cardinal H.A. Vaughan and Cardinal F. Bourne. They deal with: establishment of the New Holland Mission by Rev. J. Flynn 1818–19; selection of priests for the Mission; relations with political authorities; appointment of J.B. Polding as Vicar-Apostolic in 1834; creation of dioceses; emigration; missions in Pacific; and visit of Archbishop D. Mannix to England 1920. Correspondents include J. Flynn, P. Connolly, J.J. Therry, J.B. Polding, J.B. Pompallier and J.M.B. Serra.

11-page list available for reference.

Entry 498   Reel M2348

Name **WESTMORELAND, Charles**

Title Diary

Inclusive dates 1882–1904

Quantity 1 reel of microfilm

Location of original Ms Jane Herron, Gwent, Wales

Description
1) Diary October 1882–March 1883 of Charles Westmoreland on a voyage from Plymouth to Rockhampton on the *Melpomene,* including accounts of life on board the ship, arrival at Rockhampton, and other emigrants.

2) Two letters 1894 and 1904 written by A. Westmoreland and Charles Westmoreland to family in England.

One-page list available for reference.

Entry 499   Reel M599

Name **WHEELER, Gerald Camden (1872–1943)**

Title Manuscript and correspondence

Inclusive dates 1943–54

Quantity 1 reel of microfilm

Location of original School of Oriental and African Studies, Thornhaugh Street, Russell Square, London WC1H 0XG, England

Note
Anthropologist. In 1908 and 1909 he undertook research work in the Solomon Islands, with the assistance of the University of London, the Royal

Geographical Society and the Royal Society. His publications included *The Tribe and Intertribal Relations in Australia* (1910) and *Mono-Alu Folklore* (1926). He spent much of the latter part of his life working on a comprehensive account of the culture of the Mono-Alu people of the Western Solomon Islands.

Description
1) Incomplete typescript draft of 'The Mono-Alu People of Bougainville Strait' containing detailed descriptions of various aspects of their culture such as kinship, religion, marriage, ownership and death rites. Many of the statements are supported by verbatim quotations in the vernacular language together with translations. The draft includes a contents list and glossary of the Mono-Alu language.
2) Notes and correspondence 1953–54 of George B. Milner of the University of London with Mrs Wheeler and the Royal Anthropological Institute relating to his work on the Wheeler Papers.

Entry 500   Reel M864

Name **WHITE, James Espie (1846–1865)**
Title Journal
Inclusive dates 1863
Quantity 1 reel of microfilm
Location of original Edinburgh Central Library, George IV Bridge, Edinburgh EH1 1EG, Scotland

Note
A foreword to the journal states that the author travelled to Australia in September 1862 'to join his brother, John White, a government contractor ... building a breakwater at the Clarence River Heads, New South Wales'.

Description
Journal 1863 of White's voyage to Australia on the *Henry Fernie* September–December 1862. Most of the passengers were Irish, and White writes of their attitude to the English and Scottish passengers. He describes in detail conditions on board, entertainments arranged during the voyage, relations between the passengers, marine life observed, and deaths and burials at sea. He writes vividly of the ship's arrival at Melbourne and his first impressions of the city and its people. An appendix to the 153-page journal contains a copy of a testimonial presented to the captain and published in the *Argus* of 26 December 1862, a table recording the ship's bearings each day and a note of the destinations of his cabin mates Frederick King, Arthur Hiddle, George Samuelson and James Hall.

Entry 501   Reel M2116

Name **WIDDOWSON, Henry**
Title Journal
Inclusive dates 1825–26
Quantity 1 reel of microfilm
Location of original Mrs C. Scott, Wirral, England

Description
Journal November 1825–May 1826 kept on a voyage from England to Van Diemen's Land on the *Albion*, including accounts of life on board the ship, the weather and other passengers.

Two-page list available for reference.

Entry 502   Reel M831

Name **WILLIAM SALT LIBRARY**
Title Collections
Inclusive dates 1798–c.1890
Quantity 1 reel of microfilm
Location of original William Salt Library, 19 Eastgate Street, Stafford, Staffordshire ST16 2LZ, England

Description
1) Kirby manuscripts: letter 1880 from J. Barrett, Waimate, New Zealand, describing life in New Zealand; printed catalogue c.1905 (16 p.) of a historical exhibition aboard a ship reputed to be the *Success*. The catalogue contains lengthy notes about individual convicts and settlers associated with the *Success*, especially during its days as a prison hulk.
2) Hand, Morgan and Owen, solicitors: *New Zealand Company Terms of Purchase for a Quantity of Land in the Wellington District*, by John Ward, Secretary, New Zealand House (London, 1843); printed circular 1843 on the subject of purchase of land by Thomas C. Harington, an official of the Association for Promoting the Settlement of Otago. A map of New Zealand is included in the article.
3) Six engravings of people and views of Manila c.1798.

Two-page list available for reference.

Name **WILLS, Willam Charles**

Title Journal

Inclusive dates 1841–44

Quantity 1 reel of microfilm

Location of original Thomas Coram Foundation for Children, 40 Brunswick Square, London WC1, England

Note
In 1837–40 Wills was a steward of the Foundling Hospital (now the Thomas Coram Foundation for Children), London. In October 1841 he left England to live in Australia because of ill-health and reached Sydney in April 1842. Suitable employment was difficult to find and it was not until 20 June that he took a position as a clerk with Felix Wilson of Castlereagh Street. On 20 March 1843 he was appointed as secretary to the first Mayor of Sydney, C.H. Chambers.

Description
Journal (c.400 p.) 30 October 1841–13 January 1844, describing his voyage to Australia on the barque *Louisa* and his first two years in Australia. The journal is addressed to John Brownlow, Secretary of the Foundling Hospital. It mainly records day-to-day activities but also provides details of events leading to the formation of the first Municipal Council of Sydney.

One-page list available for reference.

Name **WILMOTH, Leslie James (1881–1963)**

Title Manuscript

Inclusive dates Undated

Quantity 1 reel of microfilm

Location of original Unknown

Description
Handwritten manuscript entitled 'The Finding of Australia'. Using printed and some original sources Wilmoth describes early Dutch, Spanish and English explorations in the Pacific, discoveries of Capt. James Cook, the background to transportation and the preparation and arrival of the First Fleet in 1788.

Name **G.W. WILSON & COMPANY**

Title Photographs

Inclusive dates c.1857–1902

Quantity 8 reels of microfilm

Location of original Aberdeen University Library, King's College, Aberdeen, Grampian AB9 2UB, Scotland

Special Conditions Requests for prints should be referred to the Keeper of Special Collections, Aberdeen University Library.

Note
George Washington Wilson (1823–1893) was established by 1857 as the leading portrait photographer of Aberdeen. In 1872, in partnership with George Brown Smith, the company G.W. Wilson and Co was formed. It employed 30 assistants and a number of staff photographers who travelled in Britain, Europe, South Africa and Australia. The company was liquidated in 1902.

Description
Photographs of Australian landscape, cities, towns and country districts, civic buildings, transport, street scenes, parks and gardens, plantations, river crossings, mining, housing, holiday scenes, birdlife, animals, and portraits of individuals, including Aborigines.

184-page list available for reference.

Name **WILSON FAMILY**

Title Papers

Inclusive dates 1814–1944

Quantity 1 reel of microfilm

Location of original Mrs Cecil Firbank, Somerset, England

Note
The Wilson Family came from Banff, Scotland. John Wilson was a merchant and shipowner. One son Capt. William Wilson was a mariner, while his other son, Sir James Milne Wilson (1812–80), after serving as a ship's officer, became manager of Hobart's Cascade Brewery and was later Premier and Colonial Secretary of Tasmania 1869–72. In 1847 James married Deborah Hope Degraves.

Description
1) Letterbook of William Wilson 1823–24 containing letters addressed to family and business associates in Sydney.

2) Notebook 1828, 1830 of a journey by John Wilson from Banff to Hobart in the brig *Sisters* and of a voyage in the South Seas in the barque *Dover*.

3) Letters 1824–34 to James and William Wilson from their sister Jane.

4) Letters 1827–49 to James and William Wilson from their parents, John and Barbara Wilson.

5) Papers 1835–80 of Sir James Milne Wilson including letters to his family and Francis Watkins of Parramatta; documents; drafts of parliamentary bills with handwritten notes; drafts of speeches; and photographs.

6) Miscellaneous family papers 1814–94.

7) Correspondence 1828–50 of the Allardyce Family, friends and business associates of the Wilsons, with a copy of the will of William Allardyce.

8) Two typescript volumes (93 p., 67 p.) and some additional papers 1935–44 relating to the history of the Wilson and Degraves Families, possibly compiled by Ada Wilson, daughter of Sir James Milne Wilson.

Two-page list available for reference.

Entry 507   Reel M935

Name **WILTSHIRE RECORD OFFICE**
Title Collections
Inclusive dates 1787–1872
Quantity 1 reel of microfilm
Location of original Wiltshire County Record Office, County Hall, Trowbridge, Wiltshire BA14 8JG, England

Description
1) Quarter Sessions Records: 12 selected bonds and contracts 1787–89 for the transportation of felons to New South Wales.

2) Boards of Guardians Records: selections 1848–58 from the minute-books of the Melksham Union relating to emigration to Australia.

3) Records 1849–51 of Wiltshire Emigration Society: accounts of the Society January–March 1851 giving details of applicants desiring to emigrate; cash account November 1850–May 1851 listing applicants by name; minute-book October 1849–December 1851 detailing the history of the development of the Society; register December 1850–May 1851 listing and giving personal details of emigrants and unsuccessful applicants; correspondence

February–June 1851 with the Colonial Land and Emigration Office, showing the names of emigrants and arrangements for travel; printed forms including abstracts from government regulations.

4) Papers 1823–29 of Calcutta merchant John Palmer, mainly comprising correspondence between John Palmer, his son Samuel J. Palmer and J.S. Brownrigg. Other correspondents include J. Burnaby, John Findall, H.W. Hobhouse, Thomas P. Courtenay, Robert Scott, M.O. Hunt, Charles Cockerell, R.C. Jenkins, Lieut. Col. Nahys and J. Deans. The correspondence deals mainly with commercial and political activities in Java, such as compensation for proprietors of spice plantations and other property at Bencoolen, Sumatra, which suffered from the transfer of Java to the Netherlands Government; the administration of Malacca; the despatch of bullion to Java; and political affairs of Java including the causes of the Java War. There is also business correspondence in Dutch and English 1825–27, mainly to J. Burnaby of Samarang, on trade in various commodities including coffee and spices.

5) 15 letters 1871–72 of Thomas E. Bate to his family, written while serving on board HMS *Iron Duke* in the Far East.

6) Printed notice 1852 of the Committee for Promoting the Emigration of Females to the Australian colonies.

7) Diary 1864–65 kept by William Chafyn Grove during a journey to Sydney on the *Vimiera* and on his travels in eastern Australia.

Seven-page list available for reference.

Entry 508   Reel M1952

Name **WOODBURY, Walter Bently (1834–1885)**
Title Letters
Inclusive dates 1852–58
Quantity 1 reel of microfilm
Location of original Royal Photographic Society, The Octagon, Milson Street, Bath, Avon BA1 1DN, England

Note
Photographer. Emigrated to Australia on the *Serampore* in 1852 and established a photographic business in Melbourne in 1855. In 1857 he went to Java and returned to England in 1862, where he invented the 'Woodbury type' photo-mechanical process.

Description
Letters written from Australia and Java, to his mother Ellen Woodbury (later Ellen Lloyd). They contain news of life in Australia, gold diggings in Victoria, establishment of photographic business in Melbourne, travels in Java, and photographs of East Indies.

Four-page list available for reference.

Entry 509   Reels M2844–2846

Name **YONGE, Sir Maurice (1899–1986)**

Title Papers

Inclusive dates 1928–78

Quantity 3 reels of microfilm

Location of original General Library, British Museum (Natural History), Cromwell Road, South Kensington, London SW7 5BD, England

Note
Worked for the Marine Biological Association, Plymouth. Appointed leader of an expedition to the Great Barrier Reef in 1927. He had a successful academic career and continued to pursue his interest and research on corals and molluscs. He published *A Year on the Great Barrier Reef* (1930) and *Oyster* (1960).

Description
Diaries, notebooks, research notes, correspondence, drafts and other papers relating to the Great Barrier Reef expedition and Yonge's extensive travels and research on corals and molluscs. Some of the diaries were kept by his wife Martha, who accompanied him on the Great Barrier Reef expedition.

Correspondents include David Stoddart, G.R. Orme, R.D. Purchon, H.C. Richards and A. Ben-Tuvia.

23-page list available for reference.

Entry 510   Reel M2519

Name **YORK CITY ARCHIVES**

Title Collections

Inclusive dates 1828–1983

Quantity 1 reel of microfilm

Location of original York City Archives, Art Gallery Building, Exhibition Square, York YO1 2EW, England

Description
1) Calendar of prisoners 1828–53 in the House of Correction, including details of convicts under sentence of transportation.
2) Calendar of prisoners 1828–33 at York Gaol.

3) Correspondence 1983 between Ann O'Donnell of Mount Gambier, South Australia, and City Solicitor concerning Pick Family.

Four-page list available for reference.

Entry 511   Reel M2766

Name **YORK MINSTER LIBRARY**

Title Collections

Inclusive dates 1885–1952

Quantity 1 reel of microfilm

Location of original York Minster Library, Deans Park, York YO1 2JD, England

Description
1) Diaries 1951–52 of Archbishop Cyril Garbett kept on his visits to Australia, New Zealand and the Pacific.
2) Letters 1885–95 of Archbishop William Thomson and his wife Zoe concerning their son Basil, his career prospects, and work in Tonga and Fiji.

Two-page list available for reference.

Entry 512   Reel M1196

Name **ZOOLOGICAL SOCIETY OF LONDON**

Title Records

Inclusive dates 1821–1903

Quantity 1 reel of microfilm

Location of original Zoological Society of London, Outer Circle, Regent's Park, London NW1 4RY, England

Note
Founded in 1826, the Society leased 20 acres in Regent's Park and in 1828 the Zoological Gardens were opened to the public. Until 1856 the Society also maintained a museum of preserved animals. Its *Scientific Proceedings* commenced in 1830 and *Transactions* in 1833. Only a small number of the early records of the Society have survived.

Description
A small collection of letters, mostly written to P.L. Sclater, relating to the discovery of new species of animals, birds and fishes in Australia, New Guinea and New Zealand, and to the conservation and exchange of animals between zoos.

Correspondents include George Bennett, John Gould, A. Gunther, G. Krefft, Lord Onslow, Sir Stamford Raffles, E.P. Ramsay and A.R. Wallace.

Four-page list available for reference.

Index

The numbers given in the index refer to entry numbers, not to page numbers.

Arrowsmith, A. 169
Art critics 189
Arthington Trust Archive 272
Arthur, Sir George 135, 314, 339, 349, 490
Arthur Balfour & Co Ltd—*see* Balfour, Arthur & Co Ltd
Artimisia, ship 327
Artists 17, 42, 56, 62, 85, 117, 130, 178, 189, 264, 291, 321, 442, 455
Artists International Association 455
Arundel, J.T. 276
Arundell, Sir George V., 8th Viscount Galway 18, 241, 355
Ashburnham parish, England 153
Ashby, Edwin 62
Ashley, H.V. 395
Ashworth, Edward 12
Ashworth, J.H., Prof. 156
Asquith, Herbert H., 1st Earl of Oxford 270
Assistance, HMS 342
Assizes 360, 415
Association for Promoting the Settlement of Otago 502
Astronomers 85, 393, 399, 464
Astronomy 210, 271, 381, 393, 399, 408
Athenaeum, periodical 23
Atkey, Sir Albert 356
Atkey, Lady Euphemia 356
Atkins, George 378
Atkins, Harry J. 378
Atkins, Richard 196
Atkinson, David 13
Atkinson, E. 53
Atkinson, Edward L. 71
Atkinson, Sir Henry 54
Atkinson, R.J. 407
Atlantis, German raider 185
Atlas I, ship 247
Atlas II, ship 247
Atomic bomb 109, 357
Atomic energy 250
Auchinleck, Sir Claude, Field Marshal 259
Auchterlonie, Gordon 448
Auckland, NZ 11, 109, 155, 200, 240, 289, 322, 352, 370, 375, 408, 410, 428, 432, 435, 457, 482, 493, 494
    drawings and paintings 12, 183, 200, 410
    immigration to 12, 319, 425
    visits to 165, 220, 340, 354, 364, 392
Auckland Islands 198
Audit Office—*see* Great Britain, Audit Office
Augusta, WA 119
Auronia, ship 188
Austin Family 190
Austral, SS 293
Australasian Federal Council 133, 192
Australasian United Steam Navigation Co 14
Australia, HMAS 206
Australia, ship 188
Australia 4, 6, 62, 64, 96, 99, 103, 109, 113, 117, 118, 119, 121, 129, 140, 141, 156, 173, 189, 194, 217, 260, 267, 272, 274, 279, 289, 291, 296, 338, 340, 344, 351, 414, 417, 442, 481, 486
    —*see also under* names of individual States, Territories and geographic regions, e.g. Northern Australia

Constitution 263
defence 51, 190, 206, 256, 345, 409, 426, 434, 451
economic conditions 20, 24, 62, 157, 206, 270, 276, 357, 370, 413, 480
exploration 84, 85, 169, 193, 246, 279, 332, 333, 439, 444, 452
federal–State relations 206, 270, 292, 347
Federation 37, 51, 133, 190, 210, 234, 288, 335, 381, 395, 434, 451
flora and fauna 57, 59, 61, 63, 66, 70, 71, 76, 116, 132, 134, 188, 190, 193, 201, 280, 320, 394, 399, 512
geology 65, 84, 85, 156, 183, 249, 332, 359
immigration to 27, 72, 79, 80, 91, 119, 123, 156, 188, 190, 230, 238, 240, 265, 271, 293, 298, 303, 327, 341, 349, 376, 381, 433, 463, 473, 491, 495
laws 284, 434
maps and charts 169, 183, 245, 432, 490
missions 100, 101, 108, 176, 279, 290, 322, 323, 469, 497
paintings, drawings and prints 62, 117, 149, 169
photographs 253
politics and government 4, 18, 30,42, 79, 85, 107, 112, 118, 133, 164, 184, 187, 206, 216, 234, 236, 259, 263, 264, 270, 286, 292, 303, 315, 326, 335, 347, 408, 413, 452, 462, 470
visits to 11, 12, 26, 36, 37, 43, 51, 54, 65, 78, 79, 109, 137, 149, 156, 164, 165, 166, 170, 188, 206, 208, 220, 229, 236, 253, 283, 287, 320, 337, 339, 341, 342, 346, 349, 356, 357, 381, 395, 396, 401, 402, 408, 413, 422, 425, 432, 437, 438, 440, 442, 447, 451, 460, 462, 464, 470, 474, 483, 511
Australian Academy of Science 170
Australian Agricultural Co 19, 225, 264, 354
Australian and New Zealand Association for the Advancement of Science 109
Australian Council for Civil Liberties 338
Australian Elizabethan Theatre Trust 259
Australian Institute of Physics 250
Australian Journalists Association (NSW) 259
Australian Labor Party 292, 315, 452
Australian League of Nations Union 164
Australian Mortgage Co Ltd 260
Australian Museum, Sydney 57
Australian Mutual Provident Society 219, 459
Australian National Socialist Party 184
Australian National University 109, 170
Australian Planning Institute 229, 442
Australian Station—*see* Royal Navy: Australian Station
Australian Transcontinental Railway 87
Authors—*see* Novelists; Poets; Writers
Auxiliary Bible Society of New South Wales 267
Aviation—*see* Civil aviation
Aviators 210
Avoca, Vic. 52
Ayers, Sir Henry 195
Aylesbury Gaol, Buckinghamshire, England 80
Ayliffe, T.H. 372
Ayre, John 96

Babbage, Charles 53
Bacchus Marsh, Vic. 163

Bisley parish, England 190
Black, Jane 478
Blackburn, David 38
Blackburn, Margaret 38
Blackwall, ship 418
Blackwall Yard 342
Blackwood, Beatrice 39
Blackwood, F.P., Capt. 246
Blackwood, Frederick, 1st Marquess of Dufferin and Ava 381
Blackwood, Vic. 231
Blackwoods, publishers 340
Blagden, Sir Charles 22, 23, 399
Blake, Leonard 251
Blake, William H., Capt. 342
Blandowski, William 40
Blankett, J., Capt. 281
Blaxland, Gregory 53, 174
Bledisloe, 1st Viscount—*see* Bathurst, Sir Charles
Blencowe, John W., Rev. 41, 317, 406
Bligh, William, Capt. 21, 22, 31, 158, 196, 264, 282, 324, 339, 340, 399, 489
Blight, F.S. 489
Bloemfontein, South Africa 337
Blomfield, James 375
Blonde, HMS 62
Blossom, Thomas 239, 290
Blossom, HMS 361, 381
Bloxam, Andrew 62, 280
Blue Coat School, Chester, England 97
Blue Mountains, NSW 53, 137, 174, 399, 473, 480
Blue Star Line 377
Blumenbach, J.F 22, 23
Blumenfeld, Ralph 236
Blundell, E. 272
Blythe, W.L. 122
Board of Guardians 31, 153, 303, 329, 468, 507
Board of Longitude—*see* Great Britain. Board of Longitude
Board of Trade—*see* Great Britain. Board of Trade
Bock, Thomas 56
Bodalla, NSW 209
Boer War, South Africa (1899–1902) 234, 237, 337
Bogese, G. 406
Bogor, Java 57
Boissier, P.M., Rev. 216
Bok, B.J. 396
Boldrewood, Rolf—*see* Browne, Thomas A.
Bombay, India 32, 301
Bonar, J., Rev. 176
Bonar Law, Andrew—*see* Law, Andrew Bonar
Bond, John J. 43
Bonham-Carter, Gerard 208
Bonham Carter, Henry 348
Bonython, Sir J. Langdon 113, 346
Bookanan, NSW 491
Books and book collecting 42, 456
Boorowa, NSW 13
Boosé, James R. 395
Booth, Charles 191
Booth, Henry, Lieut. Col. 44
Booth, Henry Jackson, Lieut. Col. 44
Booth, James 450
Booth, Mary 291

Booth, Philip 44
Booth Family 44
Booth Hill and Sons Pty Ltd 219
Booth Newman and Sons Pty Ltd 219
Boothman, Richard 268
Borden, Sir Robert 286
Borneo 37, 39, 57, 105, 129, 198, 217, 340, 366, 432, 434, 469—*see also* North Borneo
Borneo Company 236
Borrie, W.D., Prof. 395
Boschma, H. 61
Bosquet, C.J. 200
Bostock, F. 479
Bostock Family 479
Botanic Gardens
    England 394
    India 387
    Indonesia 57
Botanists 76, 120, 188, 394—*see also* Naturalists
Botany 22, 23, 57, 76, 120, 280, 394, 423, 447
    Antarctica 487
    Australia 12, 17, 116, 120, 154, 167, 169, 280, 420
    Dutch East Indies 12, 446
    France 116
    Hawaii 233
    India 387
    Pacific Islands 233
    Tahiti 233, 280
Botany Bay, NSW 162, 234, 238, 349, 382, 398, 430
    —*see also* Sydney, NSW
Bothwell, Tas. 381
Bottomley, Thomas 459
Bottomley, William 459
Boucaut, J.P. 255
Bougainville 316
Bougainville, Louis Antoine de 162, 342
Bougainville Strait, Solomon Islands 499
Bounty, HMS 21, 225, 342, 408
Bourke, Anne—*see* Thomson, Lady Anne
Bourke, Elizabeth 45
Bourke, Richard 45
Bourke, Sir Richard 45, 135, 191, 339, 384
Bourke Family 45
Bourne, E. 406
Bourne, Francis, Cardinal 497
Bourne, G.C. 431
Bourner, Sheila 46
Bourner Family 46
Bowen, Sir George F. 47, 98, 133, 146, 187, 190, 237, 256, 296, 332, 381, 394, 407, 490
Bowen, Thomas 119
Bowen, SS 137
Bower, Frederick, Prof. 188
Bower, James H.C., Lieut. 106
Bower, T.H. 71
Bowes, Arthur—*see* Smyth, Arthur Bowes
Bowes, C.H. 341
Bowie, F., Rev. 101
Bowie, Frederick 101, 386
Bowie, James 120, 394
Bowler, John W. 450
Bowles, Miss 372
Bowring, C.T. & Co Ltd 283
Box Hill, Vic. 123

Chamberlain, Joseph   234, 414, 451, 470
Chamberlin, Frederick   87
Chambers, C.H.   503
Chambers, Harry   79
Chambers, John & Son Co Ltd   413
Chambers, Samuel   274
Chambers, William, Capt.   342
Chamerouzow, L.A.   3
Champion, HMS   342
Champion Bay, WA   145
Champion of the Seas, ship   341
Changi, Singapore   109, 392, 491
Chapman Henry S.   394
Charles, Sarah   360
Charts—*see* Maps, plans and charts
Charybdis, HMS   450
Chaspoux, Pierre N., Mme   321
Chatham, HMS   361
Chatham Islands, Pacific Ocean   410
Chatterley, Mary H.   495
Chatterton, Fred, Rev.   220
Chatterton, John H.   95
Cheapside, emigrant ship   96
Cheeke, Alfred, Justice   216
Cheeseman, H.R.   79
Cheeseman, L.E.   57
Chelmsford, 1st Viscount—*see* Thesiger, Sir Frederick
        J.N.
Cheltenham, England   343
Chemists   396
Cherwell, 1st Viscount—*see* Lindemann, Frederick A.
Cheshire Quarter Sessions   96
Chesson, F.W.   3
Chester, England   97, 408
Chichester, 2nd Earl—*see* Pelham, Thomas
Chick, G.   52
Chifley, J.B.   326
Child-Villiers, Sir Victor, 7th Earl of Jersey   90
Childers, Emily   98
Childers, Hugh C.E.   24, 98, 133, 187
Childers, Rowland   98
Chile   387
Chilston, 1st Viscount—*see* Akers-Douglas, Areta
Chilton, Thomas, Mrs   438
Chimborazo, ship   364
China   12, 35, 37, 53, 105, 124, 127, 137, 184, 185, 188,
        280, 312, 420, 447
China, ship   349
Chinese in Australia   160, 319, 451, 452, 493
Chinnery, E.W.P.   203
Chisholm, Caroline   329
Chisholm, Elizabeth   290
Cholera   106
Chorlton Family   303
Christchurch, NZ   108, 172, 188, 240, 349, 447, 471
        immigration to   264
        visits to   165
Christian, Frederick W.   394, 406
Christian Brethren   99
Christie, W. Harry, Col.   337
Christina, ship   268
Christmas Island   7, 334
Christ's College, Tas.   181
Church Army   85

Church buildings—*see also* Missions and missionaries;
        see also under names of denominations
    Australia   144, 264, 330, 355, 421, 451, 480
    Melanesia   155
    New Zealand   37, 410
Church Missionary Society   100, 410
Church of England—*see* Anglican Church
Church of Melanesia   317
Church of Scotland   101
Churchill, Sir Winston S.   259, 286
Circular Head, Tas.   228, 472
Circuses   356
Citrine, Sir Walter M., 1st Baron   54
City of Adelaide, ship   154, 418, 441
City of Agra, ship   418
City of Poonah, merchant ship   342
Civil aviation   30
Clarence, merchant ship   342
Clarence River, NSW   207, 500
Clarendon, 4th Earl—*see* Villiers, George
Clark, Samuel   240
Clark, W.B., Rev.   469
Clark and Co, solicitors   240
Clarke, Sir Andrew   198
Clarke, Charles B.   394
Clarke, Cuthbert   200
Clarke, E.   100
Clarke, George, Rev.   100
Clarke, Marcus   53
Clarke, Ray   341
Clarke, Robert W.   450
Clarke, W.J.T.   14
Clarke, William B., Rev.   62, 156, 183, 280, 359, 399,
        487
Clarkson, W., Commander   272
Clay, Elizabeth   279
Clay, John   279
Clayton, Tubby, Rev.   167
Cleland, J.B.   59
Clement, John   52
Clergymen   33, 41, 42, 80, 106, 223, 226, 267, 309, 310,
        311, 341, 395, 410, 438, 469, 497, 511
Clerk, Alexander   408
Clerk, Sir George   408
Clerk, Henry   408
Clerk, James   408
Clerke, Charles, Capt.   324, 361
Cleveland Bridge Engineering Co   149
Cliff, W.J.   170
Clift, William   359
Clifton, M.W.   405
Clinton, Henry P., 5th Duke of Newcastle   1, 35, 79, 132,
        216, 345
Clio, HMS   342
Clive, Edward, 1st Earl of Powis   341
Clondalkin, Ireland   151
Clough, Arthur H.   42
Clulee, James W.   216
Clunies Ross, John   104
Clyde, convict ship   419
Clyde Navigation Trust   173
Coal—*see* Mines and mining
Coates, D.   280, 410
Coats of arms   182

Denison, Frank   132
Denison, Henry   355
Denison, Sir Hugh   462
Denison, J.E., 1st Viscount Ossington   355
Denison, William   132
Denison, Sir William T.   35, 131, 132, 177, 249, 254,
        272, 280, 296, 309, 332, 345, 355, 394
Denison Family   132
Denman, Sir Thomas, 3rd Baron   206
Dent, Tom, Rev.   323
Dent and Co   289
Denton, Derek, Prof.   109
Derby, 13th Earl—see Stanley, Edward S.
Derby, 14th Earl—see Stanley, Edward S.
Derby, 15th Earl—see Stanley, Edward H.
Derby, 17th Earl—see Stanley, Edward G.
Derby, WA   371
Dering, Sir Henry   264
Derryveagh, Ireland   269
Despard, Henry, Maj. Gen.   395
Des Voeux, Sir William   192
De Vis, Charles W.   64
Devlin, John   339
Devon, England   137
Devoy, Thomas   465
D'Eynecourt, Charles   279
Dibbs, Sir George R.   90, 107
Dicey, A.V., Prof.   263
Dick-Read, Grantley   109
Dickens, Mrs (Perth)   213
Dickens, Charles   264
Dickins, Thomas V.   352
Dickinson, A.R.   276
Dickinson, George G.   478
Dickson, Frank   136
Dickson, James   136
Dickson, Robert K., Admiral   340
Dickson Family   136
Dido, HMS   450
Digby, ship   10
Digswell Australian War Memorial Committee   217
Digswell Parish, England   217
Dilke, Sir Charles W., 2nd Baronet   42, 107
Dill, Sir John, Field Marshal   259
Dillicar, Richard   240
Dillingham, Richard   31
Dillon Family   182
Dingos   359
Diplomats   357
Dirk Hartog Island, WA   130, 162
Disbrowe, Sir Edward   1
Discovery, HMS (1776–95)   21, 342, 361
Discovery, HMS (1900–04)   71, 138
Disraeli, Benjamin, 1st Earl of Beaconsfield   139
Dissanaike, A.S., Prof.   109
Dixie, A.   59
Dixon, E.V.   79
Dixon, J.W.   79
Dixon, M.E.   279
Dixon, P.V.   79
Dixon, R.L.   163
Dobbin Family   182
Dobson, Thomas   85
Dodson, George   31

Dodson, Priscilla—see Huxley, Priscilla
Dodwell, G.F.   393
Doery, H.M.   170
Doidge, Sir Frederick   30
Dolphin, HMS   83, 328, 342, 361
Dominion Museum, Wellington, NZ   457
Dominion Office—see Great Britain. Dominion Office
Donald, W.   377
Donaldson, Stuart A.   141
Donegal, Ireland   269
Donnan, William, Lieut. Col.   447
Donnelly, Samuel   450
Donnithorne, Eliza   141
Donnithorne, James   141
Donnithorne Family   141
Dormer, Charles   479
Dormer Family   479
Dorsetshire Labourers—see Tolpuddle Martyrs
Dorsetshire Regiment (39th)   142
Double Bay, Sydney, NSW   257
Doughty, Frederic P., Admiral   447
Doughty, W.O. Edward   392
Douglas, H., Dr   354
Douglas, John   3
Douglas Alderson & Co—see Alderson, Douglas & Co
Douglass, H.G.   452
D'Ouseley, Rosamund   197
Dover, barque   506
Dover Castle, ship   342
Dowbiggin, J.S.T.   158
Dowling, Eliza   225
Dowling, Henry, Rev.   56
Dowling, Henry D.   478
Dowling, Robert   56
Downs, A.G.   36
Downside Abbey, England   144
Dowse Family   182
Draper, Capt.   335
Dring, William   238
Drogheda, Ireland   465
Drummond, Sir Francis   341
Drummond, H.N.   406
Drummond, James   280, 394
Drummond, W.M.   390
Drury, B., Capt.   246
Dryander, Jonas   23
Dublin, Ireland   419, 465
Dublin, HMS   398
Dublin University—see Trinity College Library, Dublin
Du Cane, Arthur   145
Du Cane, Sir Edmund F.   42, 145
Du Cane, Richard   145
Duchess of Northumberland, convict ship   450
Duchess of Northumberland, emigrant ship   96
Duchett, Edward   413
Duckenfield, ship   314
Duckett, E.   260
Dudley, H.T., Rev.   447
Duff, Sir Patrick   36
Duff, mission ship   387
Duff, ship   247
Dufferin and Ava, 1st Marquess—see Blackwood,
        Frederick
Duffield, W.G.   393

Gardiner, Martha 180
Gardiner, Mary 180
Gardiner, Sarah 180
Gardiner Family 180
Gardiner's Creek, Vic. 180, 408
Gardner, Joan 170
Gardner, John 479
Gardner, William A. 303
Garland, G., Lieut. Col. 44
Garland-Lester, L.V. 394
Garnet, HMS 342
Garnham, Percy C.C., Prof. 109
Garran, Andrew 462
Garran, Sir Robert R. 167, 253, 346
Garrick, Sir James 20
Garvey, Patrick J. 182
Garvey Family 182
Gascoigne, J. 31
Gascoyne-Cecil, Robert A.T., 3rd Marquess of Salisbury
        2, 234, 434, 470
Gate Pa, NZ 44, 150, 415, 449
Gaunt, Ethel 310
Gawler, George, Col. 395
Gawler, SA 469
Gawne, John M. 390
Gayndah, Qld 413
Gaywood, Ann 478
Geary Family 251
Geddes, David 450
Geddes, Sir Patrick 442
Geelong, Vic. 11, 29, 31, 42, 480
Geikie, Sir Archibald 156
Geikie, James, Prof. 249
Gell, Arthur D. 181
Gell, Eleanor I. 181
Gell, John P., Rev. 42, 181, 187
Gell Family 181, 309
Gellibrand, J. 28
Genealogy and genealogies 2, 46, 96, 137, 143, 180,
        182, 226, 228, 254, 265, 273, 306, 349, 365,
        381, 389, 435, 445, 447, 453, 479, 489, 495, 506
General Association for the Australian Colonies 395
General Graham, ship 247
General Hewett, ship 91, 233
General Roberts, ship 319
General Wellesley, ship 387
Geological Society of London 23, 183
Geological Survey Office, London 249
Geologists 7, 62, 85, 147, 148, 156, 249, 332, 383, 443,
        496
Geology
        Australia 69, 85, 249, 156, 183
        New South Wales 117, 443
        New Zealand 35, 117, 383
        Pacific Ocean 383
        surveys 249
        Tasmania 443
        Victoria 147, 443
George, David Lloyd—*see* Lloyd George, David
George, Prince, 2nd Duke of Cambridge 273
George V, King of England 79
German, William 397
Germans in Asia 184, 185
Germans in Australia 184, 185, 493

Germans in the Pacific 133, 184, 185, 187, 192, 270,
        286, 292, 395, 410, 470
Germany 184, 185, 220
Gerrald, Joseph 363
Gethethjarte, G.W.S. 280
Getty, James 381
Getty Family 381
Gibbons, L. 153
Gibbs, Alban G.H., 1st Baron Aldenham 186
Gibbs, Antony and Sons Ltd 186
Gibbs, Bright & Co 186
Gibbs, H.C. 186
Gibbs, James B. 52
Gibbs, Vicary 186
Gibraltar 12, 128, 327
Gibson, A.H. 259
Gibson, C.S. 422
Gibson, F. 170
Gibson, James 472
Gibson, John 119
Gibson, John (surgeon) 450
Gibson, Sir Robert 424
Gidley, B.C. 137
Gidley Family 137
Gifford, Edward W. 391
Gifford, Henry, Capt. 342
Gifford, John 197
Giglioni, Henry H. 237
Gilbert, John 193, 320
Gilbert, Joseph 110
Gilbert and Ellice Islands 129, 198, 395
Giles, William 478
Giles-Puller, Arthur 217
Gill, Samuel T. 178
Gillen, Francis J. 431
Gilles, O. 478
Gillfillan, John A. 442
Gillot, Joseph 413
Gilmour, Allan 197
Gilpin, William 42
Gimson, D. 215
Gipps, Sir George 193, 280
Gippsland, Vic. 97, 182
Gladstone, Mary 53
Gladstone, W.E. 1, 42, 187, 339, 345, 366, 452
Gladstone, Qld 395
Glamorganshire, Wales 341
Glanville, J. 478
Glascott Family 182
Glasgow, 7th Earl—*see* Boyle, Sir David
Glasgow, 8th Earl—*see* Boyle, Patrick J.
Glasgow, Scotland 77, 137, 173, 327, 344, 381, 408, 441,
        466
Glasson, Hannah 113
Glasson, John 491
Glasson, Mary 491
Glebe, NSW 117
Glen Innes, NSW 52
Glen Warwick station, SA 195
Glen Wilson, J.—*see* Wilson, J. Glen
Glenelg River, Vic. 436
Glover, John 314
Goderich, 1st Viscount—*see* Robinson, Frederick J.
Godley, Sir Alexander 324

Pandora, HMS 324, 418
Pankhurst, Adela—*see* Walsh, Adela Pankhurst
Papakura, Maggie—*see* Makereti
Papatoetoe, NZ 96
Papua New Guinea 57, 169, 198, 210, 235, 244, 303,
     357, 390, 409, 434, 435, 440, 442, 491, 493
  annexation 3, 133, 187, 192, 256, 380, 395
  flora and fauna 59, 62, 63, 64, 70, 134, 394
  language 406
  life and customs 39, 54, 203, 340, 442
  missions 290, 308
Pare, William 291
Paris, Edouard 162
Paris, France 321, 438
Paris Exhibition (1878) 225
Parker, Christopher C. 158
Parker, George 441
Parker, Harry 441
Parker, Jane M. 279
Parker, Sir William, Admiral 105
Parkes, Bessie N. 271
Parkes, Sir Henry 90, 107, 112, 144, 146, 187, 234,
     237, 267, 340, 348, 403, 434, 483
Parkyns, G. 447
Parmelia, ship 397
Parnell, Sir John 34
Parr, Sir James 20, 30, 173
Parr, W.F. 3
Parramatta, NSW 100, 119, 144, 196, 381, 393, 428,
     432, 447, 493, 506
Parramatta, ship 342, 491
Parramatta Gaol 432
Parramatta Observatory 271, 393, 399
Parry, Sir David 341
Parry, Griffith 341
Parry, Sir William E. 280
Pasley, Sir Charles W. 340
Passfield, 1st Baron—*see* Webb, Sidney J.
Paterson, William 280, 394
Pateshall, Nicholas, Lieut. 216
Pathologists 170
Paton, Sir George 109, 303
Paton, J.G., Rev. 3, 101
Patriarch, ship 295
Patrick, William 450
Patterson, James 234
Patteson, John C., Bishop 106, 317, 410, 461, 469
Pauton, George 432
Paymaster General—*see* Great Britain. Paymaster
    General
Payne, John B. 182
Peace Conference (1919) 286
Peace Treaty (1919) 164
Peacock, G., Prof. 339
Peacocke, Douglas P. 494
Peake, A.S. 323
Pearcey, F.G. 67
Peard, George, Lieut. 361
Pearl, HMS 450
Pearls and pearling 84, 395
Pearson, Charles H. 42, 217
Pearson, F.G. 319
Pearson, George R. 364
Pearson, Nelson V. 364

Pease, James 238
Pease, Joseph 149
Pease, Joseph R. 238
Pease Family 149, 238
Peckham, John 429
Pedder, Joseph 268
Pedley, Edward 365
Pedley, Thomas 365
Pedley, William 365
Pedley Family 365
Peek, Sir Cuthbert 464
Peel, Sir Robert, 2nd Baronet 1, 135, 329, 366, 452
Peel, Thomas 264
Pekina, SA 212
Pelham, Thomas, 2nd Earl of Chichester 367
Pelican, HMS 172
Pellew, Sir Edward, Admiral 488
Pellion, M. 162
Pelorus, HMS 143, 342, 450
Pember Reeves, W.—*see* Reeves, W. Pember
Penal reform 34, 346
Penang, Malaysia 24, 79, 152, 268, 272, 280, 290, 298,
     340, 368, 387, 488—*see also* Straits Settlements
Penang Rubber Estates Co 368
Penang Sugar Estates Co 368
Penguin, HMS 67, 342
Penhurst, 1st Baron—*see* Hardinge, Charles
Penicillin 121, 170
Peninsular and Oriental Steam Navigation Co 279, 429
Pennant, Thomas 341, 446
Penniman, T.K. 302
Pennington, Sir John F. 368
Pennymen Family 103
Penrith, England 119
Pental Island, Vic. 262
Pepler, Sir George 442
Perak, Malaysia 198, 237, 298, 368
Perceval, D. 339
Perceval, George J., 6th Earl of Egmont 490
Perceval, Spencer 34
Perceval Family 490
Percival, F.G. 249
Percy, Thomas, Dr 23
Perry, Charles, Bishop 158, 267, 469
Perry, W.W. 394
Perseus, HMS 450
Perseus, ship 247
Persia—*see* Iran
Perth, WA 108, 145, 174, 205, 214, 229, 259, 318, 322,
     352, 372, 432—*see also* Swan River, WA
  buildings 229
  immigration 395
  visits to 154, 461
Peru 406
Pestonjee Bomanjee, convict ship 279
Peterborough, England 87
Peterel, HMS 342
Peters, Edmund H. 369
Peters, John 369
Petherbridge Family 489
Petherick, E.A. 53
Petingale, John G. 370
Petre Family 158
Petrie, Sir William F. 169

Sheffield Smelting Co Ltd   413
Shelley, William   290
Shepton Mallet Gaol   425
Shelvocke, George, Capt.   324
Shenandoah, US ship   490
Sherbrooke, 1st Viscount—*see* Lowe, Robert
Sherbrooke, Viscountess—*see* Lowe, Georgiana
Sherwood, Anne   190, 204
Sherwood, Mary A.   35
Shields, Francis   378
Shields, William   234
Shillinglaw, John J.   394
Shipboard journals and logs—*see* Convict ships;
        Emigrant voyages; Royal Navy; Surgeons;
        see under names of ships
Shipping   5, 14, 73, 184, 286, 346, 470, 493
Shipping lines   5, 14, 285, 377, 429
Ships—*see* Convict ships; Emigrant voyages; Royal
        Navy; Surgeons; *see under* names of ships
Shipwrecks   210, 418
Sholl, W.   279
Short, Augustus, Bishop   217, 267, 469
Short, R.   3
Shrewsbury Gaol, England   415
Shropshire Quarter Session   415
Shuckard, William E.   280
Shuttleworth, Charles U., Major   150
Shuttleworth, Robert J.   193
Siam—*see* Thailand
Sibella, convict ship   450
Siccama, Rinso R.   450
Siddells, George   416
Sidmouth, 1st Viscount—*see* Addington, Henry
Sidney, F.W., Lieut.   246
Sillifant, John W.   405
Silver, Robert S., Prof.   188
Silver—*see* Mines and mining
Simes, I.T.   143
Simms, Frederick R.   291
Simms Motor Units Ltd   291
Simon, Sir Ernest D., 1st Baron   303
Simon, John, 2nd Baron   14
Simpson, Alex   122
Simpson, Ben   491
Sims, Phillip S.   280
Sinclair, Andrew   200
Sinclair, Sir John 280
Singapore   28, 105, 109, 122, 152, 189, 217, 272, 289,
        338, 342, 390, 392, 412, 413, 428, 441, 447,
        490—*see also* Straits Settlements
    missions   290
    photographs   37, 412, 469
    visits   115, 127, 137, 166, 167, 188, 208, 220, 337,
        375, 463, 479
Singapore, ship   438
Singer, E.   121
Siota, Solomon Islands   484
Sir Charles Napier, ship   447
Sir Edward Paget, ship   79
Sir James Hill and Sons Ltd—*see* Hill, Sir James and Sons
        Ltd
Sir Robert McAlpine & Sons Ltd—*see* McAlpine, Sir
        Robert & Sons Ltd
Sir William Bensley, convict ship   31

Sirius, HMS   38, 245, 378, 382, 430
Sirr, Henry C., Major   465
Sisters, brig   506
Skeletal remains   58, 64, 359, 375
Skinner, H.D.   39
Skipper, John M.   478
Skirving, William   363
Slack, W.H.   238
Slade, Henry   450
Sladen, Douglas   417
Slane, Ireland   465
Slattery, James   168
Small, Martha   68
Small, R.H.   327
Smethurst, J. Weston   319
Smiers, J.W.   402
Smith, Sir Andrew   280
Smith, Charles   450
Smith, Charles L.   271
Smith, Cicely F.   418
Smith, G.F. Herbert   65
Smith, George   31
Smith, H.A. McClure—*see* McClure Smith, H.A.
Smith, Humphrey H.   342
Smith, J.   394
Smith, James   189
Smith, Sir James E.   283
Smith, James W.N.   472
Smith, John (surgeon)   419
Smith, John (Tas.)   180
Smith, John A.—*see* Abel Smith, John
Smith, John L.   271
Smith, Sir Keith   474
Smith, R. Richard   379
Smith, Ralph S.   182
Smith, Sir Ross   474
Smith, Susan   441
Smith, W.H.   434
Smith, W. Saumarez, Bishop   33
Smith, W.T.   156
Smith, Walter C.   65
Smith, William   450
Smith Family   441
Smyth, Arthur Bowes   420
Smyth, P.   381
Smyth, W.H.   399
Smythe, F.   268
Snowy River region, NSW–Vic.   97
Socialism   51, 357, 491
Society for Promoting Christian Knowledge   421
Society for Promoting Natural History   280
Society for the Reform of Colonial Governments   37, 447
Society Islands   128, 233—*see also* Tahiti
Society of Friends   149, 217, 224, 422
Society of Mary (Marist Fathers)   308
Sockett, T., Rev.   372
Soddy, Frederick, Prof.   396
Soerabaya, Indonesia—*see* Surabaya, Indonesia
Sofala, NSW   258
Solander, Daniel C.   21, 23, 399, 406, 423
Solar eclipses   393, 399
Soldiers—*see* Army and defence; Army officers
Solicitors   35, 97, 103, 140, 158, 240, 432, 492, 502
Solomon Islands   57, 129, 179, 198, 276, 335, 357, 395